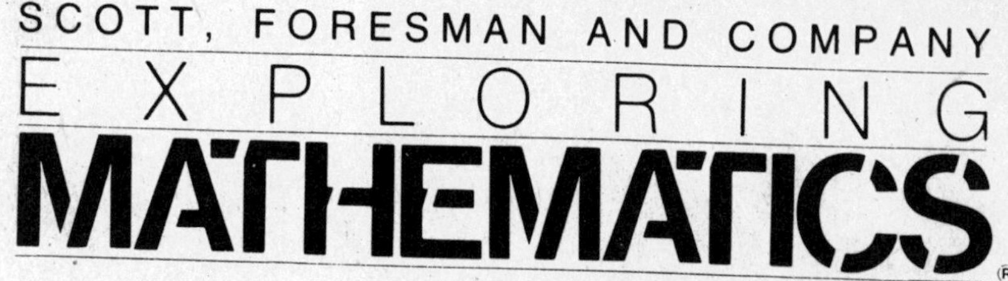

Problem Solving and Critical Thinking Sourcebook

The Activities in this Sourcebook

One activity master, along with a Teacher Notes page, is provided for each lesson in the student text. There are four categories of thinking skills, each addressing a different area of mathematical reasoning. The four categories are Problem Solving, Critical Thinking, Visual Thinking, and Decision Making.

Contents

Correlation Chart

This correlation chart is an easy-to-use reference and index for the activity masters in this book. The objective numbers that are used for the activity masters are the same numbers that are used to identify the objectives in the Student Edition.

Key

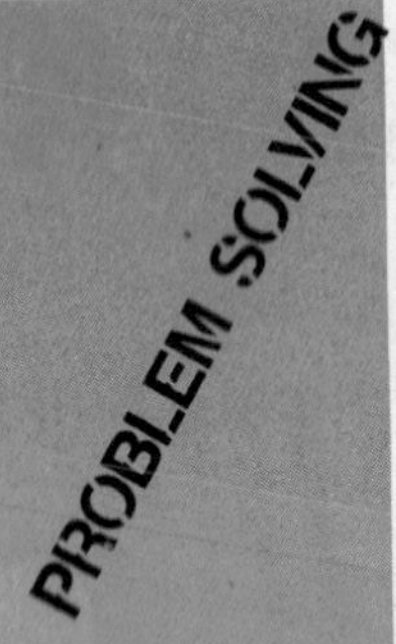

1 Write an Equation/ Number Sentence
2 Choose an Operation
3 Use a Formula
4 Make a Graph
5 Draw a Picture/ Draw a Diagram
6 Solve a Simpler Problem
7 Try and Check
8 Work Backward
9 Make a Table
10 Find a Pattern
11 Use Logical Reasoning

CRITICAL THINKING

1 Classifying and Sorting
2 Ordering and Sequencing
3 Using Logic
4 Drawing Conclusions
5 Using Number Sense
6 Finding/Extending/ Using Patterns
7 Making Generalizations
8 Reasoning with Graphs and Charts
9 Explaining Reasoning/ Justifying Answers
10 Developing Alternatives
11 Evaluating Evidence and Conclusions
12 Making and Testing Predictions

VISUAL THINKING

1 Spatial Perception
2 Visual Patterns

(transparency icon) Indicates that these Activity Masters are available as overhead transparencies.

1 Define the Problem
2 Identify the Options
3 Analyze the Options
4 Make Your Decision

Activity/ Objective Number	Use with Pages	Thinking Skills and Subskills			
		Problem Solving	Critical Thinking	Visual Thinking	Decision Making
1	4–5		2, 3		
2	[illegible]			1 (transparency)	
3	[illegible]				
4	12–		2, 8, 10		
5	14–1		2, 5		
6	16–19		2, 10		
7	22–23			1 (transparency)	
8	24–27		2, 3		
9	28–29		[illegible]		
10	30–31		[illegible]		
11	32–33				
12	34–35	1			
13	46–47				1–4
14	48–49				
15	50–51	1			
16	52–53				
17	54–57		12		
18	58–59	1			
19	60–61				
20	62–63				
21	66–67	9			
22					

Activity/ Objective Number	Use with Pages	Thinking Skills and Subskills			
		Problem Solving	Critical Thinking	Visual Thinking	Decision Making
23	68–71		3, 7, 9, 11		
24	72–73		3, 4, 6		
25	74–75	1, 9, 10			
26	76–77	9			
27	88–89	9			
28	90–91			2 (transparency)	
29	92–93		4, 12		
30	94–97				1–4
31	98–99	9			
32	100–103			1	
33	106–107	1			
34	108–109	1, 11			
35	110–111		2, 5		
36	112–113			2 (transparency)	
37	114–115	1			
38	130–131			1 (transparency)	
39	132–133				1–4
40	134–135			2 (transparency)	
41	136–137	9			
[illegible]	138–139				1–4
[illegible]	142–143		7		
[illegible]	144–145	9			

Activity/ Objective Number	Use with Pages	Thinking Skills and Subskills			
		Problem Solving	Critical Thinking	Visual Thinking	Decision Making
45	146–147		10		
46	148–149	9			
47	150–151		8		
48	162–163			1	
49	164–167				1–4
50	168–169			2	
51	170–171			1	
52	172–173	6, 9			
53	174–177		5		
54	180–181	6, 9, 10			
55	182–183	7, 10			
56	184–185			1	
57	186–187			1, 2	
58	188–189	11			
59	200–201			1	
60	202–205		3		
61	206–207				1–4
62	208–209	7			
63	210–213			2	
64	216–217	7			
65	218–219				1–4
66	220–221			1	
67	222–223		6		
68	234–237		3, 9		
69	238–241			1	
70	242–243	9			
71	244–245			1	
72	248–249	7			
73	250–251		5		
74	252–255				1–4
75	256–257	9			
76	272–275			1	
77	276–279		3, 11		
78	280–281			2	
79	282–283	7, 11			
80	286–287		3, 5		
81	288–289	1, 11			
82	290–291			1	
83	292–295				1–4
84	306–307				1–4
85	308–309		8		
86	310–311	6, 9, 10			
87	312–313	2, 11			
88	314–317		4, 9, 11		
89	320–321			1	
90	322–323			2	
91	324–325	6, 11			
92	326–327	5, 11			
93	328–329			2	
94	330–331	5, 9, 10			
95	342–343			1, 2	
96	344–345		6, 10		
97	346–347	3			
98	348–349		6, 12		
99	350–353	3			
100	356–357				1–4
101	358–359	5, 7			
102	360–361			1	
103	362–365	6, 10			

Activity/ Objective Number	Use with Pages	Thinking Skills and Subskills			
		Problem Solving	Critical Thinking	Visual Thinking	Decision Making
104	376–377		4		
105	378–381			2	
106	382–383		7		
107	384–387		8		
108	390–391		8		
109	392–395			1	
110	396–397	5, 11			
111	398–399				1–4
112	400–401	8, 9			
113	416–417			1	
114	418–419		11, 12		
115	420–421	1			
116	422–425			2	
117	428–429		3, 4, 12		
118	430–431			1	
119	432–433	1, 7			
120	434–437				1–4
121	438–439	7, 8, 11			
122	450–451			1	
123	452–453	7, 11			
124	454–457			1	
125	458–459	11			
126	460–461				1–4
127	464–465			1	
128	466–467	3			
129	468–469		5		
130	480–481	11			
131	482–483		11		
132	484–487			2	
133	490–491	5			
134	492–493			2	
135	494–495				1–4
136	496–497	7, 11			
137	508–509	6			
138	510–511				1–4
139	512–515			1	
140	516–517	2, 6			
141	518–521		5, 6		
142	524–525	4			
143	526–527			1	
144	528–529	11			
145	530–531		1, 11		
146	532–533	7			

Problem Solving and Critical Thinking Sourcebook

Purpose

Good problem solvers bring a wide variety of problem-solving strategies to bear upon a problem. After finding a solution or potential solution, they are able to look back and think critically about the solution. Successful problem solvers are resourceful and persistent in their search for a solution. The activities in this Sourcebook are designed to provide practice in problem solving and critical thinking. Students will be exposed to a wide range of problem-solving techniques. They will be given many opportunities to evaluate and criticize their solutions and decisions.

Successful problem solvers are resourceful and persistent in their search for a solution.

Many of these activities will help students recognize and understand the many mathematical and real-world problem-solving situations for which there may be more than one right answer. By focusing on the problem-solving process instead of "getting the right answer," the activities encourage alternate approaches to problem situations. As such, students will find these activities to be challenging, motivating, and interesting.

How to Use This Sourcebook

You may assign pages of the Sourcebook to individual students, small groups, or the entire class. At your discretion, students may complete a page with little or no class discussion or teacher interaction. At other times you may want to teach the pages by leading a class discussion.

You may wish to introduce the activities to the class and then let students work individually or in small-group brainstorming units, which will yield a wider variety of possible approaches than students could possibly experience on their own. In some instances, you may want to use one or more activities as "Problem(s) of the Week" and give students several days to work on them individually before discussing them as a class.

Optional Overhead Transparencies are available for thirty of the Visual-Thinking activities. They can be used in a variety of ways:

- For presenting problems to the class
- For leading class discussions
- For considering possible solutions

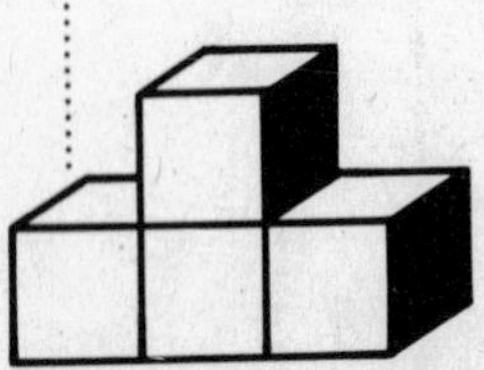

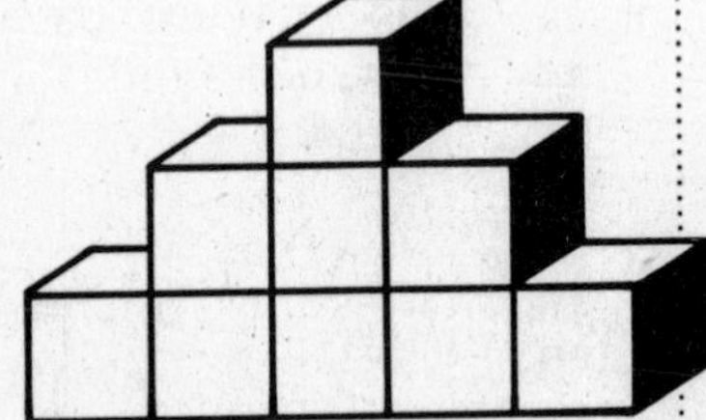

On the reverse side of each activity master is a Teacher-Notes page. A sample Teacher-Notes page is shown below, along with an explanation of its main features.

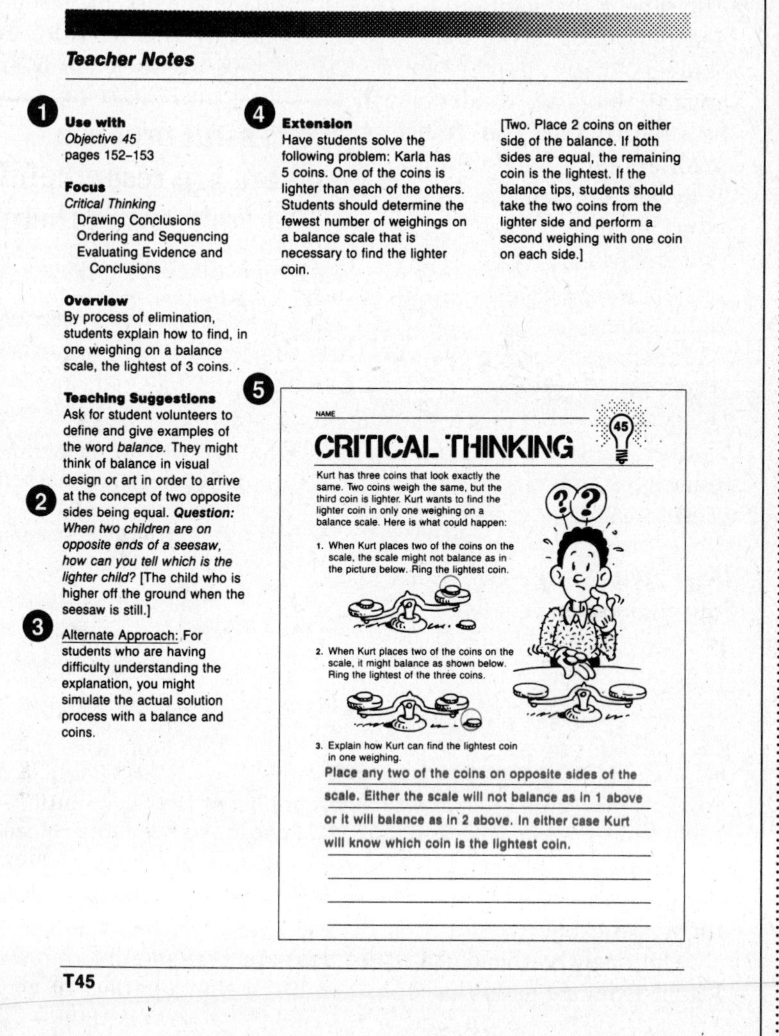

Teacher Notes

1 **Use with**
Objective 45
pages 152–153

Focus
Critical Thinking
Drawing Conclusions
Ordering and Sequencing
Evaluating Evidence and Conclusions

Overview
By process of elimination, students explain how to find, in one weighing on a balance scale, the lightest of 3 coins.

Teaching Suggestions
Ask for student volunteers to define and give examples of the word *balance*. They might think of balance in visual design or art in order to arrive at the concept of two opposite sides being equal. 2 ***Question:*** *When two children are on opposite ends of a seesaw, how can you tell which is the lighter child?* [The child who is higher off the ground when the seesaw is still.]

3 Alternate Approach: For students who are having difficulty understanding the explanation, you might simulate the actual solution process with a balance and coins.

4 **Extension**
Have students solve the following problem: Karla has 5 coins. One of the coins is lighter than each of the others. Students should determine the fewest number of weighings on a balance scale that is necessary to find the lighter coin.

[Two. Place 2 coins on either side of the balance. If both sides are equal, the remaining coin is the lightest. If the balance tips, students should take the two coins from the lighter side and perform a second weighing with one coin on each side.]

5

NAME

CRITICAL THINKING 45

Kurt has three coins that look exactly the same. Two coins weigh the same, but the third coin is lighter. Kurt wants to find the lighter coin in only one weighing on a balance scale. Here is what could happen:

1. When Kurt places two of the coins on the scale, the scale might not balance as in the picture below. Ring the lightest coin.
2. When Kurt places two of the coins on the scale, it might balance as shown below. Ring the lightest of the three coins.
3. Explain how Kurt can find the lightest coin in one weighing.
Place any two of the coins on opposite sides of the scale. Either the scale will not balance as in 1 above or it will balance as in 2 above. In either case Kurt will know which coin is the lightest coin.

T45

Focus
Identifies the category of thinking skills that the activity focuses on (Problem Solving, Critical Thinking, Visual Thinking, or Decision Making) as well as the subskills that are taught.

Question
Reveals and clarifies the substance of the activity, using leading or guiding questions. Students think through problems and are directed to a method of solution.

Alternate Approach
Offers suggestions and strategies for students to approach problems in a different way. These may be especially helpful for less-able students.

Extension
Provides opportunities for students to solve new problems that stem from the original problems.

Pupil Page
The activity master is clearly reproduced, with the answers overprinted in red.

A description of each of the four categories of thinking skills is provided on the following pages.

Problem Solving

These activities focus students' attention on solving nonroutine problems. The activities include real-world situations to stimulate interest, while highlighting nonroutine problem-solving strategies. Students will practice and extend the skills introduced in the student text, and they will apply the general method for mathematical problem solving that is developed in the text. Many of the problems can be solved using more than one strategy, thus encouraging students to develop creative methods of their own. Students will use the following nonroutine strategies:

Make a Graph
Making a graph, or in some way graphically depicting quantitative information, will help students read values between and beyond known points, as well as organize data into more useful forms.

Draw a Picture/Draw a Diagram
Representing the information in a problem in the form of a picture or diagram may help students see the conditions of the problem more clearly.

Solve a Simpler Problem
Using smaller numbers or temporarily ignoring some problem conditions often helps students find a solution method. This method is then applied to the original problem and may prove useful with more complex problems.

Try and Check
This is a systematic process of making reasonable guesses. It is often helpful when the number of possible solutions is small and when it is relatively easy to determine if a reasonable guess is correct.

Work Backward
Students examine, in counter-chronological order, the steps leading to a final result in order to discover initial conditions.

Make a Table
By making a table, students can organize large amounts of data and can often recognize hidden patterns that lead to general conjectures.

Find a Pattern
Identifying numerical and geometric patterns is often used in conjunction with making a table. Finding patterns allows students to find elegant solutions to otherwise difficult or tedious problems.

Use Logical Reasoning
Students use logic or deductive reasoning to determine reasonable processes and answers. This helps them solve a variety of problems.

In addition, the following routine strategies are used, largely at the beginning of the book, until students have been introduced to a variety of nonroutine strategies in the Student Edition.

Write an Equation/Number Sentence
Students translate real-world, quantitative situations into mathematical language.

Choose an Operation
Students decide which is the correct or best operation to use for a given problem. They may use this method with simple word problems as well as with multiple-step problems.

Use a Formula
Students use known formulas to solve mathematical problems. At upper grades, students may infer formulas to fit given data.

Critical Thinking

Critical Thinking activities challenge students to examine their own thinking about math and about related content areas. The problems and situations in these activities involve higher-order thinking skills such as analysis, synthesis, and evaluation. In becoming more aware, more critical, of their thinking, students become better problem solvers; they learn to examine and evaluate their own reasoning. Students will use the following strategies:

Classifying and Sorting
When classifying and sorting, students identify similarities and differences among objects and elements. Students also begin to group informational components according to specific characteristics.

Ordering and Sequencing
Students learn to recognize numerical and logical order and sequence.

Using Logic
Students identify logical fallacies, hidden assumptions, and illogical structures.

Drawing Conclusions
When drawing conclusions, students use deductive and inductive reasoning. They infer and draw logical, well-founded conclusions.

Using Number Sense
Students learn to judge relevance and completeness. They determine when there is too much or too little information, and they try to make well-founded estimates.

Finding/Extending/Using Patterns
While working on these problems, students interpolate and extrapolate number patterns and sequences. They may also infer mathematical properties.

Making Generalizations
Students build or propose a structure or they propose hypotheses. Students fit parts of a problem together to form a whole.

Reasoning with Graphs and Charts
Students learn to interpret numerical and graphical data. They interpolate and extrapolate needed information from graphs and charts.

Explaining Reasoning/ Justifying Answers
Students begin to explain their reasoning process and to justify and defend their answers.

Developing Alternatives
Students begin to think more flexibly when they develop alternate ways to approach and solve problems. This in turn may promote divergent and creative thinking.

Evaluating Evidence and Conclusions
Students test generalizations and logical validity. They also determine probabilities and evaluate evidence and conclusions by referring to internal or external standards.

Making and Testing Predictions
Students make predictions based on incomplete or probabilistic information. They perform experiments or use deductive reasoning to test their predictions.

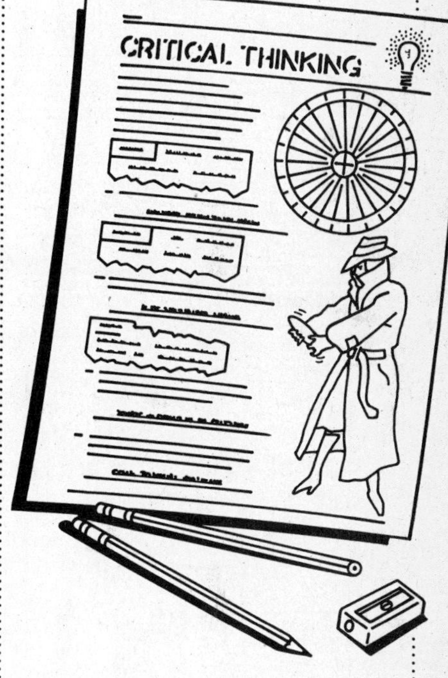

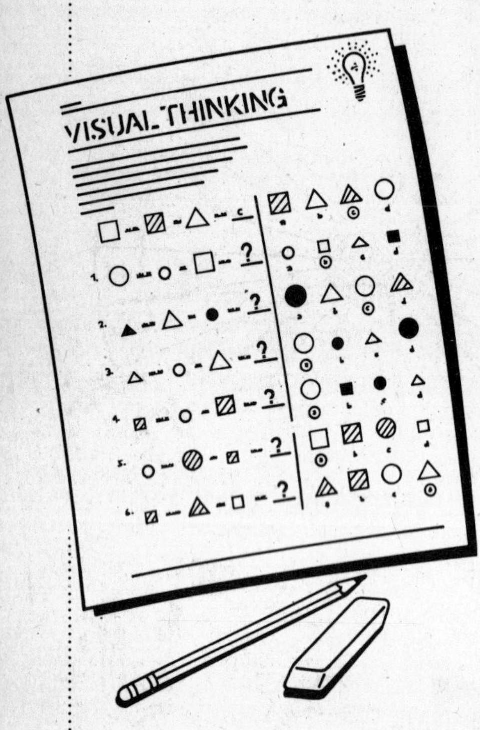

Visual Thinking

These activities exercise students' ability to perceive and mentally manipulate visual images. They also allow some students, who may not be proficient in other areas of mathematics, to excel. Additionally, students' capacity to visualize can be extremely useful to them in solving a variety of problems and in learning to think critically. Thirty of these activities are available as overhead transparencies (optional) that can be used to facilitate class discussion of the thought processes that lead to solutions. Students will use these strategies:

Spatial Perception
These activities encourage students to recognize hidden symbols or pictures and to recognize congruent or similar figures that have been slid, flipped, or turned. Students manipulate forms mentally and create mental images.

Visual Patterns
Students learn how to infer or extend visual patterns and sequences. They are also challenged by visual analogies.

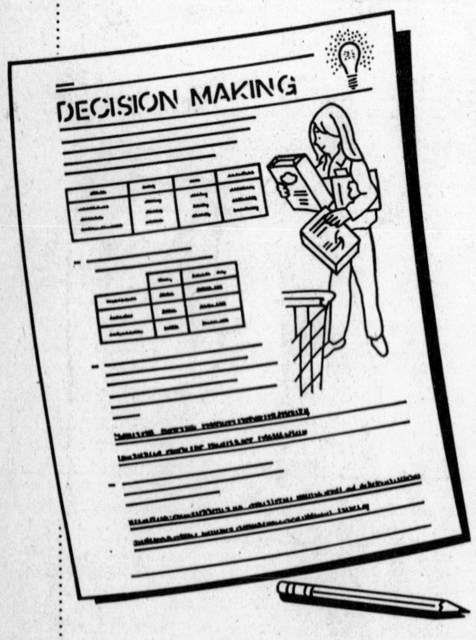

Decision Making

These activities present real-world situations that require students to make a decision. In most cases, there are no clearly right or clearly wrong answers. This gives students the opportunity to carefully weigh alternate courses of action—as well as to consider their personal experiences and preferences. The following four steps of decision making will help students make and evaluate their own decisions:

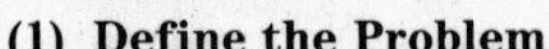

(1) Define the Problem
Students should consider why a decision is needed, what goal they wish to meet, and what tools and techniques they can use to reach their decision.

(2) Identify the Options
Students identify information that will be relevant to the decision-making process. Such information might include cost, time, rules, preferences, or practicality. Based on this information, students then develop alternative courses of action.

(3) Analyze the Options
At this stage, students consider the advantages and disadvantages of each option, considering both the positive and the negative consequences.

(4) Make a Decision
Students decide which choice is best. Students may be called on to justify their decisions with specific references to advantages and disadvantages. Because different students will weigh each advantage and disadvantage differently, this concluding step can lead to useful, worthwhile class discussion.

NAME ___

CRITICAL THINKING

Secret Agent G25 received a coded message from Agent J5. Agent G25 aligned her double-wheel decoder as shown so that J equals 5, since agents code messages according to their numbers.

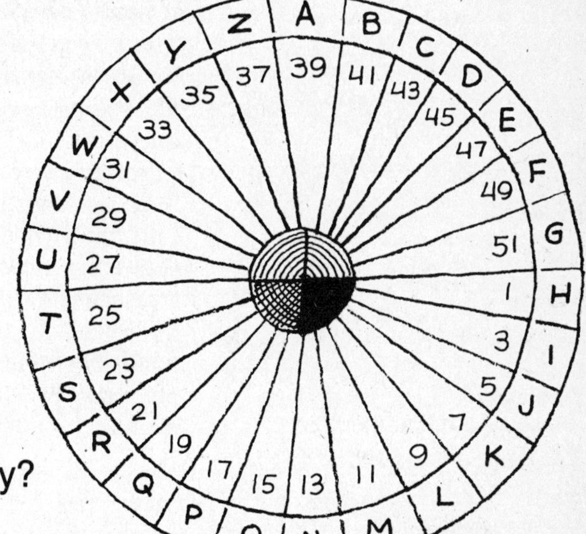

Agent J5	23-47-13-45 1-47-9-17
	21-3-51-1-25 39-31-39-35

1. What does Agent J5's message say?

___

Agent G25	29 37-1-49-51
	25-41 51-41 43-13-47-29-49

2. Agent G25 coded a message and sent it to Agent D21. What does her message say?

___

Agent F
1-33-45-39 29-21-41-41-21-33-31
21-41 5 41-45-9-9-13-41-41

3. Agent G25 received a second message, but part of the agent number was missing. Decode her message.

___

4. Make up your own agent number. On a separate sheet of paper write a coded message. Have a friend decode it.

___

Teacher Notes

Use with
Objective 1
pages 4–5

Focus
Critical Thinking
Ordering and Sequencing
Using Logic

Materials
2 index cards for each pair of students
Scissors for each pair of students
Brass fasteners

Overview
Students match and *sequence* numbers and letters to decipher coded messages.

Teaching Suggestions
Divide the class into pairs. Distribute the materials. Have each pair make its own double-wheel decoder by cutting out two different-sized circles from the index cards, and fastening them together at the center with a brass fastener. Instruct students to write the letters of the alphabet, clockwise, on the perimeter of the outer circle, and odd numerals on the inner circle. ***Question:** How do you set your double-wheel decoder for agent J5's message?* [The 5 and the *J* are aligned.] Have students decode the first message. Check each pair's answer. ***Question:** How do you set your double-wheel decoder for agent G25's message?* [The 25 and the G are aligned.] Have students decode the second message.

Students need a strategy for Problem 3. Have them search for a clue within the message. If students have difficulty, guide them to the one-letter word represented by 5. Since the only one-letter words in the English language are *A* and *I*, they must set their decoder so that either *A* or *I* is aligned with 5 and check to see if they get a sensible message. Have pairs do Problem 4 and exchange papers.

Extension
Have students send a short, coded message from agent G25. This time, they are to change the code for every letter after the first by moving the inner decoder wheel clockwise two or three places alternately. Have student partners decode the message.

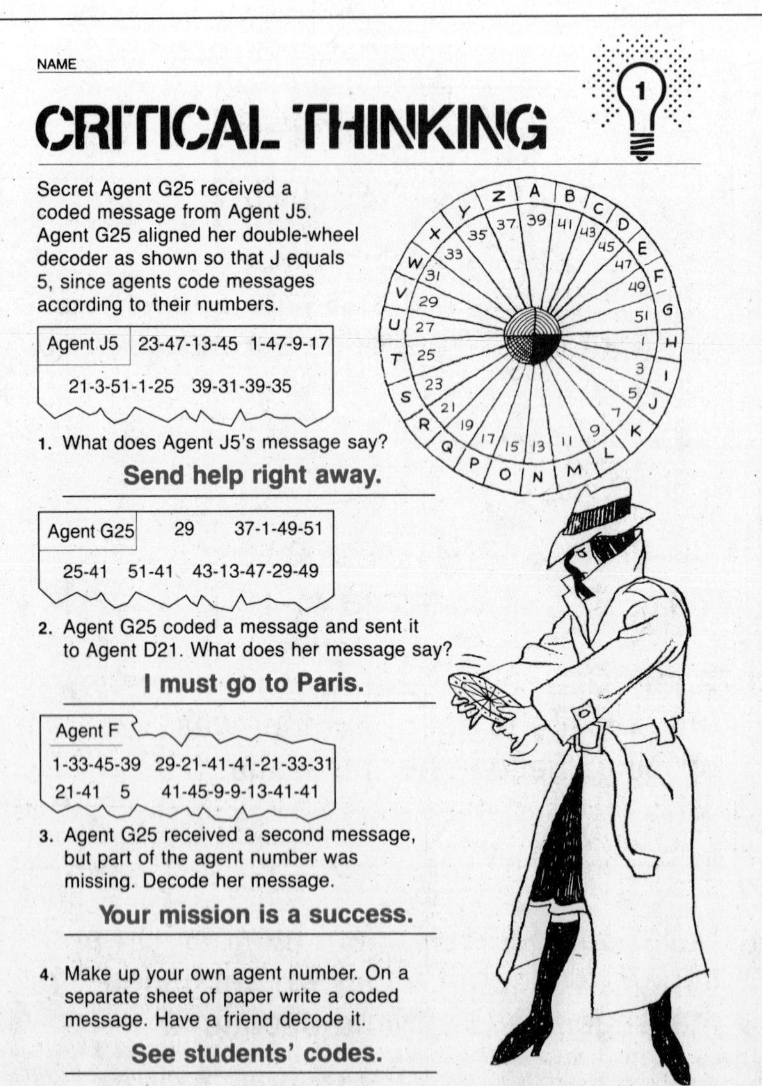

NAME
CRITICAL THINKING
1
Secret Agent G25 received a coded message from Agent J5. Agent G25 aligned her double-wheel decoder as shown so that J equals 5, since agents code messages according to their numbers.
Agent J5 23-47-13-45 1-47-9-17
21-3-51-1-25 39-31-39-35
1. What does Agent J5's message say?
Send help right away.
Agent G25 29 37-1-49-51
25-41 51-41 43-13-47-29-49
2. Agent G25 coded a message and sent it to Agent D21. What does her message say?
I must go to Paris.
Agent F
1-33-45-39 29-21-41-41-21-33-31
21-41 5 41-45-9-9-13-41-41
3. Agent G25 received a second message, but part of the agent number was missing. Decode her message.
Your mission is a success.
4. Make up your own agent number. On a separate sheet of paper write a coded message. Have a friend decode it.
See students' codes.

NAME ______________________________

VISUAL THINKING

Count the blocks in each picture. There are no hidden spaces. Each block sits on another block unless shown otherwise.

1.

______

2.

______

3.

______

4.

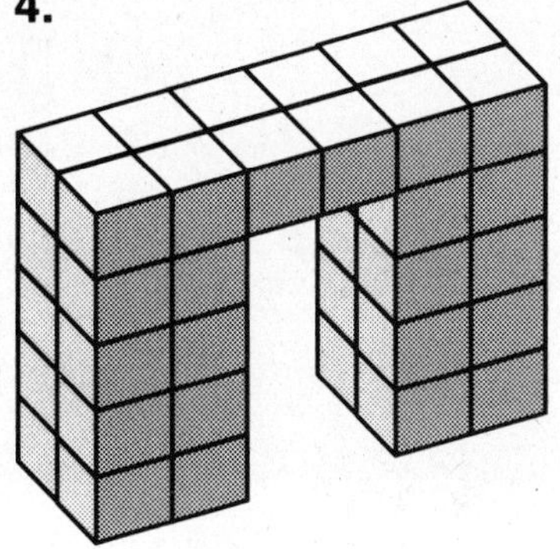

______

5.

______

6.

______

7.

______

8.

______

9.

______

Teacher Notes

Use with
Objective 2
pages 6–7

Focus
Visual Thinking
Spatial Perception

Materials
44 manipulative cubes for each group of four students
Visual Thinking transparency (optional)

Overview
Students use *spatial perception* to count all the blocks in given figures.

Teaching Suggestions
Inform students that they should look at the shape of each figure on the activity page to find a strategy or shortcut for counting the blocks. Guide students in finding a strategy for Problem 1. ***Question:*** *How does the shape of the figure in Problem 1 permit a shortcut?* [The two-layer front and rear sides are identical; so are the one-layer left and right sides. This means only the blocks on the front and left sides need to be counted. Multiplying this number by two gives the answer.]

Have students develop strategies for the rest of the problems and find the solutions. Strategies may include identifying symmetrical portions; counting individual layers; and/or counting individual stacks.

Alternate Approach: Have students use manipulative cubes to reconstruct the figures.

Extension
Have students make enlarged drawings of the figures, clearly showing all the blocks.

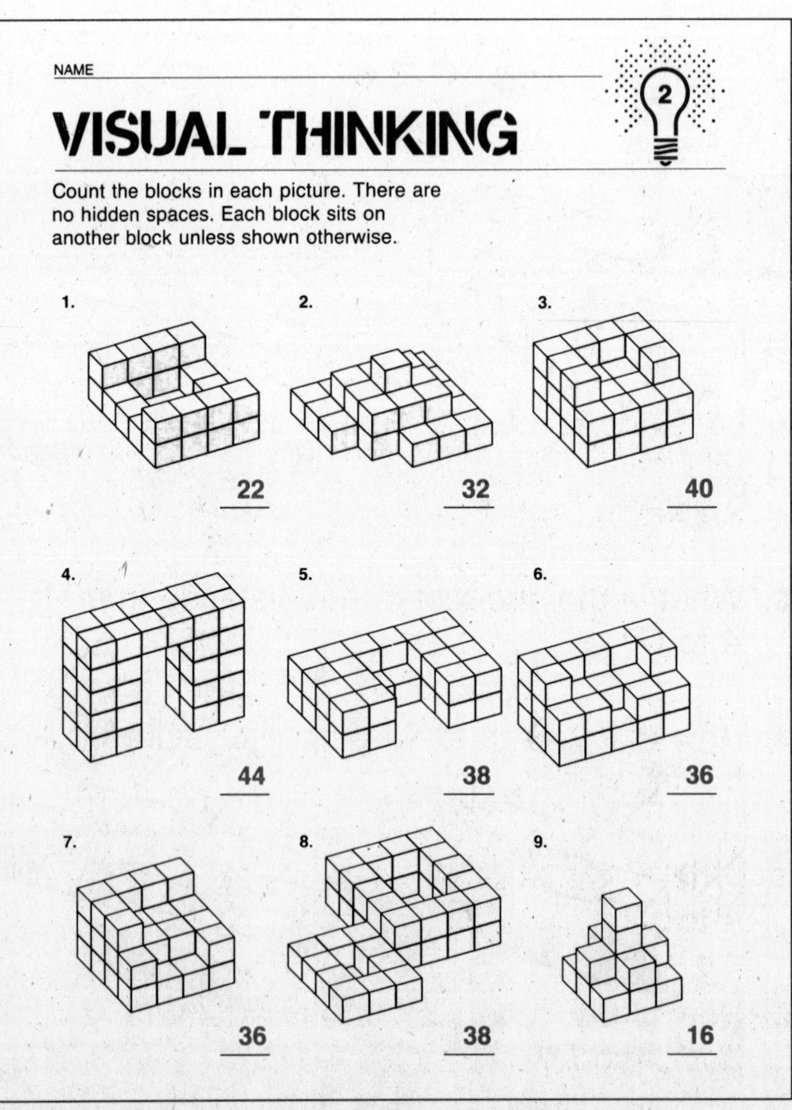

NAME
2
VISUAL THINKING
Count the blocks in each picture. There are no hidden spaces. Each block sits on another block unless shown otherwise.
1.
22
2.
32
3.
40
4.
44
5.
38
6.
36
7.
36
8.
38
9.
16

NAME ______________________________

CRITICAL THINKING

Use the street map at the right to answer the following questions.

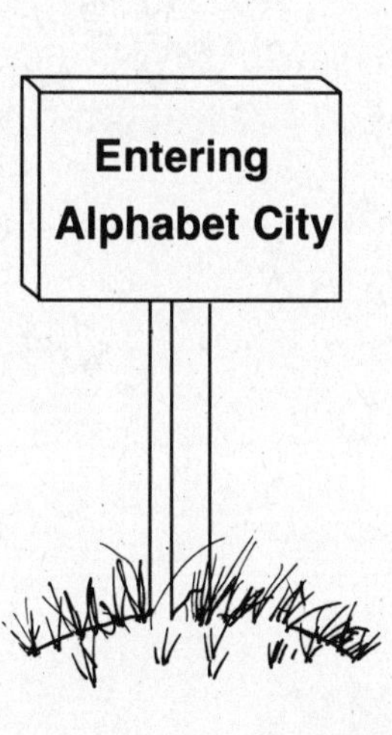

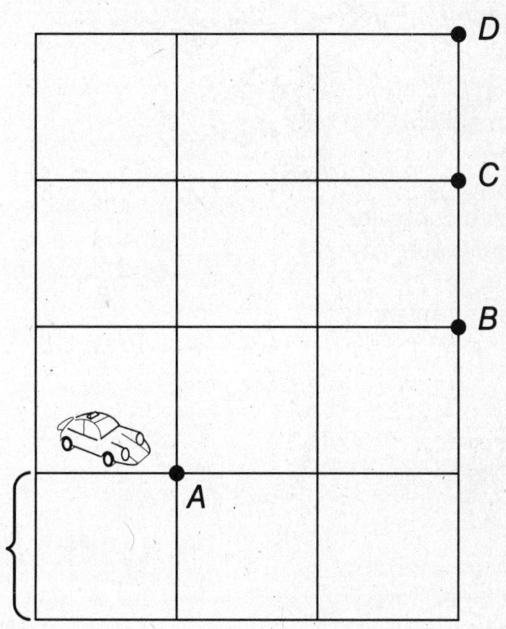

1. What is the shortest street distance in blocks from *A* to *B*? ______________

2. How many *different* paths could a taxi take to travel from *A* to *B* and travel only 3 blocks? ______________

3. What is the shortest street distance from *A* to *C*? ______________

4. How many "shortest" paths are there from *A* to *C*? ______________

5. What is the shortest street distance from *A* to *D*? ______________

6. How many "shortest" paths are there from *A* to *D*? ______________

Use after pages 8–9.

Teacher Notes

Use with
Objective 3
pages 8–9

Focus
Critical Thinking
Ordering and Sequencing
Developing Alternatives
Reasoning with Graphs and Charts

Materials
10 pipe cleaners for each student

Overview
Students find the shortest distances between points on a grid and all combinations of routes for those distances.

Teaching Suggestions
Make sure students understand that the only allowable paths are those that follow the grid lines. Discuss what "shortest distance" means in the context of the activity page. Students should realize that any direct route between points on the map is a path of minimum distance.

Encourage students to carefully keep track of the paths as they count the number of different paths between points. You may want to have students mark each path with a different colored pencil or trace each path on a separate sheet of paper.

Alternate Approach: Have students bend their pipe cleaners into the shape of each "shortest path" between two points. Making sure students do not turn the bent pipe cleaners, have them place the pipe cleaners in front of them in neat rows. The number of different pipe cleaner configurations is the number of shortest paths between two points.

Extension
Have students make each street a one-way street going in alternating directions and then find the shortest paths between the points. Suggest that they mark the grid with directional arrows to indicate the one-way streets.

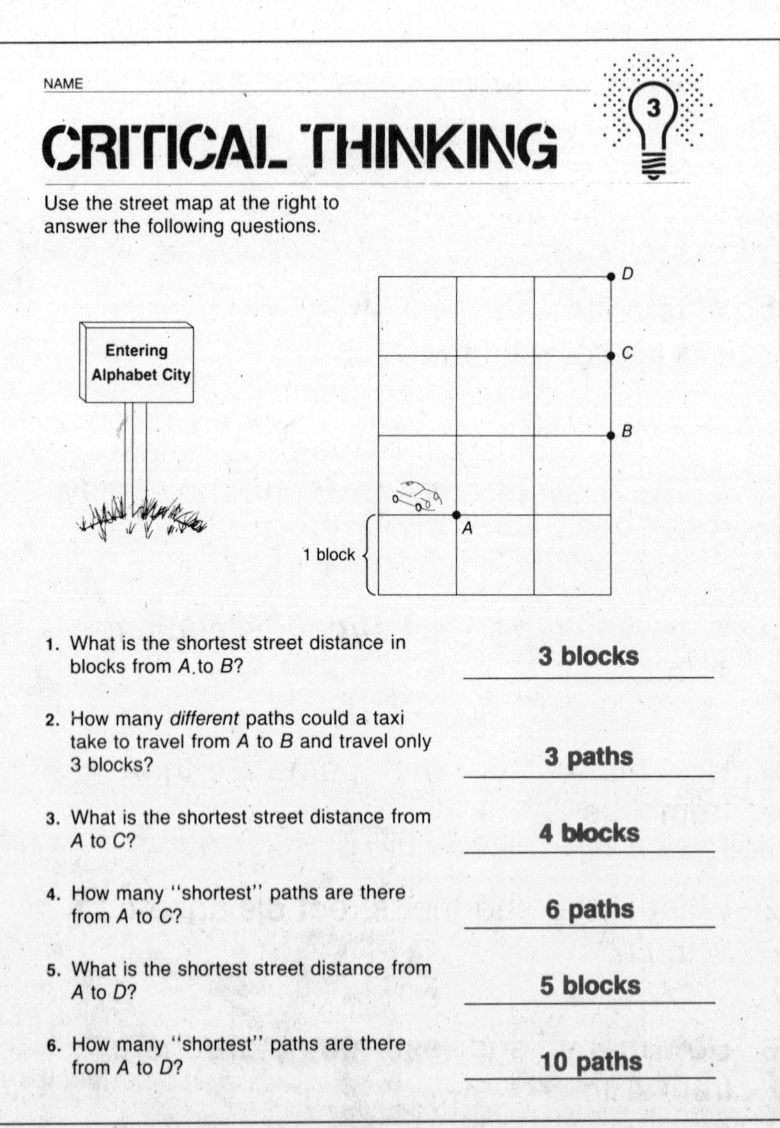

NAME
CRITICAL THINKING
3
Use the street map at the right to answer the following questions.
Entering Alphabet City
D
C
B
A
1 block
1. What is the shortest street distance in blocks from A to B?
3 blocks
2. How many different paths could a taxi take to travel from A to B and travel only 3 blocks?
3 paths
3. What is the shortest street distance from A to C?
4 blocks
4. How many "shortest" paths are there from A to C?
6 paths
5. What is the shortest street distance from A to D?
5 blocks
6. How many "shortest" paths are there from A to D?
10 paths

NAME ______________________________

CRITICAL THINKING

Numbers can be added using a clock. For example, study the addition table below for a clock with 3 numbers.

+	0	1	2
0	0	1	2
1	1	2	0
2	2	0	1

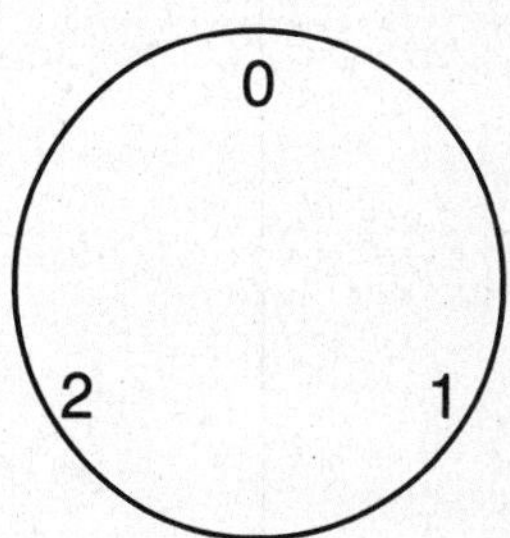

To add 0 + 2, start at the 0 on the clock and move clockwise 2 spaces. The answer is 2.

To add 2 + 2, start at the 2 on the clock and move clockwise 2 spaces. The answer is 1. Another way to look at this problem is to add 2 + 2 and get 4. Since there are only 3 numbers on the clock, you subtract 3 from 4 to get 1, which is on the clock.

1. Fill in the addition table below for a clock with 4 numbers.

+	0	1	2	3
0				
1				
2				
3				

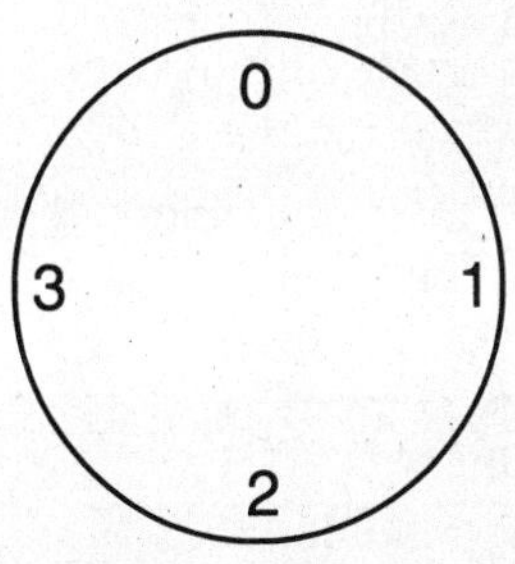

Using the clock on the right, complete the following addition problems.

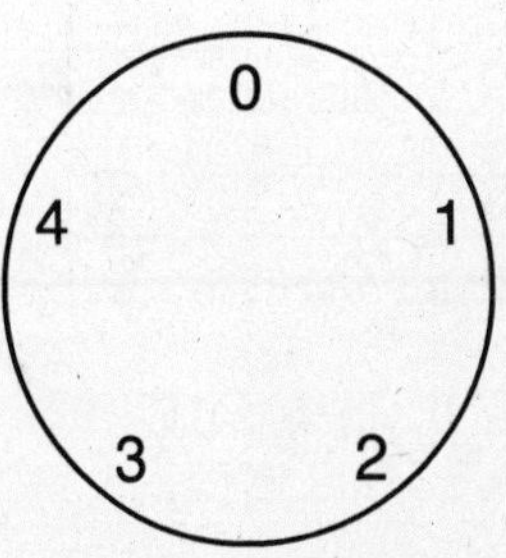

2. 1 + 3 = ___ 3. 3 + 3 = ___

4. 4 + 1 = ___ 5. 4 + 4 = ___

Teacher Notes

Use with
Objective 4
pages 10–11

Focus
Critical Thinking
Using Number Sense
Ordering and Sequencing

Overview
Students perform addition using clocks.

Teaching Suggestions
Tell students that in this activity they will be doing addition in a new way and they will get unexpected answers to simple addition problems. Have students read the example given on the activity page. Make sure students understand how to add using the clock. ***Question:*** *How would you subtract using the clock?* [Move counterclockwise instead of clockwise.]

Challenge them to try to figure out the system. Then have students complete the problems on their own. If students have difficulty, point out that each "new" answer is the same as the expected answer minus the number of digits on the clock.

You may want students to make a table for Problems 2–5. It should look like this.

+	0	1	2	3	4
0	0	1	2	3	4
1	1	2	3	4	0
2	2	3	4	0	1
3	3	4	0	1	2
4	4	0	1	2	3

Extension
Have students look for patterns in the tables. Students should concentrate on the interior of each table (the part they had to complete in Problem 1) and ignore the numbers along the outside.

Patterns which students may find include the following. Each number on the clock appears in each row and column exactly once. The first row in each table begins with 0 and increases by 1 from left to right. Succeeding rows begin with the number that is 1 more than the beginning number of the previous row. The numbers along each diagonal from upper right to lower left are the same.

NAME

CRITICAL THINKING

Numbers can be added using a clock. For example, study the addition table below for a clock with 3 numbers.

+	0	1	2
0	0	1	2
1	1	2	0
2	2	0	1

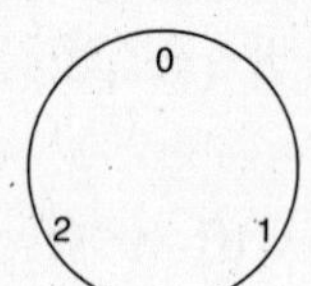

To add 0 + 2, start at the 0 on the clock and move clockwise 2 spaces. The answer is 2.

To add 2 + 2, start at the 2 on the clock and move clockwise 2 spaces. The answer is 1. Another way to look at this problem is to add 2 + 2 and get 4. Since there are only 3 numbers on the clock, you subtract 3 from 4 to get 1, which is on the clock.

1. Fill in the addition table below for a clock with 4 numbers.

+	0	1	2	3
0	**0**	**1**	**2**	**3**
1	**1**	**2**	**3**	**0**
2	**2**	**3**	**0**	**1**
3	**3**	**0**	**1**	**2**

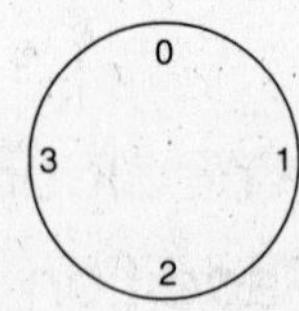

Using the clock on the right, complete the following addition problems.

2. 1 + 3 = **4**
3. 3 + 3 = **1**
4. 4 + 1 = **0**
5. 4 + 4 = **3**

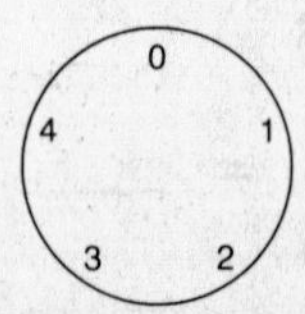

NAME ____________________

CRITICAL THINKING

Use the map of Mathtown to answer the following questions.

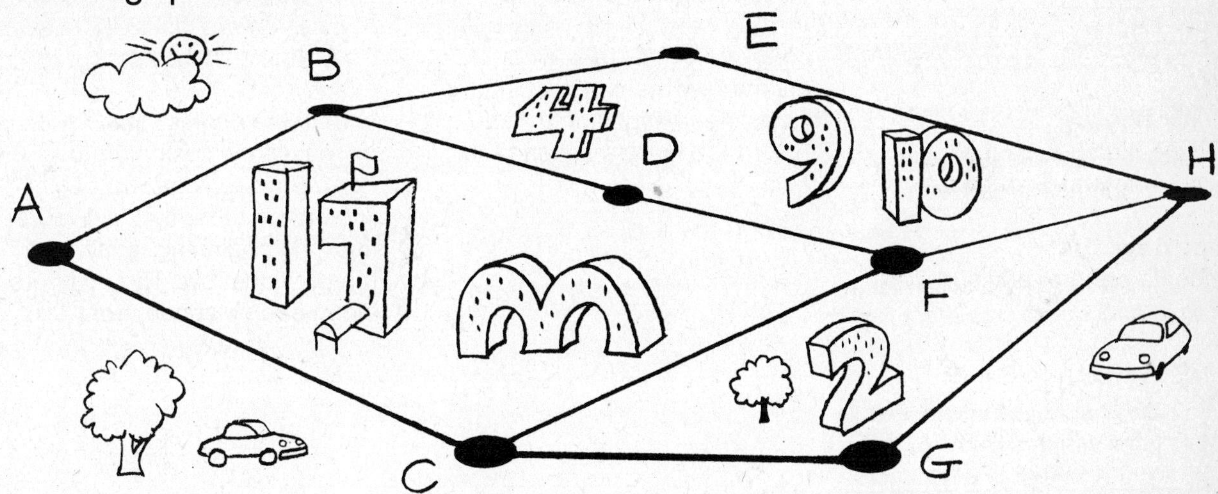

1. How many direct, or "shortest," routes are there from point *A* to point *F*? ____________________

2. For each possible route, list the points you must travel through to go from point *A* to point *F*. ____________________

3. How many direct routes take you from point *C* to point *H*? ____________________

4. For each possible route, list the points you must travel through to go from point *C* to point *H*. ____________________

5. How many direct routes take you from point *A* to point *H*? ____________________

6. For each possible route, list the points you must travel through to go from point *A* to point *H*.

____

Teacher Notes

Use with
Objective 5
pages 12–13

Focus
Critical Thinking
Ordering and Sequencing
Developing Alternatives

Overview
Students find and follow direct routes between two points on a map.

Teaching Suggestions
Make sure students understand that taking a direct route means never backtracking or moving away from your destination.

You may want to suggest that students use a tree diagram to count the number of routes. A tree diagram for Problems 1 and 2 would look like this.

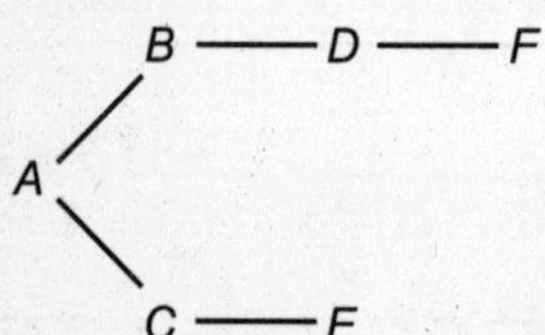

A tree diagram for Problems 5 and 6 would look like this.

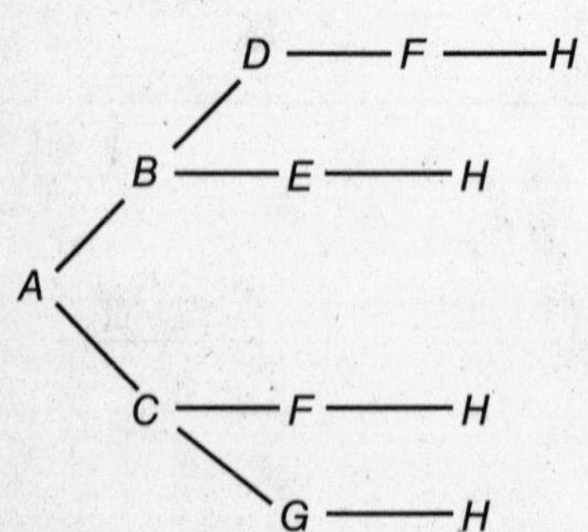

Extension
Have students draw new routes from *A* to *D, D* to *E,* and *D* to *H* (going around buildings). Then have students redo the activity.

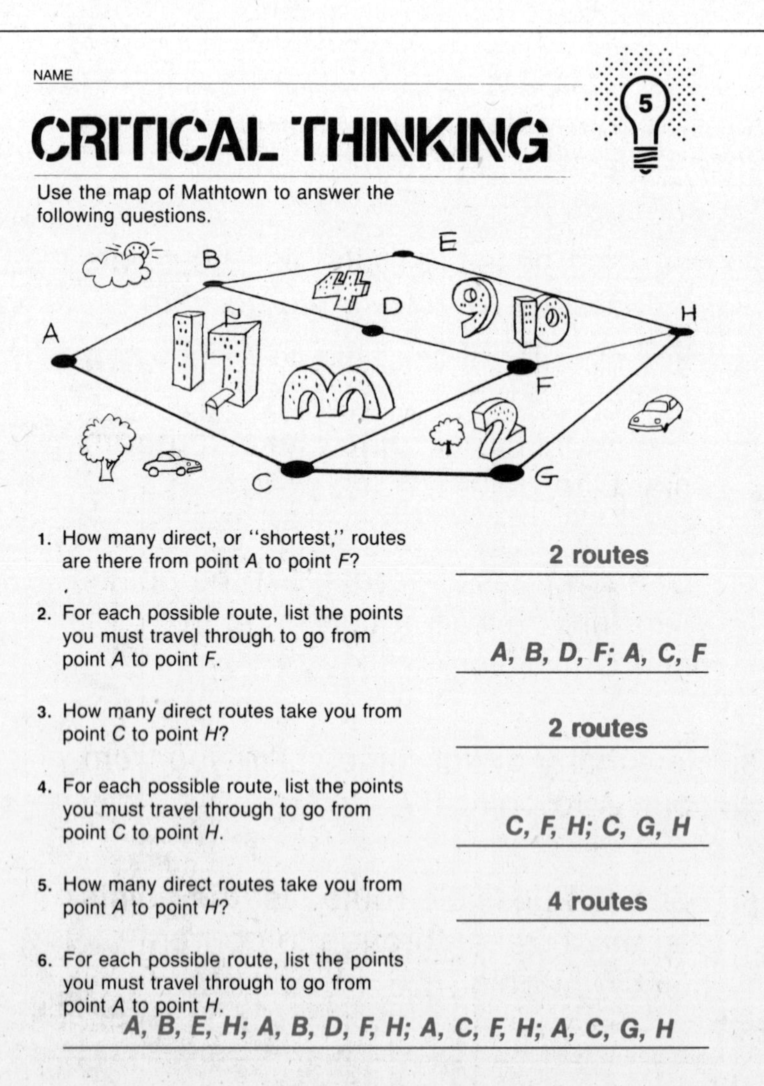

NAME

CRITICAL THINKING

5

Use the map of Mathtown to answer the following questions.

1. How many direct, or "shortest," routes are there from point *A* to point *F*? **2 routes**
2. For each possible route, list the points you must travel through to go from point *A* to point *F*. ***A, B, D, F; A, C, F***
3. How many direct routes take you from point *C* to point *H*? **2 routes**
4. For each possible route, list the points you must travel through to go from point *C* to point *H*. ***C, F, H; C, G, H***
5. How many direct routes take you from point *A* to point *H*? **4 routes**
6. For each possible route, list the points you must travel through to go from point *A* to point *H*. ***A, B, E, H; A, B, D, F, H; A, C, F, H; A, C, G, H***

NAME ____________________

VISUAL THINKING

Ring the letters of the two figures on the right that will form the figure on the left when joined. The figures may be flipped or turned, but they cannot overlap, and there cannot be gaps.

1. a. b. c. d.

2. a. b. c. d.

3. a. b. c. d.

4. a. b. c. d.

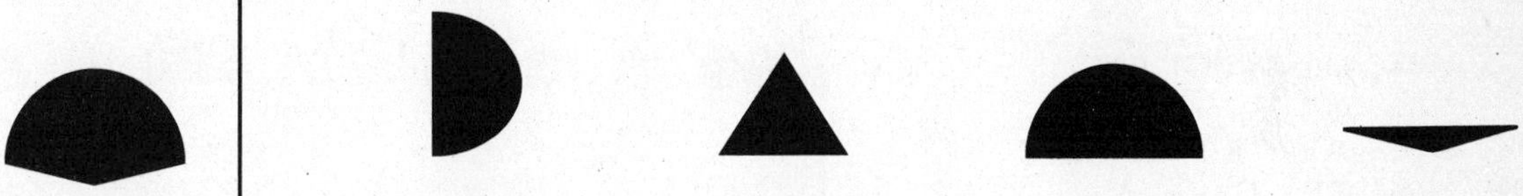

5. a. b. c. d.

6. a. b. c. d.

7. a. b. c. d.

Teacher Notes

Use with
Objective 6
pages 14–15

Focus
Visual Thinking
Spatial Perception

Materials
Index cards
Tracing paper
Cardboard
Scissors
Visual Thinking transparency (optional)

Overview
Using visual and *spatial perception,* students select the two figures that form a larger figure.

Teaching Suggestions
Students can use the edge of an index card to divide each figure on the left in two. The index card should be placed in logical areas of division: the intersection of two different shapes (Problems 1, 2, and 4), a bisection of the figure (Problems 3 and 5), or diagonals (Problem 7).

Alternate Approach: Have students make cutouts of figures identical to those on the right by using tracing paper and cardboard. Have students find the solutions by manipulating the shapes.

Extension
Have students create their own activity page with similar problems. Explain that they should make this activity page more difficult by drawing figures on the left that are made up of three separate shapes. First have students create figures for the left column. Then have them give 5 figures on the right as answer choices, including the 3 figures that form the figure on the left.

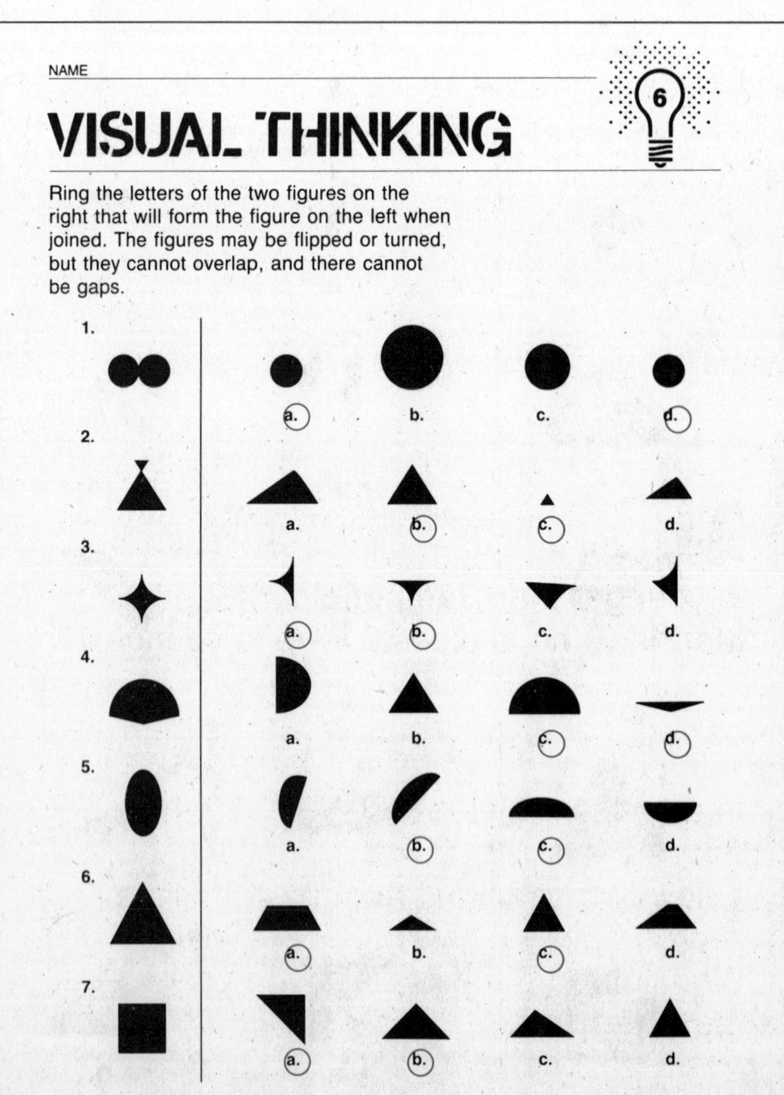

NAME

VISUAL THINKING

6

Ring the letters of the two figures on the right that will form the figure on the left when joined. The figures may be flipped or turned, but they cannot overlap, and there cannot be gaps.

1. a. b. c. d.
2. a. b. c. d.
3. a. b. c. d.
4. a. b. c. d.
5. a. b. c. d.
6. a. b. c. d.
7. a. b. c. d.

NAME ___________________________

CRITICAL THINKING

Since 15 > 9 and 9 > 3, then 15 > 3. Similarly, 102 < 519 and 519 < 520, so 102 < 520. In general

If $a > b$ and $b > c$, then $a > c$.
If $e < f$ and $f < g$, then $e < g$.

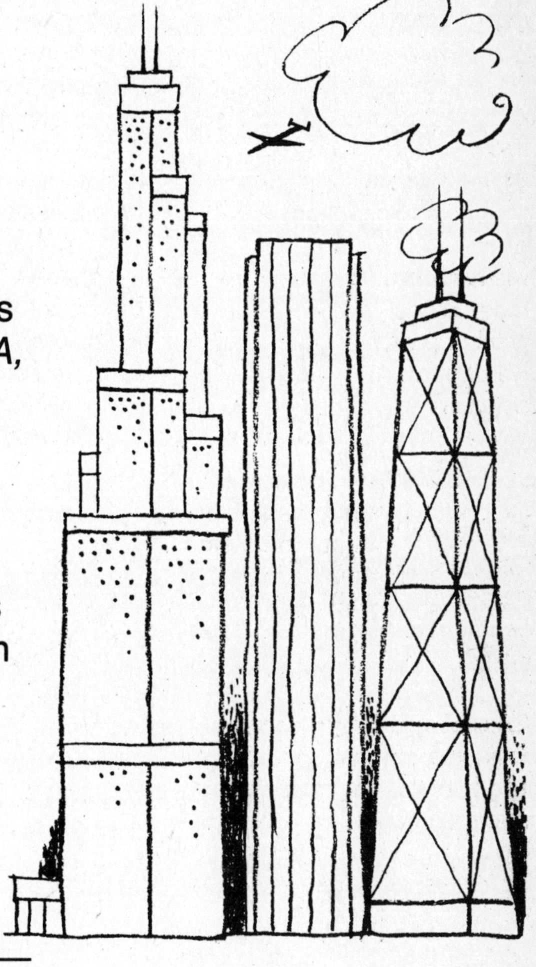

In Chicago, the Sears Tower is taller than the Amoco Building. The Amoco Building is taller than the John Hancock Center. If *S, A,* and *J* represent the heights of these buildings, then their relationship can be described as

$$S > A > J$$

Write similar relationships for the problems using the letters given in parentheses, then solve the problems.

1. Becky (*B*) is shorter than Judy (*J*), but Becky is taller than Fred (*F*). Who is tallest? Who is shortest?

____

2. Carl (*C*) is older than Joe (*J*), Pam (*P*) is younger than Martha (*M*), and Harold (*H*) is younger than Joe but older than Martha. Who is oldest? Who is youngest?

____

3. In a chess tournament, Franz (*F*) scored above Lynn (*L*) and Paul (*P*). Paul scored below Marla (*M*) but above Lynn. Jose (*J*) scored above Franz but below Marla. Who scored the highest? Who scored the lowest?

____

Teacher Notes

Use with
Objective 7
pages 16–19

Focus
Critical Thinking
Ordering and Sequencing
Using Logic

Overview
Students use *ordering and sequencing* skills to arrange series of inequalities.

Teaching Suggestions
Students should organize the information in each problem by writing an inequality for each relationship given. For instance, in Problem 1, students can express the given information by writing the inequalities $B < J$, and $B > F$.

Point out to students that it is easier to order the given information if each inequality is expressed in the same way. Thus in Problem 1, students should restate their inequalities by writing $J > B$, and $B > F$.

Alternate Approach: Have students write the information given on a number line. Have them label the right-hand side of the line as "greater," "older," or "taller," as appropriate. Students can then place the initials for each person as indicated in the problem. A sample number line for Problem 1 is shown below.

Shorter —F—B—J— Taller

NAME ______________________

CRITICAL THINKING

Since $15 > 9$ and $9 > 3$, then $15 > 3$. Similarly, $102 < 519$ and $519 < 520$, so $102 < 520$. In general

If $a > b$ and $b > c$, then $a > c$.
If $e < f$ and $f < g$, then $e < g$.

In Chicago, the Sears Tower is taller than the Amoco Building. The Amoco Building is taller than the John Hancock Center. If S, A, and J represent the heights of these buildings, then their relationship can be described as

$$S > A > J$$

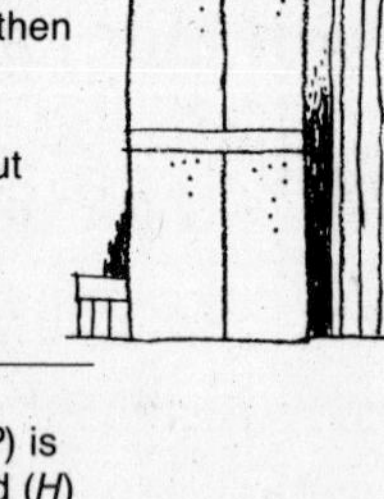

Write similar relationships for the problems using the letters given in parentheses, then solve the problems.

1. Becky (B) is shorter than Judy (J), but Becky is taller than Fred (F). Who is tallest? Who is shortest?

   $J > B > F$; Judy; Fred

2. Carl (C) is older than Joe (J), Pam (P) is younger than Martha (M), and Harold (H) is younger than Joe but older than Martha. Who is oldest? Who is youngest?

   $C > J > H > M > P$; Carl; Pam

3. In a chess tournament, Franz (F) scored above Lynn (L) and Paul (P). Paul scored below Marla (M) but above Lynn. Jose (J) scored above Franz but below Marla. Who scored the highest? Who scored the lowest?

   $M > J > F > P > L$; Marla; Lynn

NAME ____________________

CRITICAL THINKING

Numbers can be rounded in different ways.

Some calculators drop all the digits after a certain place. Therefore such calculators always round a number down.

If an item costs 3 for 1 dollar and only one is bought, a store will round the price up to 34 cents. Due to the large volume of items that a store sells, they must round up or they would lose too much profit.

In mathematics we usually round to the nearest place value.

Round each of the numbers below according to the directions.

1. Round 15.143

up to the tenths place; ________

to the nearest tenth; ________

down to the tenths place; ________

2. Round 78.7

up to the tens place; ________

to the nearest ten; ________

down to the tens place; ________

3. A grocery store sells 2 oranges for 25 cents. How much should the store charge for 5 oranges? ____________________

4. When a number was rounded to the nearest tenth it became 105.2. What could the number be?

____

Teacher Notes

Use with
Objective 8
pages 22–23

Focus
Critical Thinking
Using Number Sense

Materials
Calculators (optional)

Overview
Students *use number sense* to round numbers in different ways.

Teaching Suggestions
After students read the introductory paragraphs on the activity page, lead the class in a discussion of other situations in which decimals might be rounded. Examples include using a centimeter ruler to measure to the nearest tenth of a centimeter, estimates of populations to the nearest thousand or million, estimates of distances to the nearest mile or tenth of a mile, and banks rounding the interest on savings accounts down to the nearest hundredth. In each case, discuss whether numbers are rounded up, rounded down, or rounded to the nearest.

For Problem 4, any answer between 105.15 and 105.25 is acceptable.

Extension
Have students experiment with their calculators to see whether it rounds decimals to the nearest or truncates (rounds down). Ask students to explain how they arrive at their result.

NAME ____________________

CRITICAL THINKING

Numbers can be rounded in different ways.

Some calculators drop all the digits after a certain place. Therefore such calculators always round a number down.

If an item costs 3 for 1 dollar and only one is bought, a store will round the price up to 34 cents. Due to the large volume of items that a store sells, they must round up or they would lose too much profit.

In mathematics we usually round to the nearest place value.

Round each of the numbers below according to the directions.

1. Round 15.143
   - up to the next tenth; **15.2**
   - to the nearest tenth; **15.1**
   - down to the next tenth; **15.1**

2. Round 78.7
   - up to the next ten; **80**
   - to the nearest ten; **80**
   - down to the next ten; **70**

3. A grocery store sells 2 oranges for 25 cents. How much should the store charge for 5 oranges? **63 cents**

4. When a number was rounded to the nearest tenth it became 105.2. What could the number be?

   Possible answer: 105.19

NAME

CRITICAL THINKING

Estimates can be made high or low depending on the purpose of the estimate.

Choose whether to estimate high or low for each of the situations and explain why.

1. An engineer is designing a bridge. She needs to estimate the strength of the supports (how much weight each support will hold). Should she estimate the strength as higher or lower than it actually needs to be?

2. Ralph is estimating the time it will take to drive from home to a job interview. If he wants to be sure to arrive on time, should he estimate his driving speed higher or lower than it probably will be?

3. Wally is painting a room. When buying the paint, should he buy the amount of paint based on an estimate that is higher or lower than what he thinks he will need?

4. Stacey is estimating how long it will take to word process a report. To be sure she completes the report on time, should she estimate her word processing speed higher or lower than it actually is?

Use after pages 24–27.

Teacher Notes

Use with
Objective 9
pages 24–27

Focus
Critical Thinking
Developing Alternatives
Using Logic

Overview
Students choose whether to estimate values high or low under different conditions.

Teaching Suggestions
Discuss with students various situations that call for making estimates. Answers might include how much food to buy for a group or how much money to allow for a purchase.

Encourage students to make "If, then" statements for the high and low alternatives in each problem on the activity page. In Problem 1, such statements might look like this: If strength is higher, then the bridge holds more weight. If strength is lower, then the bridge holds less weight. Looking at these two alternatives, students choose the one that gives the more desirable results. ***Question:*** *What "If, then" statement can be used with Problem 2?* [If speed is lower, then Ralph must leave earlier. If speed is higher, then Ralph must leave later.] Have students choose the preferable alternative. Then have students finish the problems on their own, using this method.

Extension
Have students create a schedule and materials list for a pretend class project to paint the classroom with three coats of paint. Say that it takes from 8–16 hours for each coat of paint to dry. Students can only paint during school hours, and each can of paint covers from 100–200 square feet. Have students share their estimates in a large group discussion.

NAME

CRITICAL THINKING

Estimates can be made high or low depending on the purpose of the estimate.

Choose whether to estimate high or low for each of the situations and explain why.

1. An engineer is designing a bridge. She needs to estimate the strength of the supports (how much weight each support will hold). Should she estimate the strength as higher or lower than it actually needs to be?

   Higher; wants an extra safety factor

2. Ralph is estimating the time it will take to drive from home to a job interview. If he wants to be sure to arrive on time, should he estimate his driving speed higher or lower than it probably will be?

   Lower; leaves extra time for unexpected delays

3. Wally is painting a room. When buying the paint, should he buy the amount of paint based on an estimate that is higher or lower than what he thinks he will need?

   Higher; better to have extra paint than not enough

4. Stacey is estimating how long it will take to word process a report. To be sure she completes the report on time, should she estimate her word processing speed higher or lower than it actually is?

   Lower; build in maximum typing time

NAME

CRITICAL THINKING

To finish the roof of her dollhouse, Lori needs to combine scraps of wood that add up to the lengths shown on the blueprint below. Use the given board lengths to complete the table.

Scrap board	Length (cm)
A	13.6
B	12.8
C	5.9
D	5.2

Scrap board	Length (cm)
E	15.1
F	7.7
G	10.6
H	9.7

Board	Length	+	Board	Length	=	Total (cm)
		+			=	15.8
		+			=	18.7
		+			=	21.3
		+			=	24.8

Teacher Notes

Use with
Objective 10
pages 28–29

Focus
Critical Thinking
Using Number Sense
Reasoning with Graphs and Charts
Classifying and Sorting

Overview
Students choose lengths of wood that add up to a given sum.

Teaching Suggestions
Encourage students to look at the chart on the activity page for two pieces of scrap board whose combined lengths equal any one length specified on the blueprints. Have them enter the boards and their lengths in the proper places in the table. For the first line in the table, adding the two decimals must leave an 8 in the tenths place. This permits the following combinations: 13.6 and 5.2, 5.2 and 10.6, 15.1 and 7.7, 15.1 and 9.7. Among these only 5.2 and 10.6 add up to 15.8. Students can use the process of elimination to reduce the number of choices as they work through the chart.

Students can also round all lengths to the nearest centimeter. Using the rounded lengths, students can identify pairs of boards that are likely to add to the correct lengths. These pairs are then checked using the actual lengths.

Alternate Approach: A slower but easier method is this: Beginning with the total in line 1 of the table, students should subtract each scrap board length (beginning with A) from 15.8 until they get a difference equal to the length of another scrap board on the chart. These two lengths should then be entered in the chart and crossed out on the list. The rest of the table can be completed in the same manner.

Extension
Say that Lori changed the slope of the roof so that she now needs two lengths that add up to 20.3 cm. Ask students what combinations will work. [15.1 and 5.2; 10.6 and 9.7]

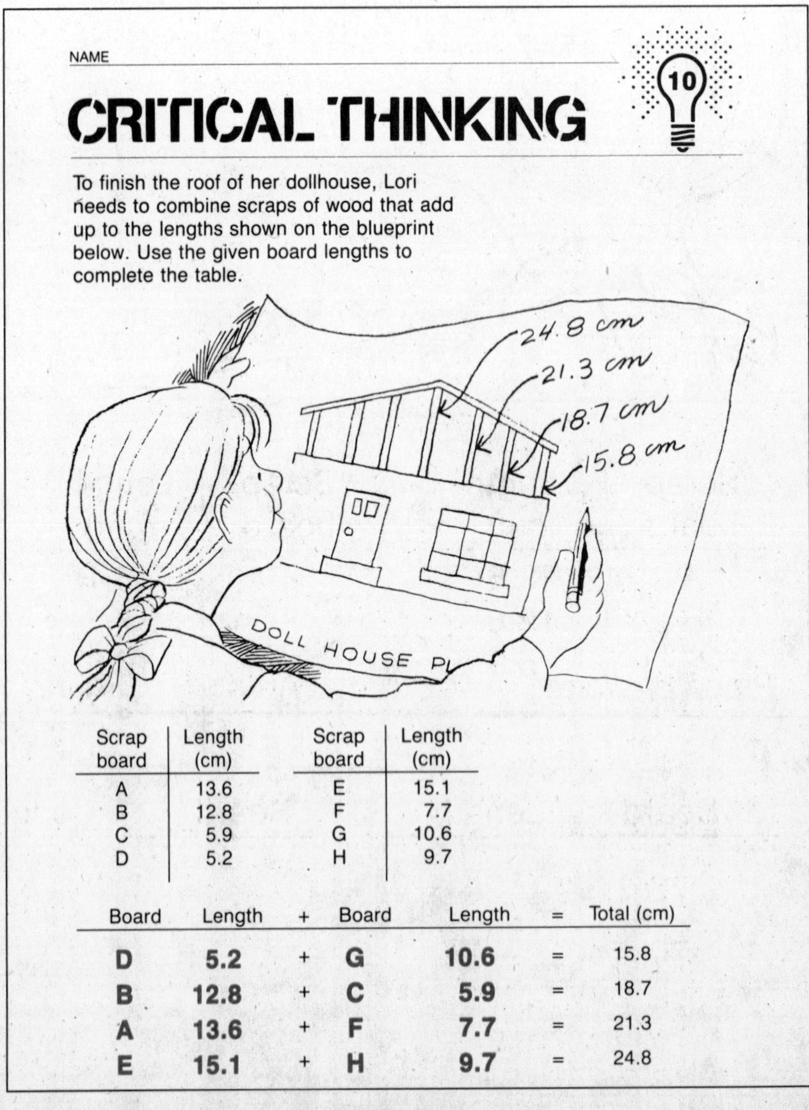

NAME

CRITICAL THINKING 10

To finish the roof of her dollhouse, Lori needs to combine scraps of wood that add up to the lengths shown on the blueprint below. Use the given board lengths to complete the table.

Scrap board	Length (cm)	Scrap board	Length (cm)
A	13.6	E	15.1
B	12.8	F	7.7
C	5.9	G	10.6
D	5.2	H	9.7

Board	Length	+	Board	Length	=	Total (cm)
D	**5.2**	+	**G**	**10.6**	=	15.8
B	**12.8**	+	**C**	**5.9**	=	18.7
A	**13.6**	+	**F**	**7.7**	=	21.3
E	**15.1**	+	**H**	**9.7**	=	24.8

NAME

CRITICAL THINKING

Roger is making a model ship from balsa wood. He has some lengths of wood that have to be cut to the correct lengths needed. He wants to cut the wood so he has as many waste pieces as possible that are at least 8 cm long. Complete the table below to show how Roger should cut the wood.

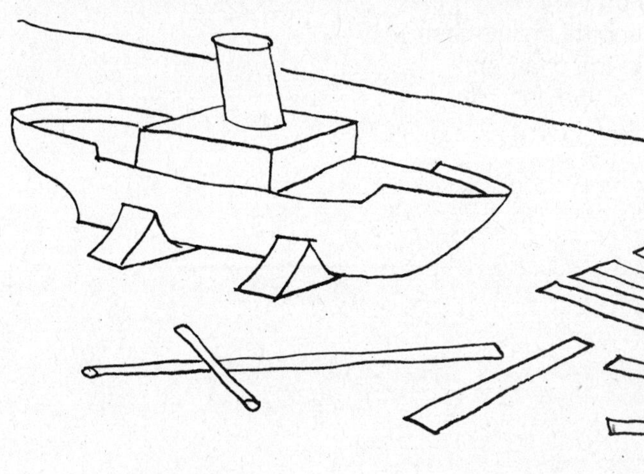

Piece of wood (cm)	Correct length needed (cm)
103.8	38.5
67.6	57.1
96.3	61.4
79.5	72.0
70.2	85.2
43.2	95.3

Piece of wood	–	Correct length	=	Waste (cm)
103.8	–		=	
96.3	–		=	
79.5	–		=	
70.2	–		=	
67.6	–		=	
43.2	–		=	

Use after pages 30–31.

Teacher Notes

Use with
Objective 11
pages 30–31

Focus
Critical Thinking
Ordering and Sequencing
Using Number Sense
Classifying and Sorting

Overview
Students make a plan for cutting pieces of wood, leaving as many scraps as possible that are at least 8 centimeters long.

Teaching Suggestions
Through discussion, encourage students to come up with a strategy to complete the table on the activity page.
Questions: *Which piece or pieces of wood can be cut to make the longest length needed (95.3 cm) and provide a waste piece 8 cm or longer?* [Only the longest piece, 103.8 cm] *Which piece or pieces of wood can be cut to make the second longest length needed (85.2 cm) and provide a waste piece 8 cm or longer?* [Only the second longest piece, 96.3 cm] Students should see that the table must be completed by listing the correct lengths in decreasing order to correspond with the pieces of wood.

Extension
Tell students that Roger discovers he doesn't need the 95.3 cm length. Have students figure out his new options. [Larger pieces of waste wood can be used to make the correct lengths.]

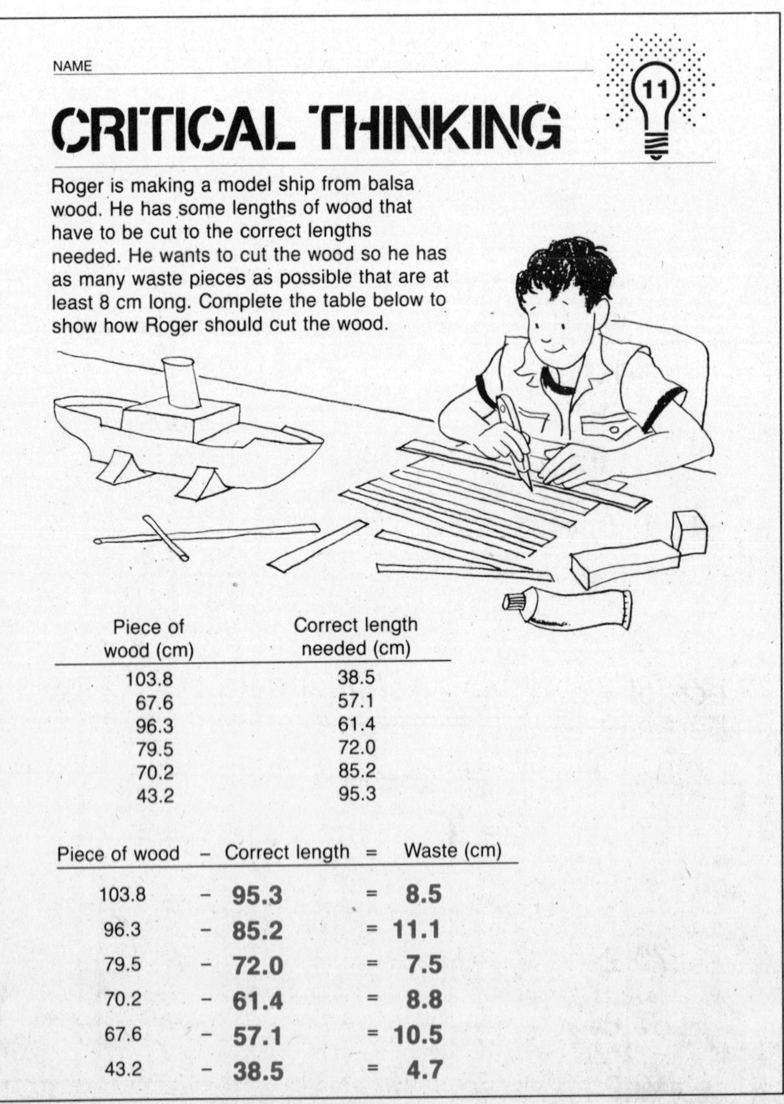
NAME

CRITICAL THINKING

11

Roger is making a model ship from balsa wood. He has some lengths of wood that have to be cut to the correct lengths needed. He wants to cut the wood so he has as many waste pieces as possible that are at least 8 cm long. Complete the table below to show how Roger should cut the wood.

Piece of wood (cm)	Correct length needed (cm)
103.8	38.5
67.6	57.1
96.3	61.4
79.5	72.0
70.2	85.2
43.2	95.3

Piece of wood	–	Correct length	=	Waste (cm)
103.8	–	**95.3**	=	**8.5**
96.3	–	**85.2**	=	**11.1**
79.5	–	**72.0**	=	**7.5**
70.2	–	**61.4**	=	**8.8**
67.6	–	**57.1**	=	**10.5**
43.2	–	**38.5**	=	**4.7**

NAME ____________________

DECISION MAKING

Use the drawing and the following information to complete the chart.

Adam has the weights shown on the right. He is setting up a barbell so that the total weight is 70 pounds. He always sets up the barbell so that

- the weights on both sides are equal;
- the same kinds of weights are used on each side;

1. Complete the chart in as many ways as possible.

Left Side			Right Side		
15 lb	10 lb	5 lb	15 lb	10 lb	5 lb

2. How do you think Adam should set up the barbell? Explain.

____

____

____

____

Teacher Notes

Use with
Objective 12
pages 32–33

Focus
Decision Making

Materials
Pan balance
Mass weights: four 15 gm, six 10 gm, and six 5 gm

Overview
Students complete a chart for different symmetrical weight combinations.

Teaching Suggestions
Ask a student volunteer to explain how a balance works. Elicit the idea that in order to balance, the weight on both sides needs to be the same. Since the weights used on both sides of the bar discussed on the activity page must be identical, students need only complete the left side of the chart and copy their results onto the right side. ***Questions:*** *How much must each side weigh?* [35 lb] *How many weights of each kind are available on each side?* [Two 15-lb, three 10-lb, three 5-lb] Have students complete the chart. There are two possible answers for Problem 2: two 15-lb weights and one 5-lb weight; one 15-lb weight and two 10-lb weights.

Alternate Approach: Have students pretend that the mass weights for the pan balance are Adam's barbell weights, weighing pounds instead of grams. Have students divide the mass weights into identical groups of two—one group per pan. Have students find all symmetrical combinations for 70 gm ("70 lb") by actually balancing them on the pan balance.

Extension
Tell students that Adam has gotten so strong that he now needs 90 lb on the bar. Have students complete the problems on the activity page for a 90 lb bar.

Left side			Right side		
15 lb	10 lb	5 lb	15 lb	10 lb	5 lb
2	1	1	2	1	1
2	0	3	2	0	3
1	3	0	1	3	0
1	2	2	1	2	2
0	3	3	0	3	3

NAME ______________________

DECISION MAKING

Use the drawing and the following information to complete the chart.

Adam has the weights shown on the right. He is setting up a barbell so that the total weight is 70 pounds. He always sets up the barbell so that

- the weights on both sides are equal;
- the same kinds of weights are used on each side;
- the fewest number of weights is used.

1. Complete the chart in as many ways as possible.

Left Side			Right Side		
15 lb	10 lb	5 lb	15 lb	10 lb	5 lb
2	0	1	2	0	1
1	2	0	1	2	0
1	1	2	1	1	2
0	3	1	0	3	1
0	2	3	0	2	3

2. How do you think Adam should set up the barbell? Explain.

Possible answer: Use 1 fifteen-pound weight and 2 ten-pound weights on each side. This uses the fewest amount possible and they are all nearly the same size.

NAME ______________________

PROBLEM SOLVING

A store buys items at a wholesale price, adds a markup, and sells the items at the retail price. This can be shown as follows.

retail price	=	wholesale price	+	mark-up

1. Store and Pour charges $90 for a crystal pitcher after marking it up $48. What is the pitcher's wholesale price? ______________

2. Tall Tales sells a book that has a wholesale price of $3.99 and a markup of $4.00. What is the book's retail price? ______________

3. Music Makers sells a child's drum set for $49.95. Its wholesale price is $25.69. What is its markup? ______________

4. Billy's Bagels sells bagels that cost 10¢ to make. The markup for each bagel is 15¢. What is the retail price of a bagel? ______________

5. Hangup's normally sells a shirt for $28.00, but they put the shirt on sale by cutting the markup in half. The wholesale price is $15.80. What is the sale price? ______________

Teacher Notes

Use with
Objective 13
pages 34–35

Focus
Problem Solving
Write an Equation

Overview
Students solve problems for retail price, wholesale price, and markup using a simple equation.

Teaching Suggestions
Lead a discussion about retail pricing with students. ***Question:*** *How do stores make a profit on the items that they sell?* [They add a markup to the wholesale price of each item.] Have students copy the three-box equation shown on the activity page for each problem on the sheet. Have students leave enough room for numbers to be written in the boxes. There should be one three-box equation for each of Problems 1–4 and two three-box equations for Problem 5. Have students solve Problems 1–4 by filling in the boxes and solving the equations.

For Problem 5, have students first figure out the markup on the original price of $28.00 [$12.20]; next have students figure out the sale price by halving the original markup.

Extension
Explain to students that businesses often represent their markups in terms of percentage. ***Questions:*** *In Problems 1 and 2, what is the markup as a percentage of the wholesale price?* [To one decimal place, 114.3%; 100.3%] *In Problems 3 and 4, what is the markup as a percentage of the retail price?* [48.57%; 60%]

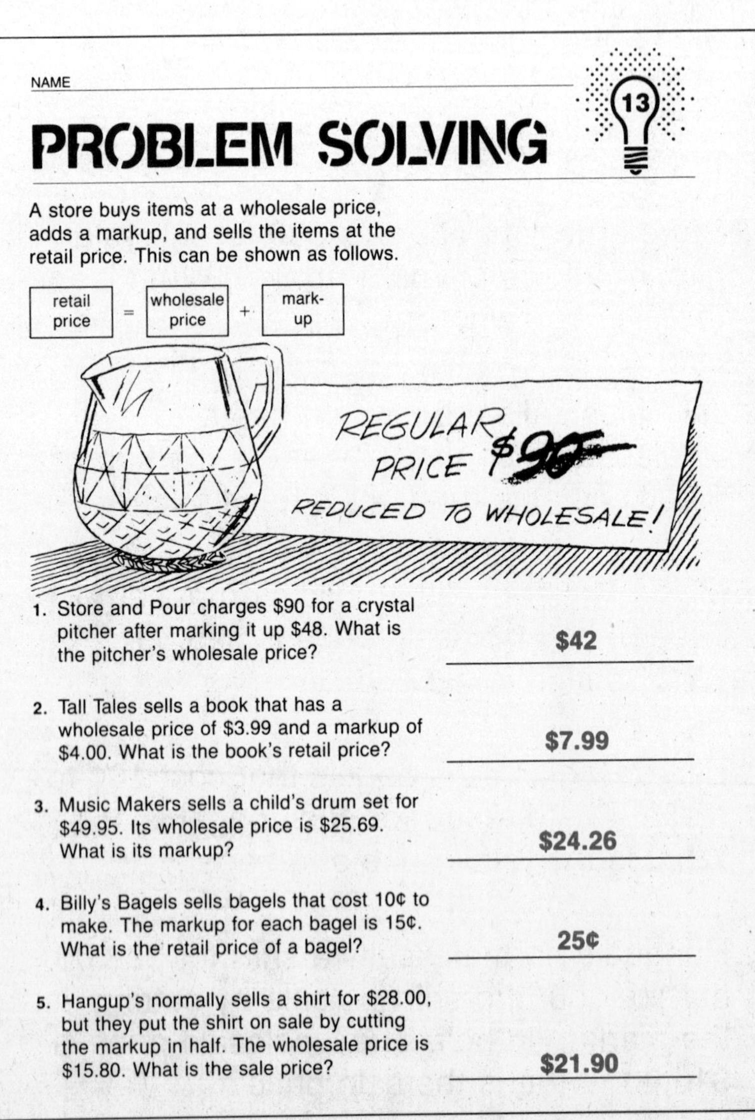
NAME ______

PROBLEM SOLVING

13

A store buys items at a wholesale price, adds a markup, and sells the items at the retail price. This can be shown as follows.

retail price	=	wholesale price	+	mark-up

1. Store and Pour charges $90 for a crystal pitcher after marking it up $48. What is the pitcher's wholesale price? **$42**

2. Tall Tales sells a book that has a wholesale price of $3.99 and a markup of $4.00. What is the book's retail price? **$7.99**

3. Music Makers sells a child's drum set for $49.95. Its wholesale price is $25.69. What is its markup? **$24.26**

4. Billy's Bagels sells bagels that cost 10¢ to make. The markup for each bagel is 15¢. What is the retail price of a bagel? **25¢**

5. Hangup's normally sells a shirt for $28.00, but they put the shirt on sale by cutting the markup in half. The wholesale price is $15.80. What is the sale price? **$21.90**

NAME ____________________

VISUAL THINKING

Ring the figure on the right that is either an enlargement or reduction of the figure on the left.

1. 

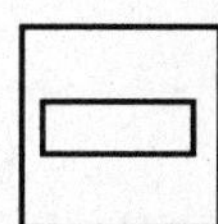  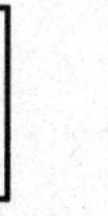 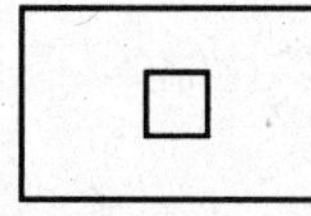 

a. b. c. d.

2. 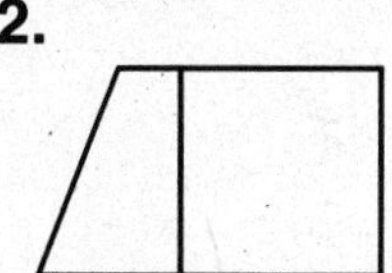

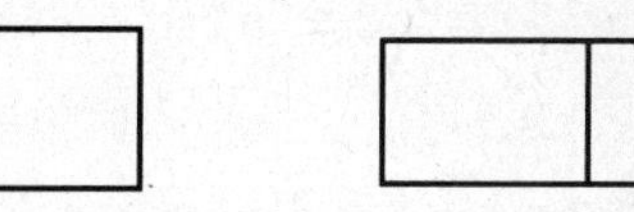

a. b. c. d.

3. 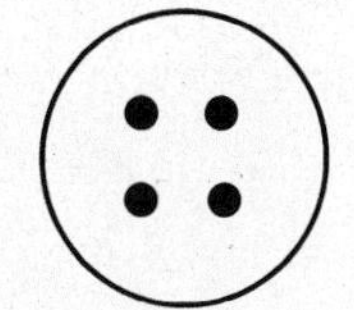

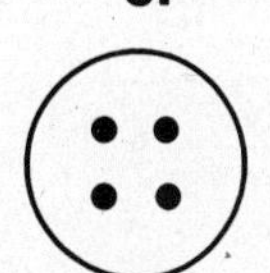 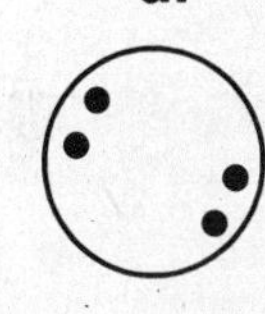

a. b. c. d.

4. 

a. b. c. d.

5. 

 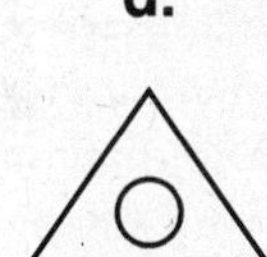 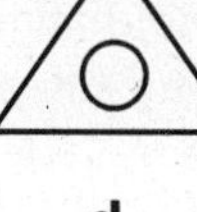

a. b. c. d.

6. 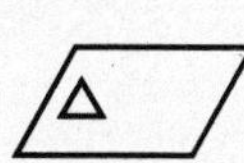

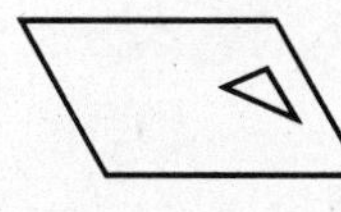 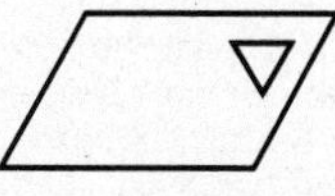

a. b. c. d.

7. 

a. b. c. d.

8. 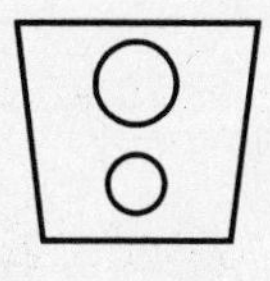

  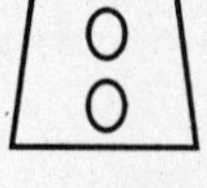

a. b. c. d.

Teacher Notes

Use with
Objective 14
pages 46–47

Focus
Visual Thinking
Spatial Perception

Materials
Transparent rulers
Visual Thinking transparency (optional)

Overview
Students match a figure with its enlargement or reduction.

Teaching Suggestions
As students work through the problems, guide them to observe that certain properties of the original figure are preserved in the enlargement (reduction). For example, lines that are straight in the original are also straight in the enlargement. ***Question:*** *Do angle measures change when a figure is enlarged or reduced?* [No] The positions of parts of the figure relative to each other are preserved. That is, the figure is not flipped or turned when it is enlarged.

Alternate Approach: If students are having difficulty matching the figures, allow them to use transparent rulers to measure the shapes for the first problem only. Then encourage them to solve the remaining problems visually.

Extension
If a photocopier that enlarges and reduces is available, have students experiment with specific size changes. For example, students can work in pairs: one student can draw a figure and reduce (or enlarge) it, say, to 75% of its actual size; the other student can try to estimate the percent of size change (without measuring).

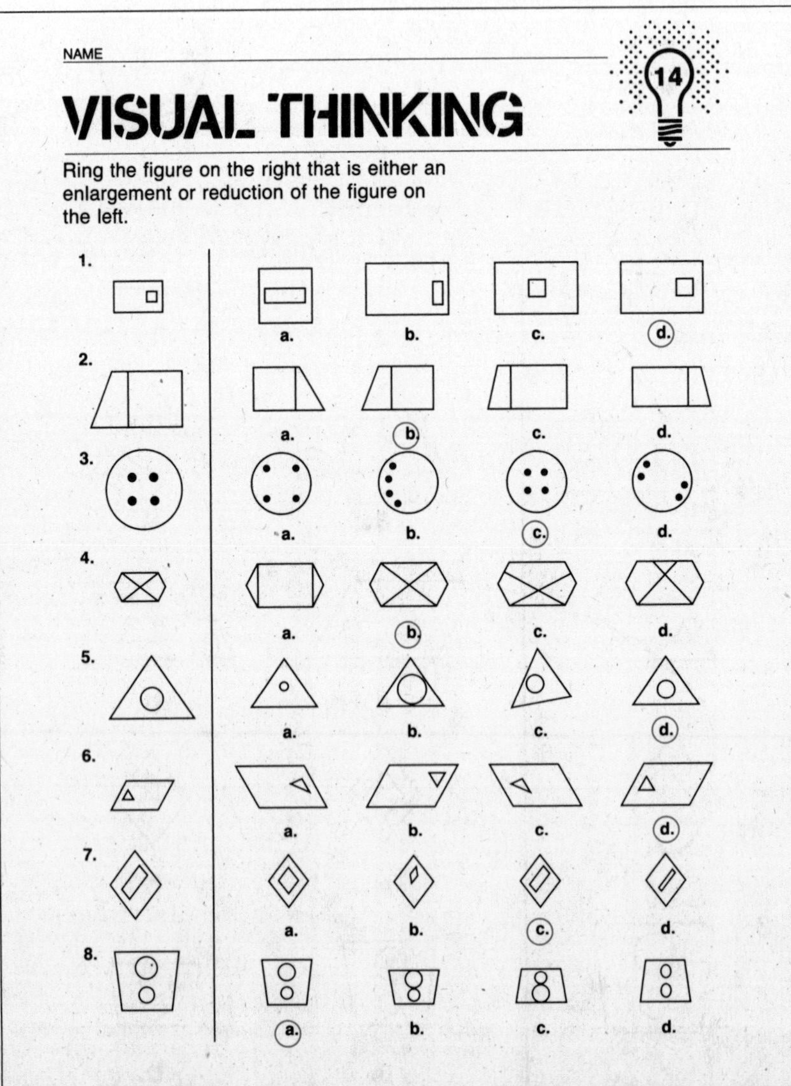

NAME ______________________________

CRITICAL THINKING

Five families live on the island shown below. Each family has a boat landing of its own. Each family wants a private path from their house to their boat dock. Dock A belongs to the family in House A, Dock B to the family in House B, and so on.

1. Draw a path from each house to its boat dock. None of the five paths should cross.

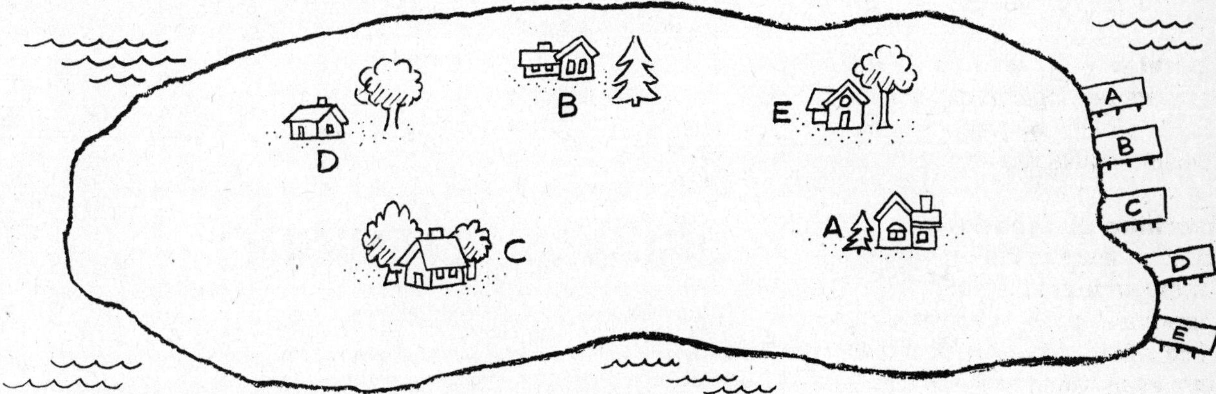

2. Suppose Family E and Family A decide to trade docks. Show how this would change the paths on the diagram below. Would this be a helpful trade for the families? Explain your answer.

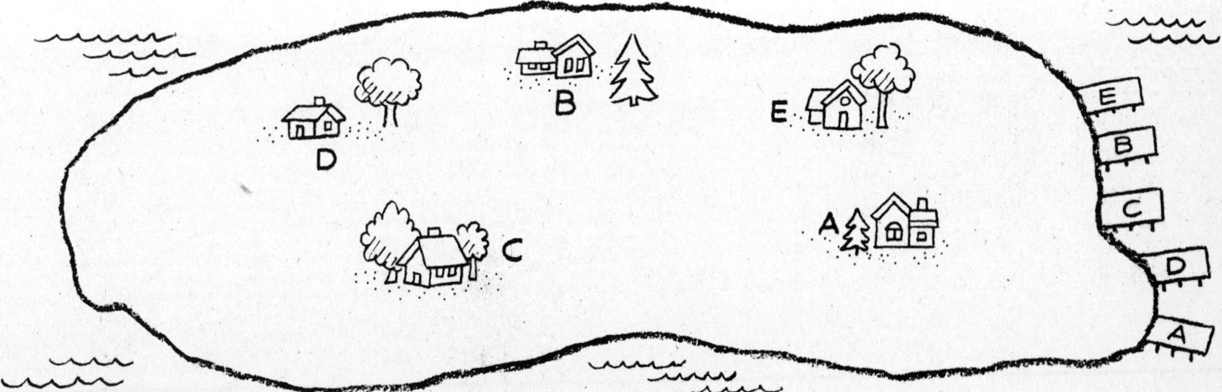

____

____

Teacher Notes

Use with
Objective 15
pages 48–49

Focus
Critical Thinking
Using Logic
Developing Alternatives
Finding and Extending Patterns

Materials
Colored yarn or string

Overview
Students *use logic* to develop alternate paths between sets of matched points.

Teaching Suggestions
Arrange desks in the classroom to simulate the houses and docks. Divide students into groups of five pairs each. Give each pair of students a long piece of different colored yarn to represent their path. Have students make as many different paths to the appropriate docks as possible.

Extension
Photocopy simple mazes found in many local newspaper "puzzle pages" or in puzzle books. Have students complete the mazes. If a maze has more than one solution, allow students to use different colored pencils to trace the different paths.

Ask students to trace the figure below without lifting the pencil from the page and without tracing over any line. One possible solution is shown.

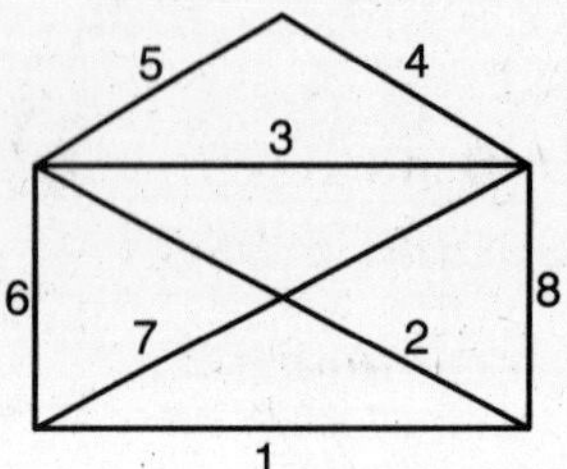

NAME ______________________

CRITICAL THINKING

Five families live on the island shown below. Each family has a boat landing of its own. Each family wants a private path from their house to their boat dock. Dock A belongs to the family in House A, Dock B to the family in House B, and so on.

1. Show how the families could lay out five paths that do not cross.

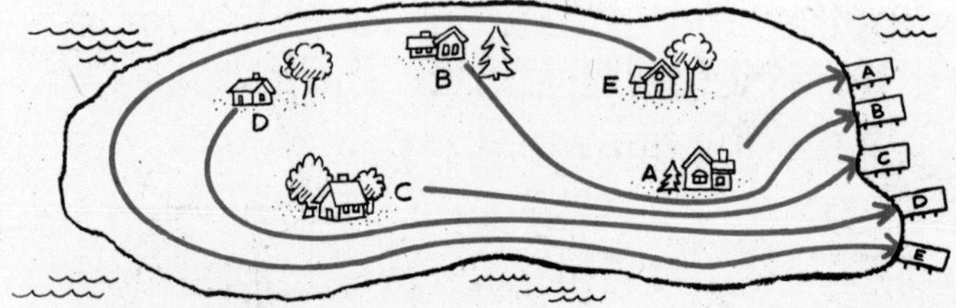

2. Suppose Family E and Family A decide to trade docks. Show how this would change the paths on the diagram below. Would this be a helpful trade for the families? Explain your answer.

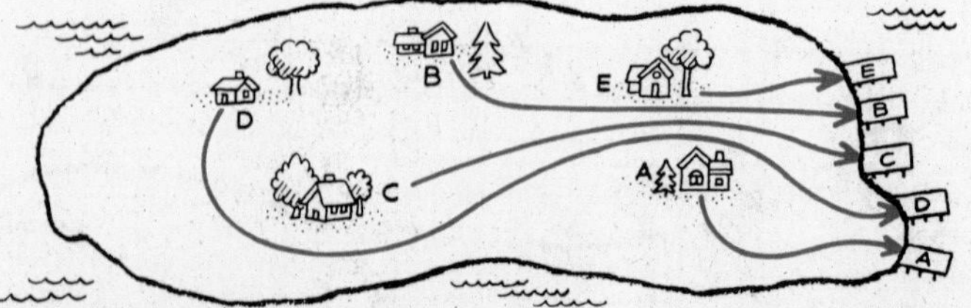

It would be helpful. Most families would have a shorter distance to travel.

NAME ____

PROBLEM SOLVING

Suppose a pair of rabbits has 8 baby rabbits in a litter. Each of these baby rabbits grows up and produces another 8 baby rabbits. These new rabbits grow up to produce another 8 baby rabbits each, and so on. Use this information to answer the problems.

1. Write an equation to show the total number of rabbits in the first ten generations. Count the first two rabbits as the first generation.

____

____

2. If an average-sized cage can hold twenty adult rabbits, how many cages will be needed to hold the first and second generation of rabbits? The first through third? The first through fourth generations?

____

3. If the building these rabbits are housed in can support 1,000,000 pounds and each adult rabbit weighs 5 pounds, how many generations of rabbits will the building support?

____

Teacher Notes

Use with
Objective 16
pages 50–51

Focus
Problem Solving
Write an Equation

Materials
Calculator (optional)

Overview
Students write an expression using exponents to determine the number of rabbits in successive generations.

Teaching Suggestions
Guide students to see that the total number n of rabbits in a given generation g is $n = 2 + 8 + 8^2 + 8^3 + ... + 8^{g-1}$. ***Questions:*** *How could you write the number of rabbits produced during the third generation using exponents?* [8^2] *How could you write the number of rabbits produced during the fourth generation using exponents?* [8^3]

For Problem 2, make sure that students realize that they must include a cage to accommodate the rabbits that remain after dividing the total into groups of 20.

Problem 3 can be solved by taking the total number of rabbits in 6 generations (37,450) and multiplying this by the weight of each rabbit. The weight of 6 generations of rabbits is 187,250 pounds.

In a similar way, students can find that the total weight of the rabbits in 7 generations is 299,594 × 5 or 1,497,970 lb.

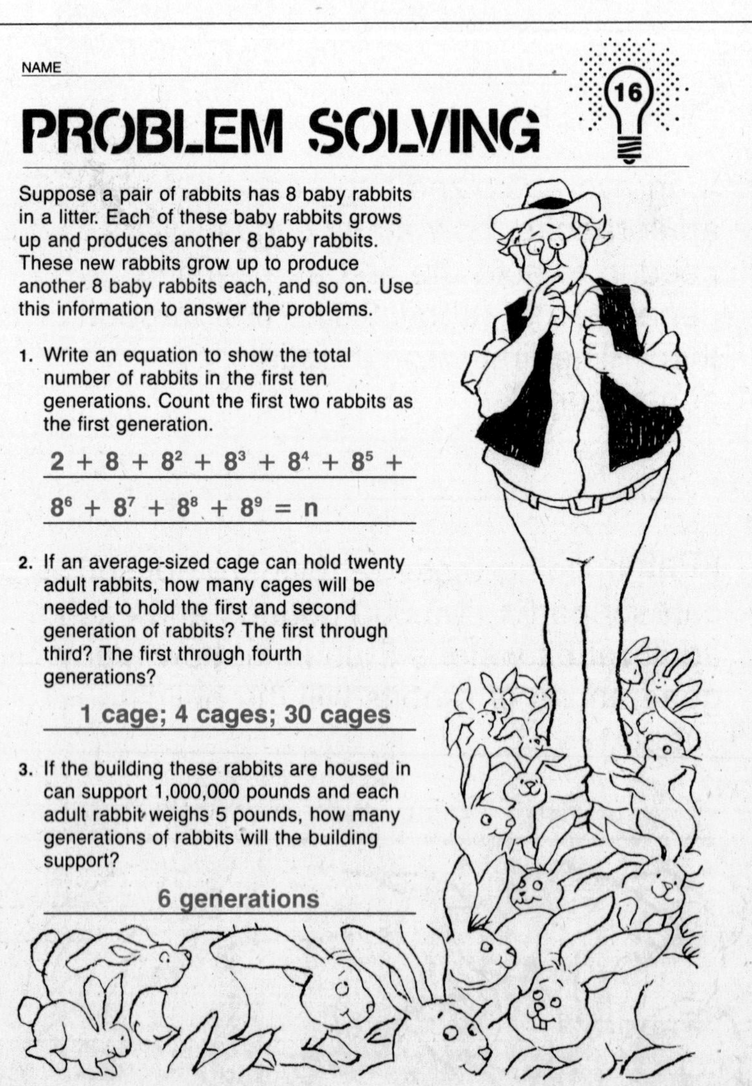
NAME ____________

16

PROBLEM SOLVING

Suppose a pair of rabbits has 8 baby rabbits in a litter. Each of these baby rabbits grows up and produces another 8 baby rabbits. These new rabbits grow up to produce another 8 baby rabbits each, and so on. Use this information to answer the problems.

1. Write an equation to show the total number of rabbits in the first ten generations. Count the first two rabbits as the first generation.

   $2 + 8 + 8^2 + 8^3 + 8^4 + 8^5 + 8^6 + 8^7 + 8^8 + 8^9 = n$

2. If an average-sized cage can hold twenty adult rabbits, how many cages will be needed to hold the first and second generation of rabbits? The first through third? The first through fourth generations?

   1 cage; 4 cages; 30 cages

3. If the building these rabbits are housed in can support 1,000,000 pounds and each adult rabbit weighs 5 pounds, how many generations of rabbits will the building support?

   6 generations

NAME ______________________________

VISUAL THINKING

Find the pattern in each of these block arrangements. Draw the next figure in the pattern, then write a description of the pattern.

1.

Pattern: ______________________________

____

2.

Pattern: ______________________________

____

3.

Pattern: ______________________________

____

4.

Pattern: ______________________________

____

Teacher Notes

Use with
Objective 17
pages 52–53

Focus
Visual Thinking
Visual Patterns

Overview
Students determine patterns in successive figures made by adding blocks to an existing figure.

Teaching Suggestions
It may be useful to allow students to use colored pencils to shade the same blocks in each of the figures to help them determine the patterns used. For example, in Problem 3, students could shade the first figure blue. Those same blocks should be blue in successive figures. The additional blocks in the second figure could be colored red; therefore, the second figure would be blue and red. Yellow could be added to the third figure, and so on.

Extension
Have students develop their own block patterns, exchange papers, and analyze each others' patterns.

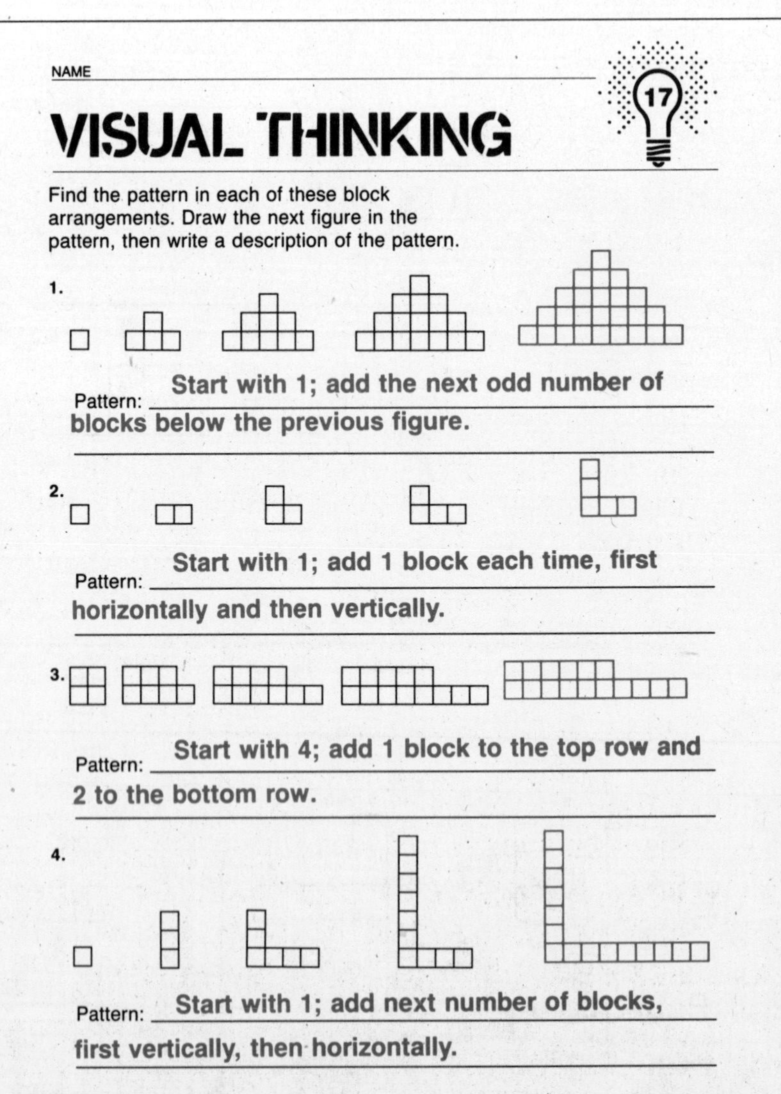

NAME

VISUAL THINKING

17

Find the pattern in each of these block arrangements. Draw the next figure in the pattern, then write a description of the pattern.

1.

Pattern: **Start with 1; add the next odd number of blocks below the previous figure.**

2.

Pattern: **Start with 1; add 1 block each time, first horizontally and then vertically.**

3.

Pattern: **Start with 4; add 1 block to the top row and 2 to the bottom row.**

4.

Pattern: **Start with 1; add next number of blocks, first vertically, then horizontally.**

NAME ______________________________

CRITICAL THINKING

Use the pictures of the dinosaurs below to solve the problems.

1. Which dinosaur do you estimate is longer, torosaurus or stegosaurus? ______________

2. Suppose stegosaurus is 20 feet long. Johnny estimates the length of apatosaurus to be 40 feet, while Ted estimates it to be 50 feet. Who is closer? Explain your answer.

____

____

3. Imagine a box big enough to ship a life-size model of torosaurus. How many times longer than that would a box have to be to ship a life-size model of apatosaurus? How many times taller?

____

Use after pages 54–57.

Teacher Notes

Use with
Objective 18
pages 54–57

Focus
Critical Thinking
Making and Testing Predictions

Materials
String

Overview
Students make and test estimates of sizes of dinosaurs from pictures.

Teaching Suggestions
After students have completed the problems, ask them to decide if their estimates would be better tested using a wooden stick or a piece of string. Students should realize that the string, being flexible, would yield better results than the stick, especially when estimating the size of apatosaurus, whose tail is curled.

Alternate Approach: Give students pieces of string to test their estimates.

Extension
Show students the optical illusion in the next column. Ask them to guess which of the hat's dimensions is greater, its height or width. [Possible answer: Its height] Have a volunteer measure the hat to see that the width is actually greater.

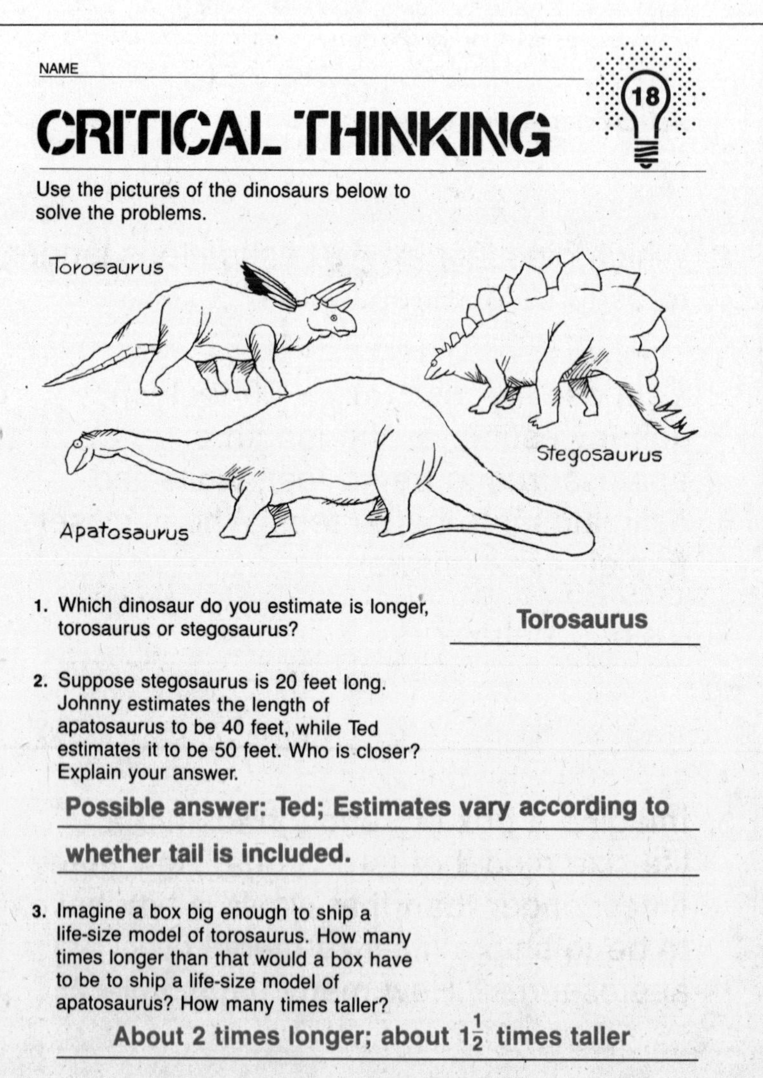

NAME ____________

CRITICAL THINKING

18

Use the pictures of the dinosaurs below to solve the problems.

1. Which dinosaur do you estimate is longer, torosaurus or stegosaurus? **Torosaurus**

2. Suppose stegosaurus is 20 feet long. Johnny estimates the length of apatosaurus to be 40 feet, while Ted estimates it to be 50 feet. Who is closer? Explain your answer.
Possible answer: Ted; Estimates vary according to whether tail is included.

3. Imagine a box big enough to ship a life-size model of torosaurus. How many times longer than that would a box have to be to ship a life-size model of apatosaurus? How many times taller?
About 2 times longer; about $1\frac{1}{2}$ times taller

NAME ______________________________

PROBLEM SOLVING

Jill's Gasoline Station is in Canada. The price on her sign refers to Canadian dollars and the British imperial gallon.

Bob's Gasoline Station is in the United States. The price on his sign refers to U.S. dollars and the U.S. gallon.

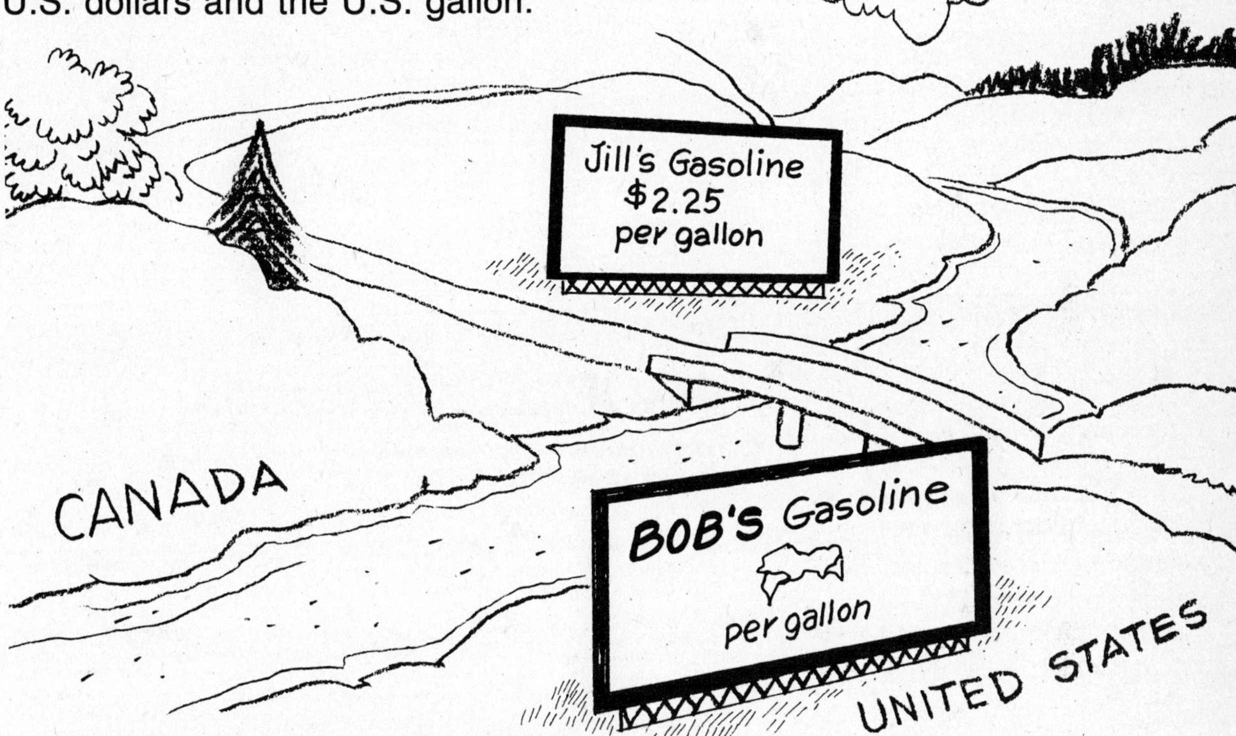

1. One imperial gallon is equal to 1.2 U.S. gallons. How many U.S. gallons would $6.75 in Canadian money buy at Jill's gas station? ______________

2. Suppose $1.00 in Canadian currency has the same value as $.80 in U.S. currency. What is the value of $2.25 (Canadian) in U.S. currency? ______________

3. What price in U.S. dollars should be posted on Bob's sign if he wants to charge the same as Jill does for an equal amount of gasoline? ______________

Use after pages 58–59.

Teacher Notes

Use with
Objective 19
pages 58–59

Focus
Problem Solving
Write an Equation

Overview
Students write and solve equations to determine a U.S. equivalent for Canadian measures and money.

Teaching Suggestions
For Problem 1, students must first compute the number of imperial gallons $6.75 would buy. ***Question:** How many imperial gallons would $6.75 in Canadian money buy?* [3] Multiplying this result by 1.2 equals 3.6 U.S. gallons.

Problem 2 can be solved by writing a proportion between Canadian and U.S. dollars and solving for the unknown.

Canadian dollars → / U.S. dollars → $\frac{1}{0.80} = \frac{2.25}{n}$

$n = 0.80 \times 2.25 = 1.8$

Problem 3 can also be solved by a proportion.

U.S. dollars → / U.S. gallons → $\frac{1.80}{1.20} = \frac{n}{1}$

Extension
Inform students that foreign-exchange rates fluctuate daily. Find the current rate of the Canadian dollar. Let students also solve the problems using this rate if it differs from $0.80 U.S.

Ask students to find exchange rates for various foreign currencies in the business sections of large newspapers. Then have them calculate the cost of their favorite school lunch in another country.

NAME

PROBLEM SOLVING

19

Jill's Gasoline Station is in Canada. The price on her sign refers to Canadian dollars and the British imperial gallon.

Bob's Gasoline Station is in the United States. The price on his sign refers to U.S. dollars and the U.S. gallon.

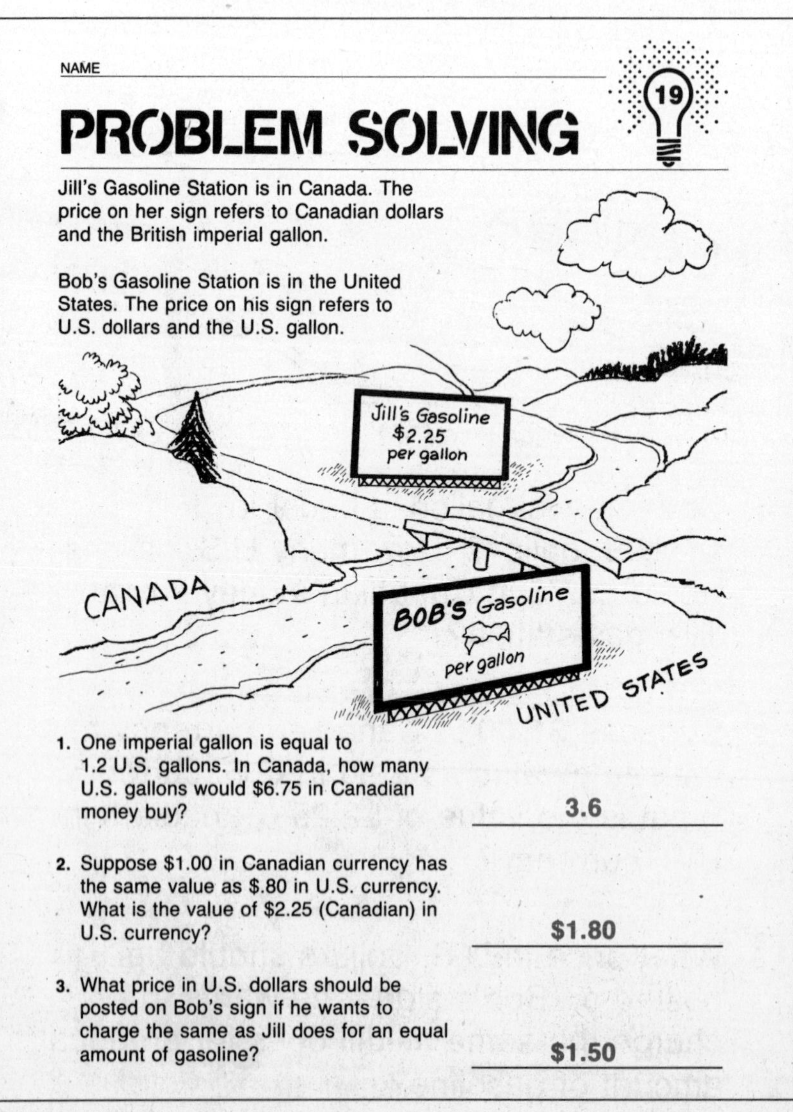

1. One imperial gallon is equal to 1.2 U.S. gallons. In Canada, how many U.S. gallons would $6.75 in Canadian money buy? **3.6**
2. Suppose $1.00 in Canadian currency has the same value as $.80 in U.S. currency. What is the value of $2.25 (Canadian) in U.S. currency? **$1.80**
3. What price in U.S. dollars should be posted on Bob's sign if he wants to charge the same as Jill does for an equal amount of gasoline? **$1.50**

NAME ______________________________

VISUAL THINKING

Ring the letters of the two figures on the right that will form the figure on the left when joined. The figures may be flipped or turned, but they cannot overlap, and there cannot be gaps.

1. a. b. c. d. e.

2. a. b. c. d. e.

3. a. b. c. d. e.

4. a. b. c. d. e.

5. a. b. c. d. e.

6. a. b. c. d. e.

7. a. b. c. d. e.

Teacher Notes

Use with
Objective 20
pages 60–61

Focus
Visual Thinking
Spatial Perception

Materials
Visual Thinking transparency (optional)
Jigsaw puzzle pieces

Overview
Students determine which two of five given figures can be used to form a given larger figure.

Teaching Suggestions
This activity may be only moderately difficult for some students, but somewhat more difficult for others. If students appear to need help, suggest that they use a small index card to cover parts of the original figure in order to see properties of the figure more clearly. The activity may also be done as a class using the visual thinking transparency.

Alternate Approach:
Associating the figures with known objects might also help some students. For example, Figure 1 resembles a coin, Figure 2 a sheet of paper, and so on.

Extension
Obtain pieces of jigsaw puzzles whose colors are the same and whose edges are very similar. Puzzles with 1,000 pieces or more work well. Give each student 10 or more of the pieces, making sure ahead of time that some pieces do connect while others do not. Do not let students look at the picture of the completed puzzle. Have students guess and test which pieces will fit together.

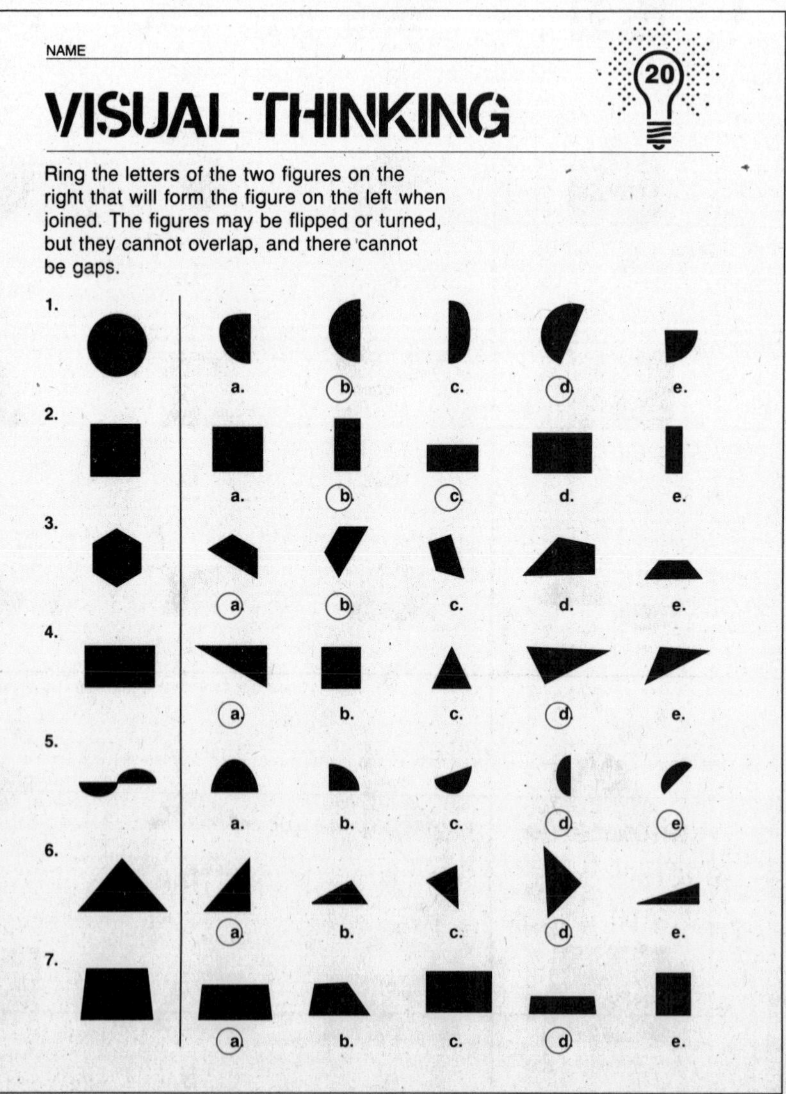

NAME ______________________________

DECISION MAKING

Frances is trying to limit her intake of fat and sodium. Checking the nutritional content of the cereals she likes to eat for breakfast, she found the following information:

Brand	Serving	Fat	Sodium
Crunchettes	28.3 g	2.3 g	60.5 mg
Flakoids	28.3 g	4.1 g	70.2 mg
Bran-o-Rama	28.3 g	4.6 g	49.3 mg

1. Complete the table below.

   Weekly Amounts (1 serving per day)

	Fat (g)	Sodium (mg)
Crunchettes		
Flakoids		
Bran-o-Rama		

2. How much fat and sodium will Frances consume if she eats one serving of Crunchettes for 4 days and one serving of Flakoids for 3 days? If she eats Bran-o-Rama for 3 days and Flakoids for 4 days?

____

____

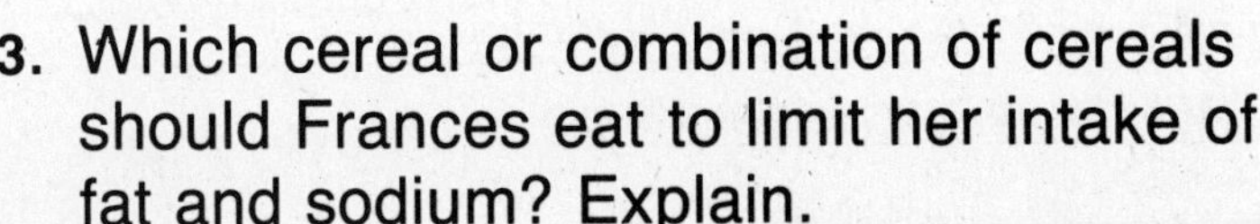

3. Which cereal or combination of cereals should Frances eat to limit her intake of fat and sodium? Explain.

____

____

Teacher Notes

Use with
Objective 21
pages 62–63

Focus
Decision Making

Overview
Students compute the amounts of certain nutrients in breakfast cereals to determine which provides the least fat and sodium. They must then decide which cereal (or combination of cereals) will limit intake of fat and sodium.

Teaching Suggestions
To complete the table, students must multiply the amount of fat and sodium per serving by the number of days in a week.

Explain that there are recommended daily allowances (RDAs) for nutrients, determined by the Food & Drug Administration. The recommended daily allowance for adults and children for sodium is 500 mg per day. (This is a reduction of the 1,100–3,300 mg per day that was once acceptable.) The recommended safe allowance for adults and children for fat is approximately 30% of a person's caloric intake per day. ***Question:*** *How many servings of Flakoids would Frances have to eat in a day to meet the recommended safe allowance for sodium?* [Approximately 7]

Extension
Have students research food packages to find out how the various nutrients in each product compare to the daily recommended allowances. They might find some information by reading a book about sensible eating or by calling a nutrition specialist. The Federal Government also publishes materials explaining the RDAs for all nutrients.

Based on this information, have students propose a sensible diet for the class for one week.

NAME

DECISION MAKING

21

Frances is trying to limit her intake of fat and sodium. Checking the nutritional content of the cereals she likes to eat for breakfast, she found the following information:

Brand	Serving	Fat	Sodium
Crunchettes	28.3 g	2.3 g	60.5 mg
Flakoids	28.3 g	4.1 g	70.2 mg
Bran-o-Rama	28.3 g	4.6 g	49.3 mg

1. Complete the table below.
   Weekly Amounts (1 serving per day)

	Fat (g)	Sodium (mg)
Crunchettes	16.1	423.5
Flakoids	28.7	491.4
Bran-o-Rama	32.2	345.1

2. How much fat and sodium will Frances consume if she eats one serving of Crunchettes for 4 days and one serving of Flakoids for 3 days? If she eats Bran-o-Rama for 3 days and Flakoids for 4 days?
   C&F: fat 21.5 g, sodium 452.6 mg;
   B&F: fat 30.2 g, sodium 428.7 mg

3. Which cereal or combination of cereals should Frances eat to limit her intake of fat and sodium? Explain.
   Possible answer: Mix Crunchettes and Bran-o-Rama;
   average fat: 3.45 g, average sodium: 54.9 g

NAME ___________________________________

PROBLEM SOLVING

Anna, Jose, and Glenn entered a walk-a-thon to raise money for charity. The 12-mile walk had 5 checkpoints (*A*,*B*,*C*,*D*,*E*); one every 2 miles. Anna, Jose, and Glenn began entering their times on a table.

1. Complete the table, assuming the patterns shown will continue.

	Start to *A* (min)	*A* to *B* (min)	*B* to *C* (min)	*C* to *D* (min)	*D* to *E* (min)	*E* to Finish (min)
Anna	39	41	43			
Jose	46	45	44			
Glenn	44	44	44			

2. Who reached the halfway point of the walk-a-thon first? How long did it take? ____________________

3. Who reached the halfway point last? How long did it take? ____________________

4. Which checkpoint did Jose and Glenn reach at the same time? ____________________

5. Who finished the walk-a-thon first? How long did it take? ____________________

Teacher Notes

Use with
Objective 22
pages 66–67

Focus
Problem Solving
Make a Table

Overview
Students complete a table using patterns in the given data to determine how long it took each of three walkers to reach various points in a 12-mile walk.

Teaching Suggestions
To complete the table, students should determine that Anna's times increased by 2 minutes from checkpoint to checkpoint; Jose's times decreased by one minute; and Glenn's rate of walking was constant. Point out that students must assume these patterns will remain constant for the remaining distance.

Extension
Anna arrived at checkpoint *E* 5 minutes before Jose and Glenn did. Assume that each walker travels at a constant rate between checkpoints. Tell students to find the approximate point at which Jose passed Anna. [Approximately 26 minutes after Jose passed checkpoint *E*, or about 1-1/4 miles from checkpoint *E*]

NAME

PROBLEM SOLVING

22

Anna, Jose, and Glenn entered a walk-a-thon to raise money for charity. The 12-mile walk had 5 checkpoints (*A,B,C,D,E*); one every 2 miles. Anna, Jose, and Glenn began entering their times on a table.

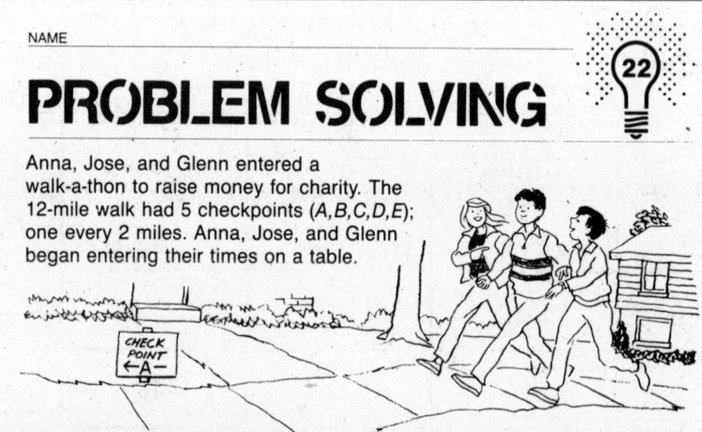

1. Complete the table, assuming the patterns shown will continue.

	Start to *A* (min)	*A* to *B* (min)	*B* to *C* (min)	*C* to *D* (min)	*D* to *E* (min)	*E* to Finish (min)
Anna	39	41	43	**45**	**47**	**49**
Jose	46	45	44	**43**	**42**	**41**
Glenn	44	44	44	**44**	**44**	**44**

2. Who reached the halfway point of the walk-a-thon first? How long did it take? **Anna; 123 minutes**

3. Who reached the halfway point last? How long did it take? **Jose; 135 minutes**

4. Which checkpoint did Jose and Glenn reach at the same time? **Checkpoint *E***

5. Who finished the walk-a-thon first? How long did it take? **Jose; 261 minutes**

NAME ____________________

CRITICAL THINKING

People use reasoning to form conclusions about a situation. In one kind of reasoning "If..., then..." statements are used.

Example:
If..., then... statement:
If our class raises enough money, then we can go on a field trip.
Fact: Our class raises enough money.
Conclusion: We can go on a field trip.

Complete each exercise to show the same kind of reasoning used in the example.

1. If..., then... statement:
If the dinosaur is a torosaurus, then it has horns.

Fact: The dinosaur is a torosaurus.

Conclusion: ____________________

2. If..., then... statement:
If the dinosaur is a tyrannosaurus rex, then it has many sharp teeth.

Fact: ____________________

Conclusion: ____________________

3. If..., then... statement:
If the dinosaur is a ankylosaurus, then it has bony armor on its back.

Fact: ____________________

Conclusion: ____________________

Teacher Notes

Use with
Objective 23
pages 68–71

Focus
Critical Thinking
Using Logic
Making Generalizations
Justifying Answers
Evaluating Evidence and Conclusions

Overview
Students evaluate logic statements to form conclusions about the physical characteristics of certain kinds of dinosaurs.

Teaching Suggestions
After students have completed the problems, emphasize the subtleties of logic by posing the following statement: *If a dinosaur has horns, it is a Torosaurus.* If any of the students think this is a true statement, refer them to the worksheet for Objective 18, which shows a horned Stegosaurus. This example illustrates that the converse of an "If . . . , then . . ." statement is, in general, not true.

Extension
Have students write their own logic statements. Suggest using familiar objects and situations. Have them exchange statements with one another and decide if the statements always hold true.

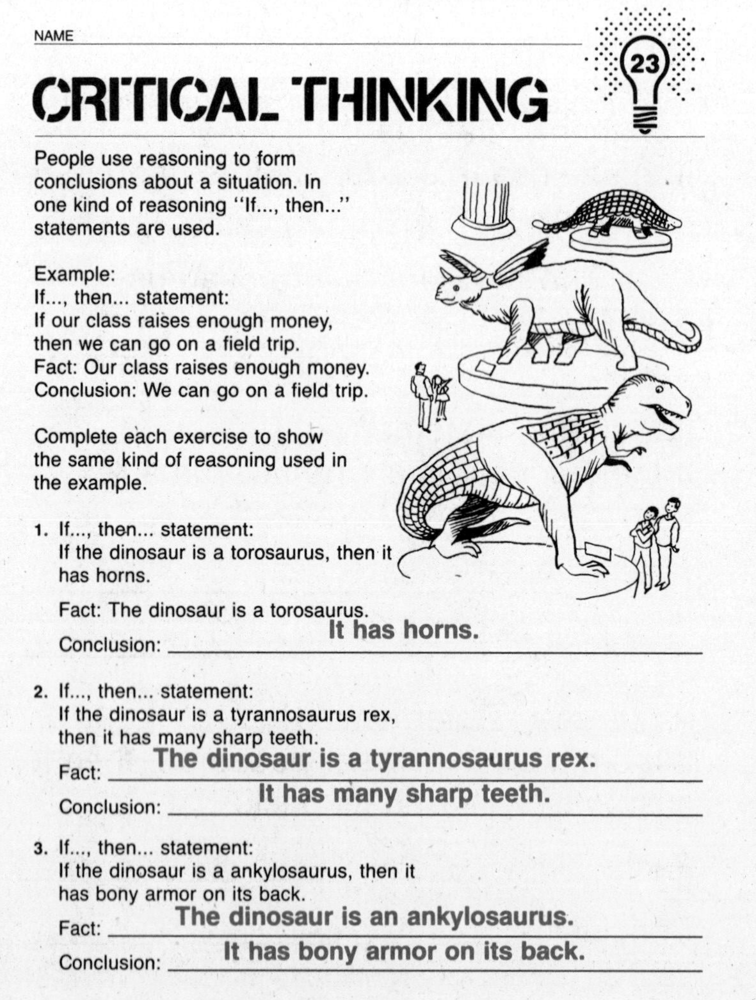

NAME ______________________

23

CRITICAL THINKING

People use reasoning to form conclusions about a situation. In one kind of reasoning "If..., then..." statements are used.

Example:
If..., then... statement:
If our class raises enough money, then we can go on a field trip.
Fact: Our class raises enough money.
Conclusion: We can go on a field trip.

Complete each exercise to show the same kind of reasoning used in the example.

1. If..., then... statement:
If the dinosaur is a torosaurus, then it has horns.
Fact: The dinosaur is a torosaurus.
Conclusion: **It has horns.**

2. If..., then... statement:
If the dinosaur is a tyrannosaurus rex, then it has many sharp teeth.
Fact: **The dinosaur is a tyrannosaurus rex.**
Conclusion: **It has many sharp teeth.**

3. If..., then... statement:
If the dinosaur is a ankylosaurus, then it has bony armor on its back.
Fact: **The dinosaur is an ankylosaurus.**
Conclusion: **It has bony armor on its back.**

NAME

CRITICAL THINKING

Georgia stretched a rubberband on a pegboard to form the figure below.

Then Georgia removed some pegs to see how the figure would change. On the pegboards below, some pegs have been removed. Draw how the rubberband shape shown above would change on each one.

1. 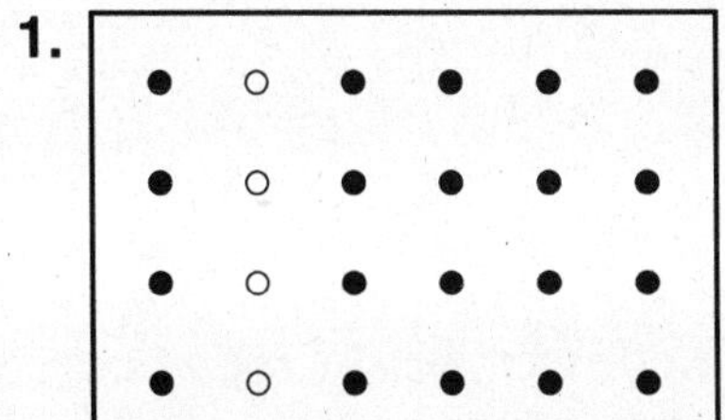

2. 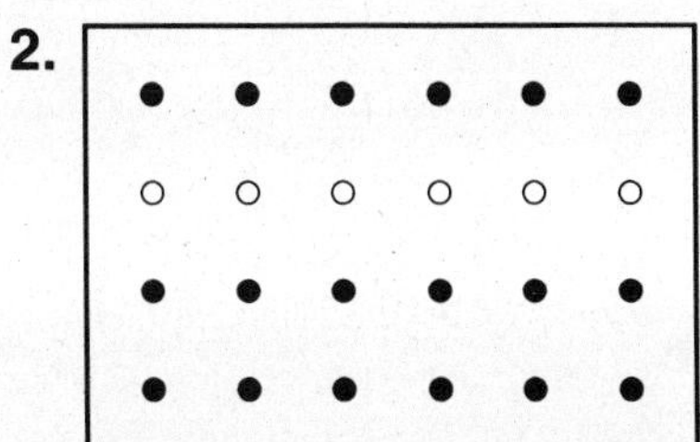

3. 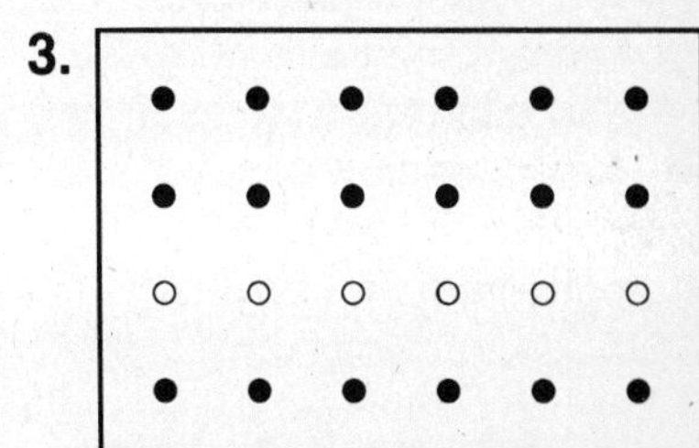

4. 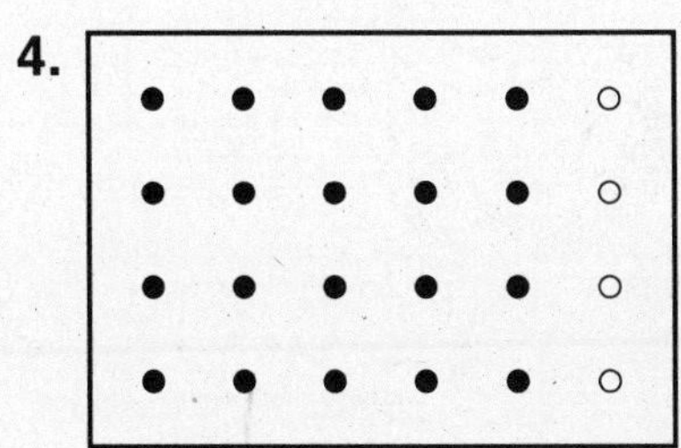

5. 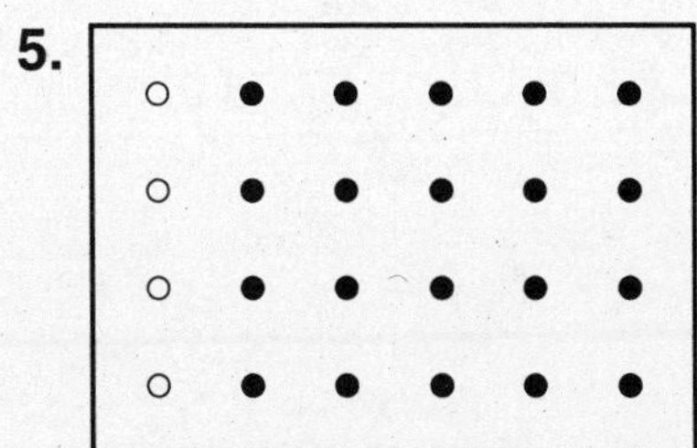

6. 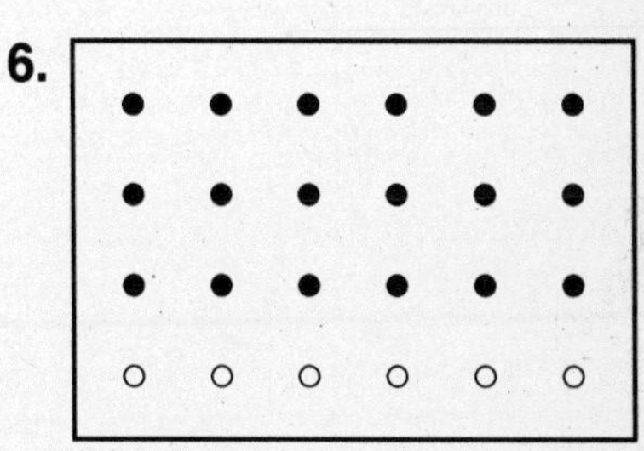

Teacher Notes

Use with
Objective 24
pages 72–73

Focus
Critical Thinking
Using Logic
Drawing Conclusions
Extending Patterns

Overview
Students *use logic* to *draw conclusions* about the behavior of a rubber band on a pegboard. They use these conclusions to *extend patterns* on different pegboards.

Teaching Suggestions
Before students try to do the problems, make sure students study Georgia's original figure to determine whether the rubberband is to the left or right or is above or below each peg. This is a critical step in determining each solution.

For more practice, reproduce Georgia's pegboard with different numbers removed from different rows as in the example below.

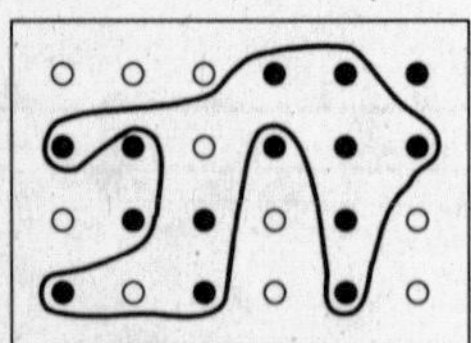

Extension
Obtain a few knitting tubes used by children to knit. Make sure there are at least 10 pegs in each knitter. Allow students to wrap the yarn around different numbers of pegs to form different stitches and patterns. Have students compare and contrast their results.

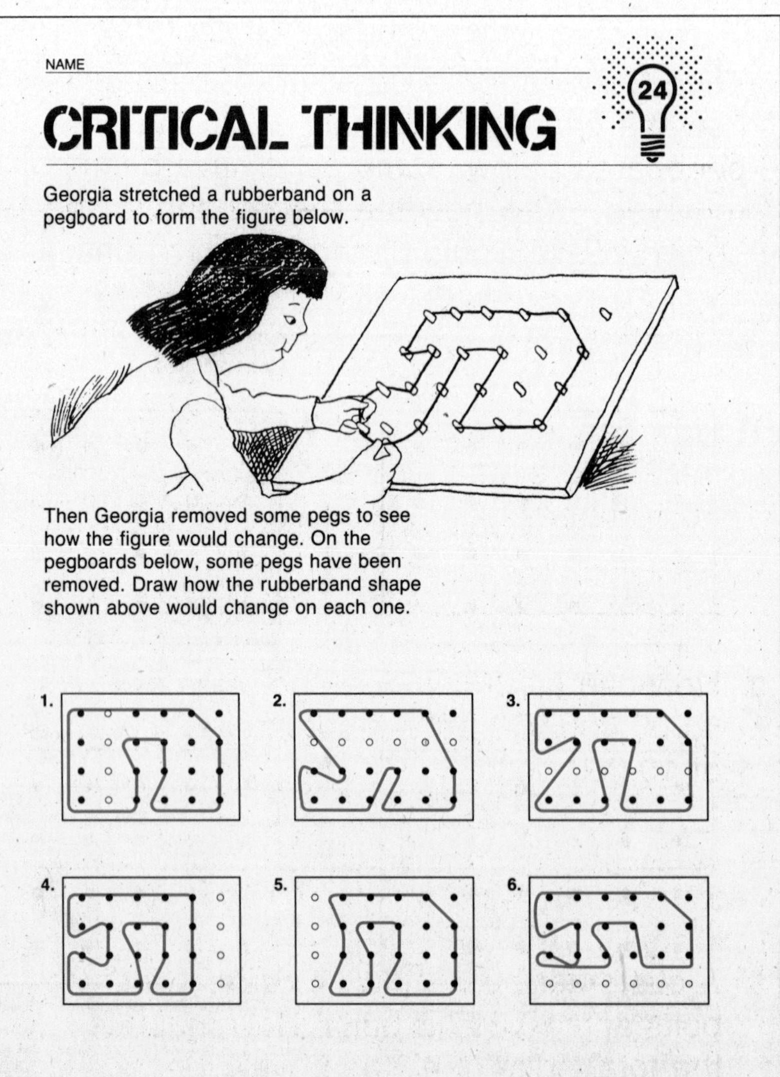
NAME

CRITICAL THINKING

24

Georgia stretched a rubberband on a pegboard to form the figure below.

Then Georgia removed some pegs to see how the figure would change. On the pegboards below, some pegs have been removed. Draw how the rubberband shape shown above would change on each one.

1. 2. 3. 4. 5. 6.

NAME ______

PROBLEM SOLVING

Lynn sells packages of bolts in a hardware store. The bolts can be sold in packages of 10, 100, 1,000, or 10,000. Complete the table to solve the problems.

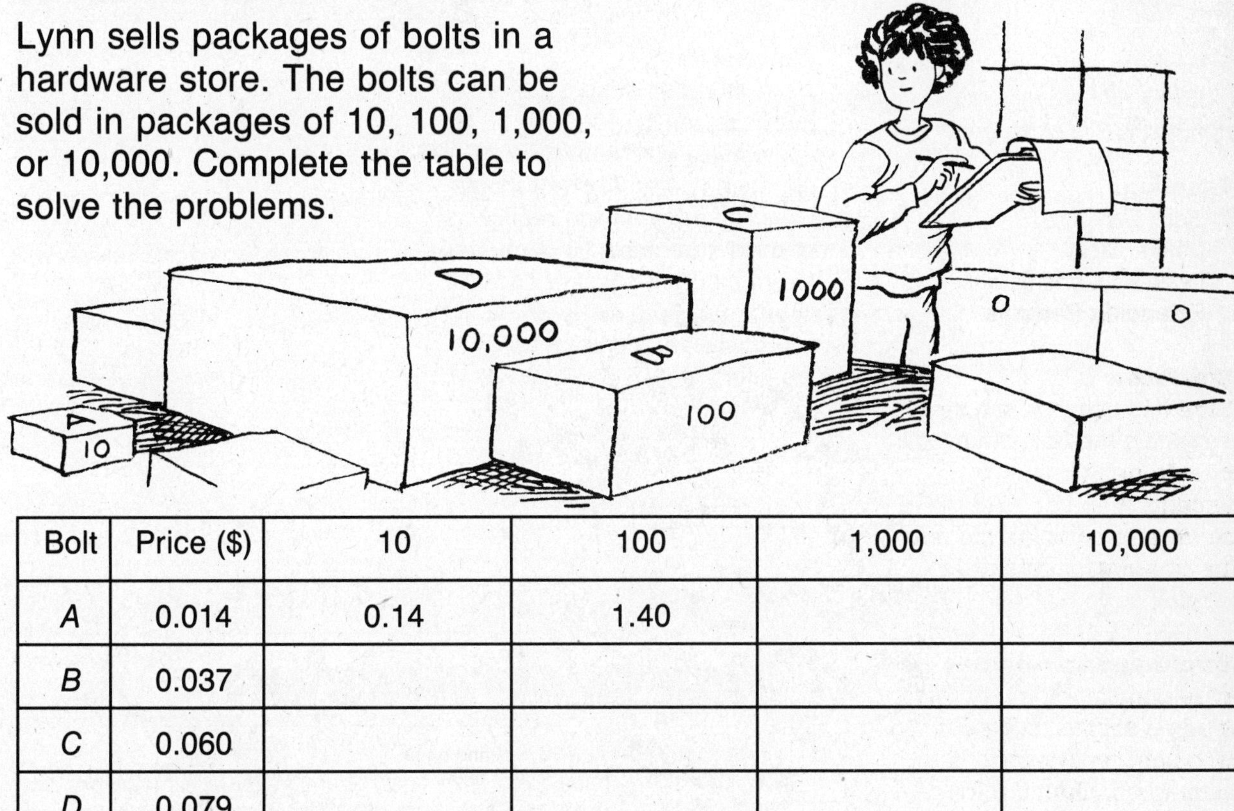

Bolt	Price ($)	10	100	1,000	10,000
A	0.014	0.14	1.40		
B	0.037				
C	0.060				
D	0.079				
E	0.103				

1. How can Lynn compute the price of 1,000,000 bolts if she knows the price of 10,000 bolts?

______

2. How can Lynn compute the price of 1,000,000,000 bolts if she knows the price of 10,000 bolts?

______

3. A customer buys 1,000 *A* bolts, 1,000 *B* bolts and 10,000 *E* bolts. How much is the total price of all the bolts? ______

Teacher Notes

Use with
Objective 25
pages 74–75

Focus
Problem Solving
Make a Table
Find a Pattern
Write an Equation

Overview
Students complete a table by computing the cost of several items from their unit prices. Students then use patterns in the table to compute the cost of a combination of different items.

Teaching Suggestions
While completing the table, students should recognize that each consecutive price is a factor of 10. ***Question:*** *What would you have to spend for bolts if you were building an object that required 10 A bolts, 101 B bolts, 1,500 D bolts, and an E bolt?* [$0.14 + $4.07 + $118.50 + $1.03 = $123.74] Make sure students realize that the bolts are sold only in the packages listed. Thus, the minimum number of B bolts that must be purchased is 110.

Extension
Have students suppose that the bolts can be sold individually and have them compute how much they would have to spend for the number of bolts described. [$122.48]

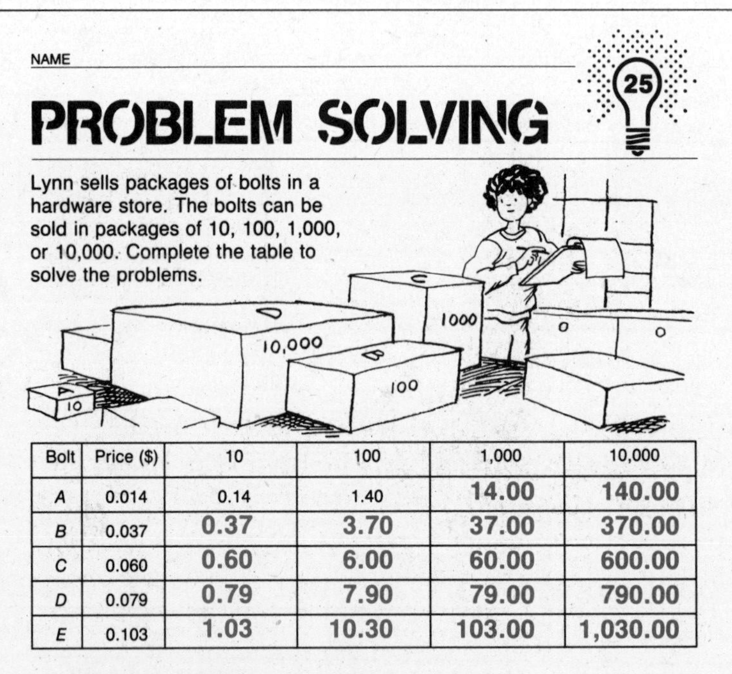

NAME

PROBLEM SOLVING

25

Lynn sells packages of bolts in a hardware store. The bolts can be sold in packages of 10, 100, 1,000, or 10,000. Complete the table to solve the problems.

Bolt	Price ($)	10	100	1,000	10,000
A	0.014	0.14	1.40	**14.00**	**140.00**
B	0.037	**0.37**	**3.70**	**37.00**	**370.00**
C	0.060	**0.60**	**6.00**	**60.00**	**600.00**
D	0.079	**0.79**	**7.90**	**79.00**	**790.00**
E	0.103	**1.03**	**10.30**	**103.00**	**1,030.00**

1. How can Lynn compute the price of 1,000,000 bolts if she knows the price of 10,000 bolts?

   Multiply the price by 100.

2. How can Lynn compute the price of 1,000,000,000 bolts if she knows the price of 10,000 bolts?

   Multiply the price by 100,000.

3. A customer buys 1,000 *A* bolts, 1,000 *B* bolts and 10,000 *E* bolts. How much is the total price of all the bolts? **$1,081**

NAME

PROBLEM SOLVING

Dr. Melior is planning to send radio messages from Earth to other planets in the solar system. Complete the table below to help solve the problems. Assume that the planets' orbits are circular.

Note: Solar system is not drawn in proportion.

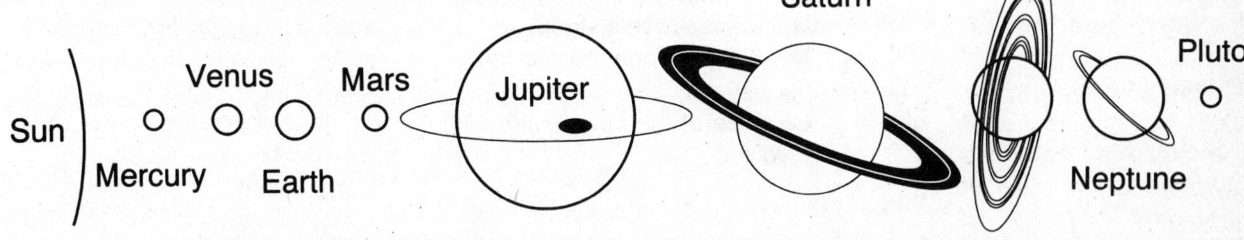

Planet	Average mean distance from Sun (millions of miles)	Shortest distance from from Earth (millions of miles)	Largest distance from from Earth (millions of miles)
Mercury	36.3		
Venus	66.96		
Earth	93		
Neptune	2799.3		
Pluto	3701.4		

1. A message is sent to Neptune when Earth and Neptune are on the same side of the sun. What is the shortest distance the message may travel?

2. A message is sent to Venus when Earth and Venus are on opposite sides of the sun. What is the longest distance the message may travel?

3. A message is sent to Mercury when Earth and Mercury are on the same side of the sun. What is the shortest distance the message may travel?

4. A message is sent to Pluto when Earth and Pluto are on opposite sides of the sun. What is the longest distance the message may travel?

Teacher Notes

Use with
Objective 26
pages 76–77

Focus
Problem Solving
Make a Table

Overview
Students complete a table of interplanetary distances and use the data to solve word problems.

Teaching Suggestions
Explain that the mean is a middle point between two extremes—in this case, the greatest and least distance of each planet from the sun. The planets' orbits are actually elliptical, but since we are using the mean distances, we can assume the orbits are circular. Sketch the sun on the chalkboard and surround it with nine ovals to represent the orbits of its planets. ***Question:*** *If a planet were positioned on the opposite side of the sun than the Earth, how would you compute the distance between the planets?* [Add their mean distances from the sun.] Suggest that students sketch the locations of the sun, Earth, Venus, and Pluto for Problems 2 and 4, if they have difficulty visualizing their locations.

Point out that to compute the distances asked for in Problems 2 and 4 more accurately, students would have to include the diameter of the sun (864,000 miles) in their calculations. This would, however, change the answers very slightly (less than 1%) because of the large distances involved.

Extension
Ask students to find the mean distance from the sun to Mars, Jupiter, Saturn, and Uranus. Ask them to imagine that they are able to travel through space in a vehicle that gets 1,000,000 miles to the gallon! Have them calculate the number of gallons of gas they would need for various interplanetary trips.

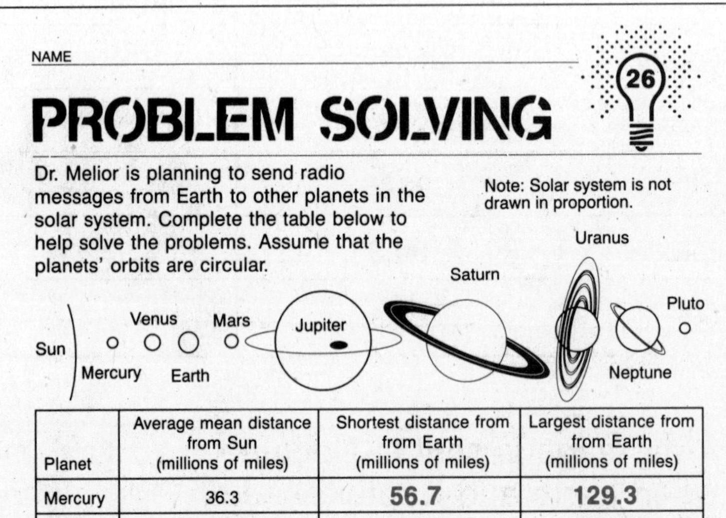

NAME

PROBLEM SOLVING

26

Dr. Melior is planning to send radio messages from Earth to other planets in the solar system. Complete the table below to help solve the problems. Assume that the planets' orbits are circular.

Note: Solar system is not drawn in proportion.

Planet	Average mean distance from Sun (millions of miles)	Shortest distance from from Earth (millions of miles)	Largest distance from from Earth (millions of miles)
Mercury	36.3	56.7	129.3
Venus	66.96	26.04	159.96
Earth	93	---	---
Neptune	2799.3	2706.3	2892.3
Pluto	3701.4	3608.4	3794.4

1. A message is sent to Neptune when Earth and Neptune are on the same side of the sun. What is the shortest distance the message may travel?

   2706.3 million miles

2. A message is sent to Venus when Earth and Venus are on opposite sides of the sun. What is the longest distance the message may travel?

   159.96 million miles

3. A message is sent to Mercury when Earth and Mercury are on the same side of the sun. What is the shortest distance the message may travel?

   56.7 million miles

4. A message is sent to Pluto when Earth and Pluto are on opposite sides of the sun. What is the longest distance the message may travel?

   3794.4 million miles

NAME ___

PROBLEM SOLVING

The winner of the World Series in baseball is the first team that wins 4 games out of a possible 7. For example, a team could win 4 games in a row, or it could win the first and second game, lose the third game, then win the next 2 games.

How many different ways are there to win the World Series?

One way to solve this problem is to list all the possibilities on a separate sheet of paper.

Games	1	2	3	4	5	6	7
	W	W	L	W	W		

Solve each problem.

1. How many ways could a team win the Series by playing 4 games? ___
2. How many ways could a team win the Series by playing 5 games? ___
3. How many ways could a team win the Series by playing 6 games? ___
4. How many ways could a team win the series by playing 7 games? ___
5. What is the total number of ways that a team can win the World Series? ___

Teacher Notes

Use with
Objective 27
pages 88–89

Focus
Problem Solving
Make a Table

Overview
Students examine all the different ways of winning the World Series by *making a table* to list all the possibilities.

Teaching Suggestions
Begin by discussing the World Series with students. Have a volunteer read the first paragraph. Make sure students realize that after four games are won by a team, no more games are played. Work through Problem 1 with the class. Suggest that everyone use *W* for "win" and for *L* for "loss."

Have students work Problem 2 independently. ***Questions:*** *If the series is over in 5 games, how many losses were there?* [1] *Is the last game a win or loss and why?* [A win because if it were a loss, the series would have been won in the first four games.]

Make sure students use a systematic strategy for listing all of the possibilities in order. For Problem 3, there are 10 ways to win a 6-game series:
LLWWWW; LWLWWW; LWWLWW;
LWWWLW; WLLWWW; WLWLWW;
WLWWLW; WWLLWW; WWLWLW;
WWWLLW.

For Problem 4, there are 20 ways to win a 7-game series:
LLLWWWW; LLWLWWW; LLWWLWW;
LLWWWLW; LWLLWWW; LWLWLWW;
LWLWWLW: LWWLLWW; LWWLWLW;
LWWWLLW; WLLLWWW; WLLWLWW:
WLLWWLW; WWLLLWW; WWLLWLW;
WWLWLLW; WWWLLLW; WLWLLWW;
WLWWLLW; WLWLWLW.

For Problem 5, add all the previous answers to find that the World Series can be won in 35 different ways.
(1 + 4 + 10 + 20 = 35)

Extension
A team wins the Series in 5 games, using 3 starting pitchers. Pitchers A and B pitched 2 games each. Pitcher C pitched 1 game. In how many different ways could they have pitched? [30]

AABBC	BBAAC	CAABB	AABCB
BBACA	CABAB	AACBB	BBCAA
CABBA	ABBCA	BAACB	CBBAA
ABBAC	BAABC	CBABA	ABABC
BABAC	CBAAB	ABCAB	BACBA
ABCBA	BACAB	ABACB	BABCA
ACBAB	BCABA	ACABB	BCBAA
ACBBA	BCAAB		

NAME ______________________________

PROBLEM SOLVING

27

The winner of the World Series in baseball is the first team that wins 4 games out of a possible 7. For example, a team could win 4 games in a row, or it could win the first and second game, lose the third game, then win the next 2 games.

How many different ways are there to win the World Series?

One way to solve this problem is to list all the possibilities on a separate sheet of paper.

Games	1	2	3	4	5	6	7
	W	W	L	W	W		

Solve each problem.

1. How many ways could a team win the Series by playing 4 games? **1**
2. How many ways could a team win the Series by playing 5 games? **4**
3. How many ways could a team win the Series by playing 6 games? **10**
4. How many ways could a team win the series by playing 7 games? **20**
5. What is the total number of ways that a team can win the World Series? **35**

NAME ______________________________

VISUAL THINKING

In each row, study the first set of figures to determine the pattern that is shown. Ring the letter of the figure to the right of the line that best completes the second set of figures.

1.

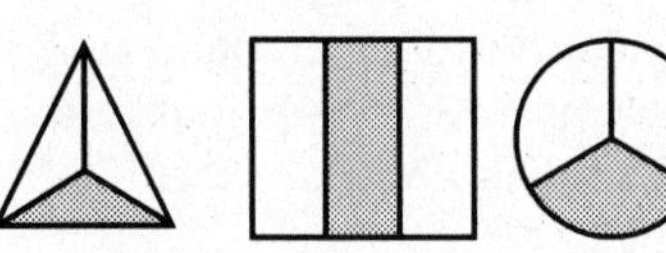  ? 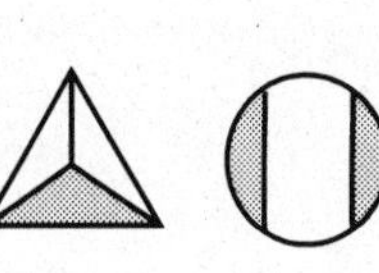 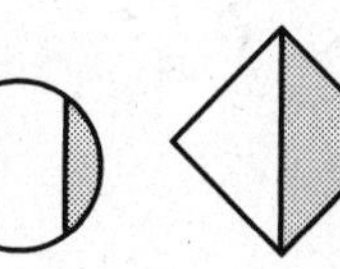

a. b. c. d.

2.

   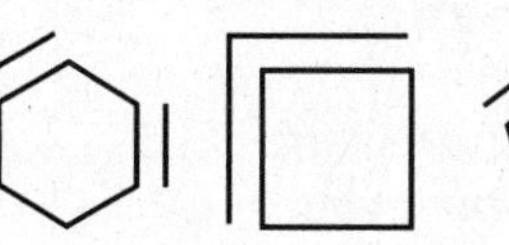 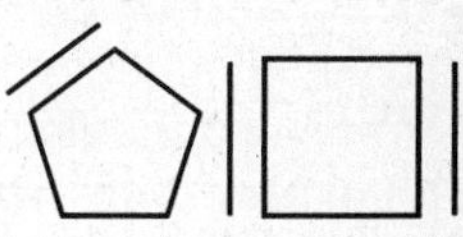

a. b. c. d.

3.

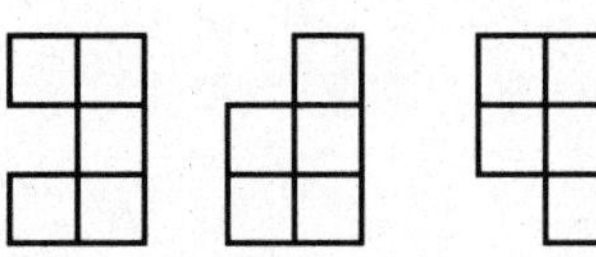 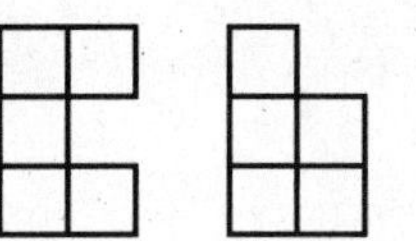  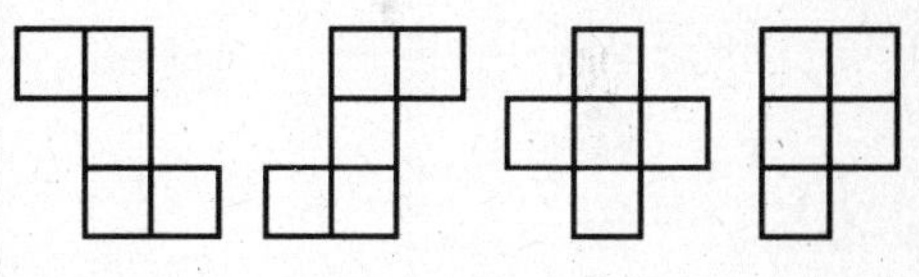

a. b. c. d.

4.

 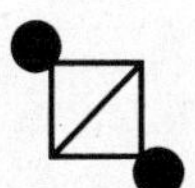 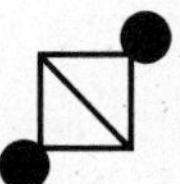 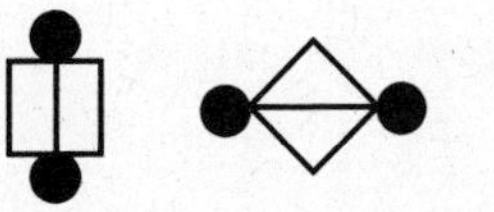  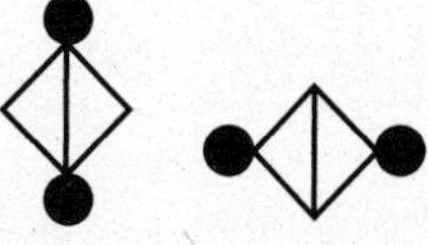 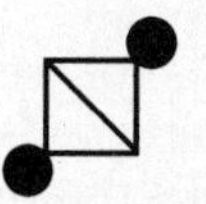 

a. b. c. d.

5.

 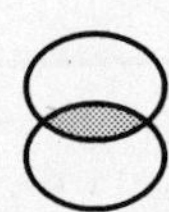 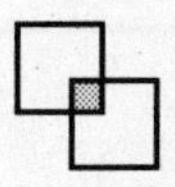 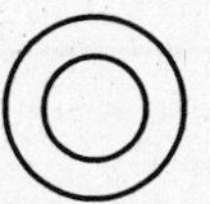 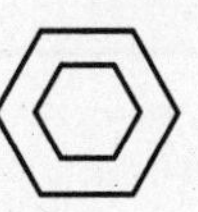 ? 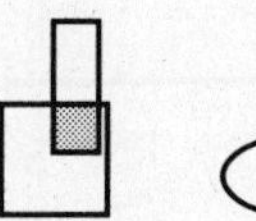 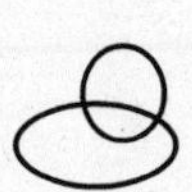  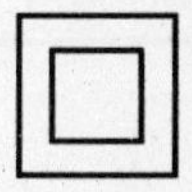

a. b. c. d.

Teacher Notes

Use with
Objective 28
pages 90–91

Focus
Visual Thinking
Visual Patterns

Materials
Visual Thinking transparency (optional)

Overview
Students recognize the relationship in a *visual pattern* and use this same relationship to complete the pattern.

Teaching Suggestions
Have students begin by examining the first problem. ***Question:*** *How would you describe the first pattern in Problem 1?* [Possible answer: Each figure is divided into 3 parts and one is shaded.] Call students' attention to the similarities and differences between the first and second group. ***Questions:*** *How would you describe the second pattern in Problem 1?* [Each figure is divided in two and one part is shaded.] *Which figure best completes the pattern? Why?* [C, because it is the only one divided into 2 parts.] The remaining problems can be approached similarly. In the second part of Problem 2, the outer lines are on two adjacent sides. In Problem 3, each figure in the second column is a flip of the figure in the first column.

In Problem 4, the black dots in the second column are endpoints of the inner segments. In Problem 5, each figure in the second column is comprised of two similar figures, one inside the other.

Alternate Approach: Use the Visual Thinking transparency and do this page as a class activity.

Extension
Have students make up their own problems using only 1 column of figures. Each student should make up 5 sets of figures. They should draw the figures along with 4 answer choices for each problem and exchange with a partner. Challenge them to make up patterns with different criteria than those shown in the activity.

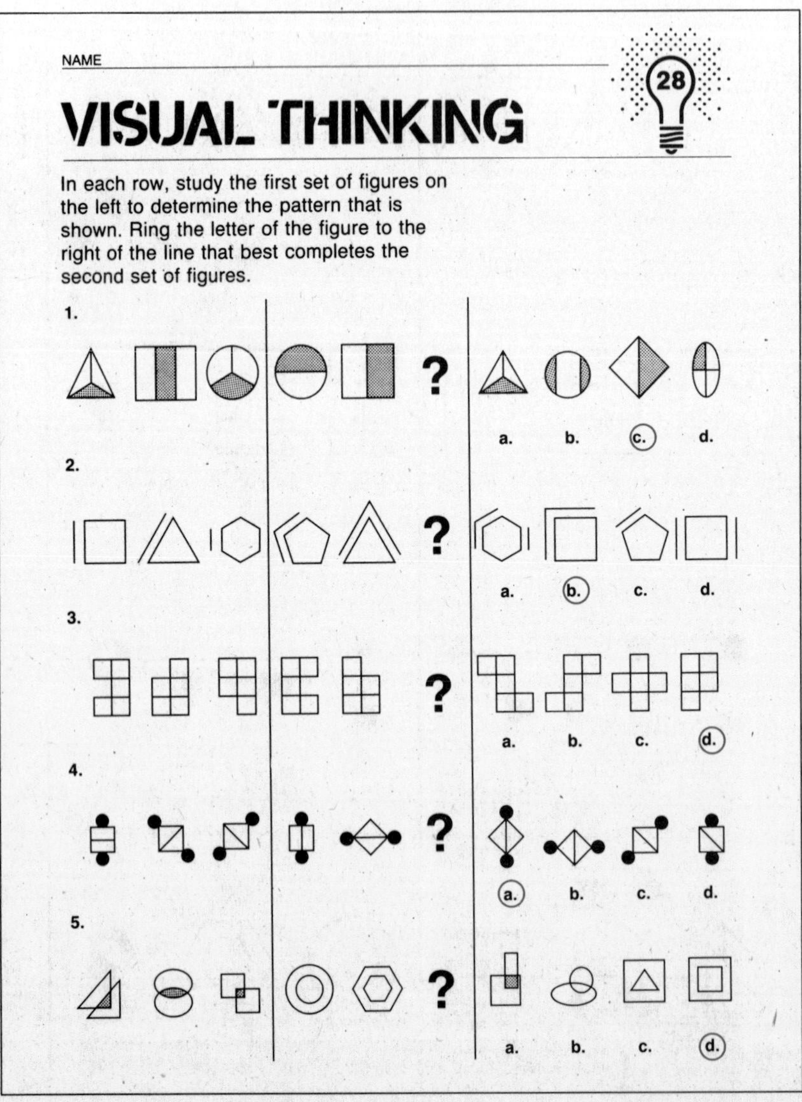

NAME ______________________________

CRITICAL THINKING

A peanut vendor ran out of bags for peanuts. He made paper tubes from sheets of paper, each measuring $8\frac{1}{2}$ inches by 11 inches, and taped the tubes to cardboard bases. He made both tubes shown at right.

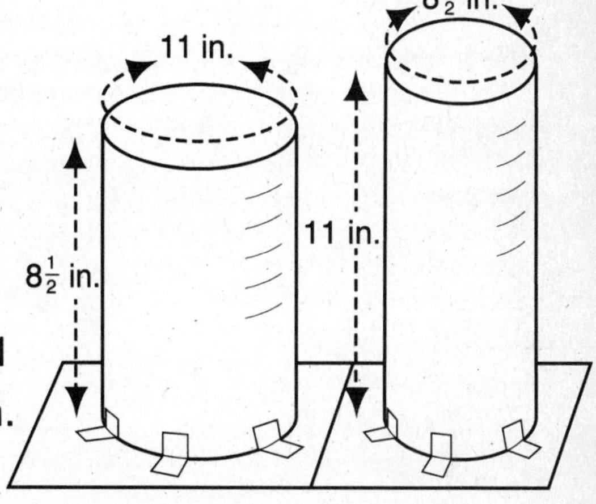

1. Find out if both tubes will hold the same amount of peanuts. Make a prediction, then use sheets of paper $8\frac{1}{2}$ inches by 11 inches and tape to check your prediction. If necessary, use foam peanuts to measure which holds more.

   My prediction: ______________________________

   What Actually Happened: ______________________________

2. Make another pair of cylinders from two nonsquare sheets of paper that are the same size as each other but not the same as the sheets used in Problem 1. Will they hold the same amount?

   My prediction: ______________________________

   What Actually Happened: ______________________________

3. Based on your observations, what can you say about visually estimating the amount that paper tubes will hold?

   My prediction: ______________________________

   ____

   ____

   ____

Teacher Notes

Use with
Objective 29
pages 92–93

Focus
Critical Thinking
Making and Testing Predictions
Drawing Conclusions

Materials
8-1/2″ x 11″ paper
Tape
Scissors
Plastic pellets, puffed cereal, or other lightweight, uniform material

Overview
Students analyze the relationship of a cylinder's circumference and its height to its volume.

Teaching Suggestions
Introduce the activity by reviewing the terms *cylinder, volume,* and *surface.* Do not, however, introduce the formula for calculating the volume of a cylinder.

Demonstrate the procedure for assembling the cylinders. Tape together two 8-1/2″ × 11″ sheets of paper, one 8-1/2 inches tall and the other 11 inches tall. Tape the base of each cylinder to another sheet of paper as shown on the pupil page.

Students should complete Problem 1 by making their own models and testing them. Each student will fill the containers, count the contents, and use the results to compare the volume of the cylinders.

For Problem 2, each student should record the size of the paper and the results.

Have students discuss Problem 3. Encourage them to compare their results in Problems 1 and 2, and discuss any differences between their predictions and what actually happened.

Students should find that when the dimensions of the cylinders are reversed (height and circumference of the base), the shorter cylinder will hold more. In general, an increase in the circumference of a cylinder has a greater effect on volume than an identical increase in height.

NAME ______________________________

CRITICAL THINKING

A peanut vendor ran out of bags for peanuts. He made paper tubes from sheets of paper, each measuring $8\frac{1}{2}$ inches by 11 inches, and taped the tubes to cardboard bases. He made both tubes shown at right.

1. Find out if both tubes will hold the same amount of peanuts. Make a prediction, then use sheets of paper $8\frac{1}{2}$ inches by 11 inches and tape to check your prediction. If necessary, use foam peanuts to measure which holds more.
   My prediction: **Possible answer: the shorter tube.**
   What Actually Happened: **The shorter tube will hold more.**

2. Make another pair of cylinders from two nonsquare sheets of paper that are the same size as each other but not the same as the sheets used in Problem 1. Will they hold the same amount?
   My prediction: **Possible answer: No, they will not.**
   What Actually Happened: **The shorter one will hold more.**

3. Based on your observations, what can you say about visually estimating the amount that paper tubes will hold?
   My prediction: **Answers will vary.**

NAME ____________________

DECISION MAKING

Joey, Cheryl, and Lupe went to the museum to see the dinosaur exhibit. They wanted to buy posters in the gift shop for souvenirs. The cards were priced as shown. Joey had 80¢, Cheryl had $2.30, and Lupe had $2.50.

DINOSAUR POSTERS
90¢ each
3 for $2.50
Set of 7 for $5.00

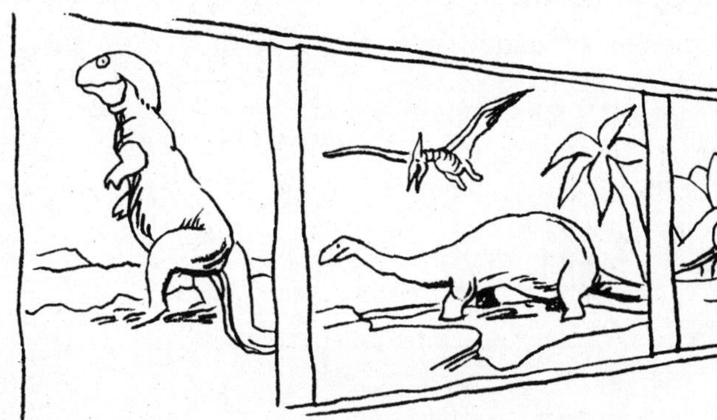

1. How many dinosaur posters can each buy with his or her own money?

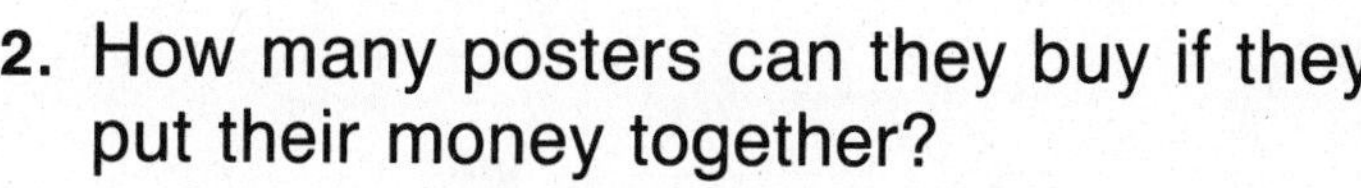

____

2. How many posters can they buy if they put their money together?

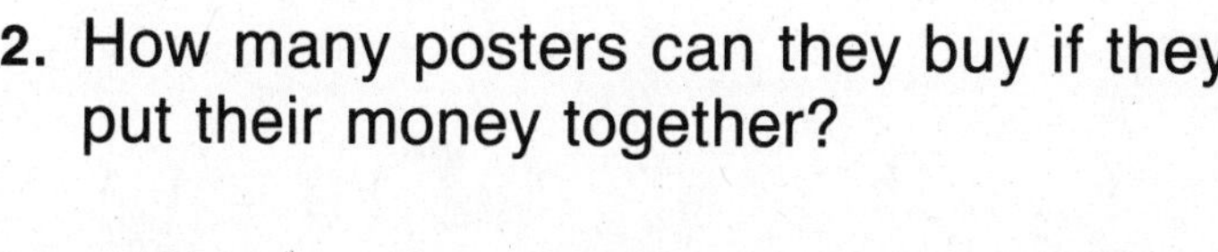

____

3. If they put their money together, how much do you think each should contribute? Explain your answer.

____

____

4. How many posters should each one receive? Explain your answer.

____

____

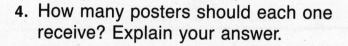

Teacher Notes

Use with
Objective 30
pages 94–97

Focus
Decision Making

Overview
Students compare the number of posters that three people can purchase individually or collectively.

Teaching Suggestions
For Problem 1, students should observe that Joey can almost buy one poster and Cheryl can almost buy three. Lupe has exactly enough money for three posters.

For Problem 2, students should begin by adding the three amounts of money. ***Questions:*** *How much money do the three people have all together?* [$5.60] *What is the best deal they can make? Why?* [7 for $5.00; this gives the cheapest price per poster (about $0.72)] *How much money is left over?* [$0.60]

Problems 3 and 4 may be discussed together. For Problem 3, students may say that the three should each pay a multiple of the unit cost (about $0.72) and then receive the number of posters they paid for: Joey—one poster, $0.72; Cheryl—three posters, $2.14; Lupe—three posters, $2.14.

Extension
Tell students that the museum also sells miniature models of dinosaurs. The prices are 1 for $0.50; 3 for $1.30; 7 for $3.00; and 12 for $5.15. What is the best deal that the 3 friends can make if they pool their money and buy models instead? [They can get 13 models for $5.60 by buying 2 sets of 3 for $1.30 and 1 set of 7 for $3.00. If they buy 12 for $5.15, they will not have enough money to purchase any more.]

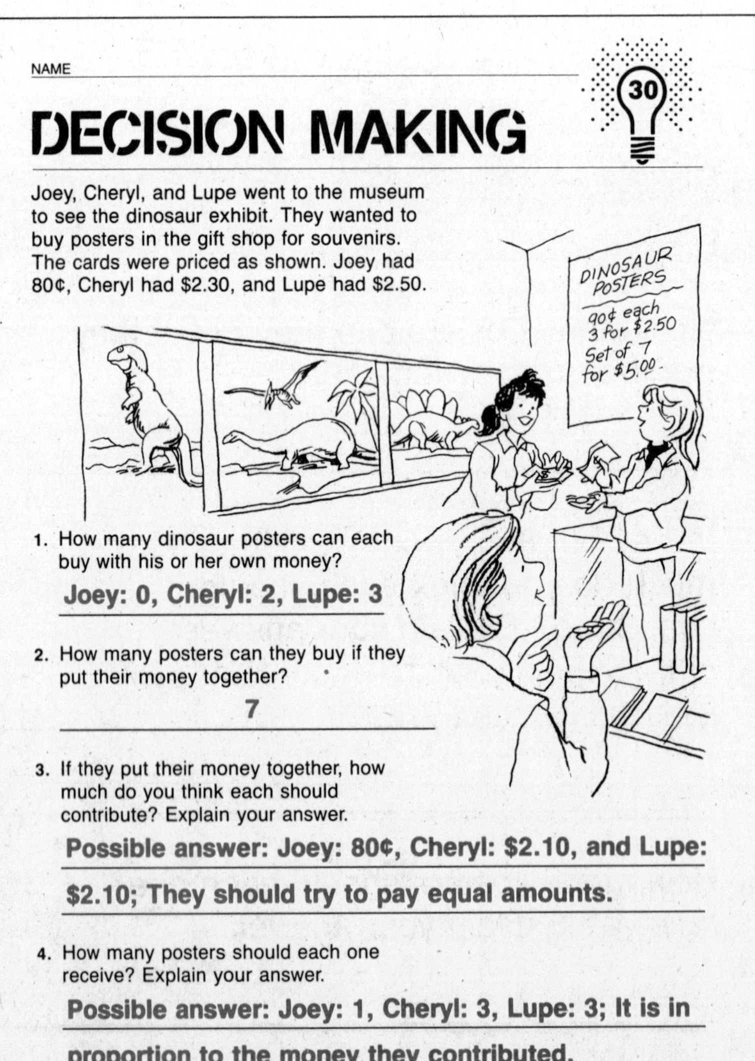

NAME

30

DECISION MAKING

Joey, Cheryl, and Lupe went to the museum to see the dinosaur exhibit. They wanted to buy posters in the gift shop for souvenirs. The cards were priced as shown. Joey had 80¢, Cheryl had $2.30, and Lupe had $2.50.

1. How many dinosaur posters can each buy with his or her own money?
   Joey: 0, Cheryl: 2, Lupe: 3
2. How many posters can they buy if they put their money together?
   7
3. If they put their money together, how much do you think each should contribute? Explain your answer.
   Possible answer: Joey: 80¢, Cheryl: $2.10, and Lupe: $2.10; They should try to pay equal amounts.
4. How many posters should each one receive? Explain your answer.
   Possible answer: Joey: 1, Cheryl: 3, Lupe: 3; It is in proportion to the money they contributed.

NAME ______________________________

PROBLEM SOLVING

Two bakers are considering different plans for selling their bran muffins. Benny plans to sell his first muffin for $0.01, the second for $0.02, the third for $0.04, the fourth for $0.08, and so on, doubling the cost of each additional muffin. Bart plans to sell the first muffin for $0.10, the second for $0.20, the third for $0.30, and so on.

1. How much did each baker receive for selling one dozen muffins?

____

2. If they each sold 18 muffins, how much would each baker receive?

____

3. If they each sold 24 muffins, how much would each baker receive?

____

____

Teacher Notes

Use with
Objective 31
pages 98–99

Focus
Problem Solving
Make a Table

Materials
Calculators (optional)

Overview
Students compare two pricing systems for bran muffins, one using addition and one using multiplication.

Teaching Suggestions
Have students calculate how much each baker will charge for the 4th muffin. [Bart, $0.40; Benny, $0.08] Ask which baker they think will charge less for the 12th muffin. [Answers will vary.] Then have students calculate how much each baker will charge for the 12th muffin. [Bart, $1.20; Benny, $20.48]

To answer Problems 1, 2, and 3, students should *make a table* for the total cost of the number of muffins. If calculators are available, you might let students use them to complete the table. The table in the next column is completed through 12 muffins. For Problem 2, students should extend it to 18 muffins and for Problem 3 to 24 muffins.

Muffins sold	Bart received	Benny received
1	$0.10	$ 0.01
2	$0.30	$ 0.03
3	$0.60	$ 0.07
4	$1.00	$ 0.15
5	$1.50	$ 0.31
6	$2.10	$ 0.63
7	$2.80	$ 1.27
8	$3.60	$ 2.55
9	$4.50	$ 5.11
10	$5.50	$10.23
11	$6.60	$20.47
12	$7.80	$40.95

NAME

PROBLEM SOLVING

Two bakers are considering different plans for selling their bran muffins. Benny plans to sell his first muffin for $0.01, the second for $0.02, the third for $0.04, the fourth for $0.08, and so on, doubling the cost of each additional muffin. Bart plans to sell the first muffin for $0.10, the second for $0.20, the third for $0.30, and so on.

1. How much did each baker receive for selling one dozen muffins?

   Benny: $40.95; Bart: $7.80

2. If they each sold 18 muffins, how much would each baker receive?

   Benny $2,621.43; Bart: $17.10

3. If they each sold 24 muffins, how much would each baker receive?

   Benny: $167,772.15; Bart: $30.00

NAME ______________________________

VISUAL THINKING

In each row, the first cube has been turned twice. Ring the letter of the symbol that is on the bottom of the last cube. The first one has been done for you.

1. ⊠ a. ○ b. □ c. • d. ⊕ e. × (f.)

2. ⊠ a. ○ b. □ c. • d. ⊕ e. × f.

3. ⊠ a. ○ b. □ c. • d. ⊕ e. × f.

4. ⊠ a. ○ b. □ c. • d. ⊕ e. × f.

5. ⊠ a. ○ b. □ c. • d. ⊕ e. × f.

6. ⊠ a. ○ b. □ c. • d. ⊕ e. × f.

7. ⊠ a. ○ b. □ c. • d. ⊕ e. × f.

Teacher Notes

Use with
Objective 32
pages 100–103

Focus
Visual Thinking
Spatial Perception

Materials
Number cubes
Tape

Overview
Students analyze three views of cubes marked with 6 different symbols to determine which symbol is on the bottom in the last picture.

Teaching Suggestions
Explain that each cube has 6 different symbols on it. Encourage students to verbalize how the cube has been turned each time. ***Questions:*** *How would you describe the first turn in Problem 1?* [Possible answer: side turned 90° clockwise] *How would you describe the second turn?* [Possible answer: top turned 90° clockwise.] Be sure they see that this turn will put the X on the bottom.

For Problems 2, 3, and 5, students must look at both the first and second pictures.

In Problems 4, 6, and 7, cubes are turned 180° in the first turn. In Problems 4 and 6, the second turn is 90° and in Problem 7 it is 180°.

Alternate Approach: Have students tape appropriate symbols on a number cube, turning the cube as indicated. After the second turn they can look at the bottom to determine the answer.

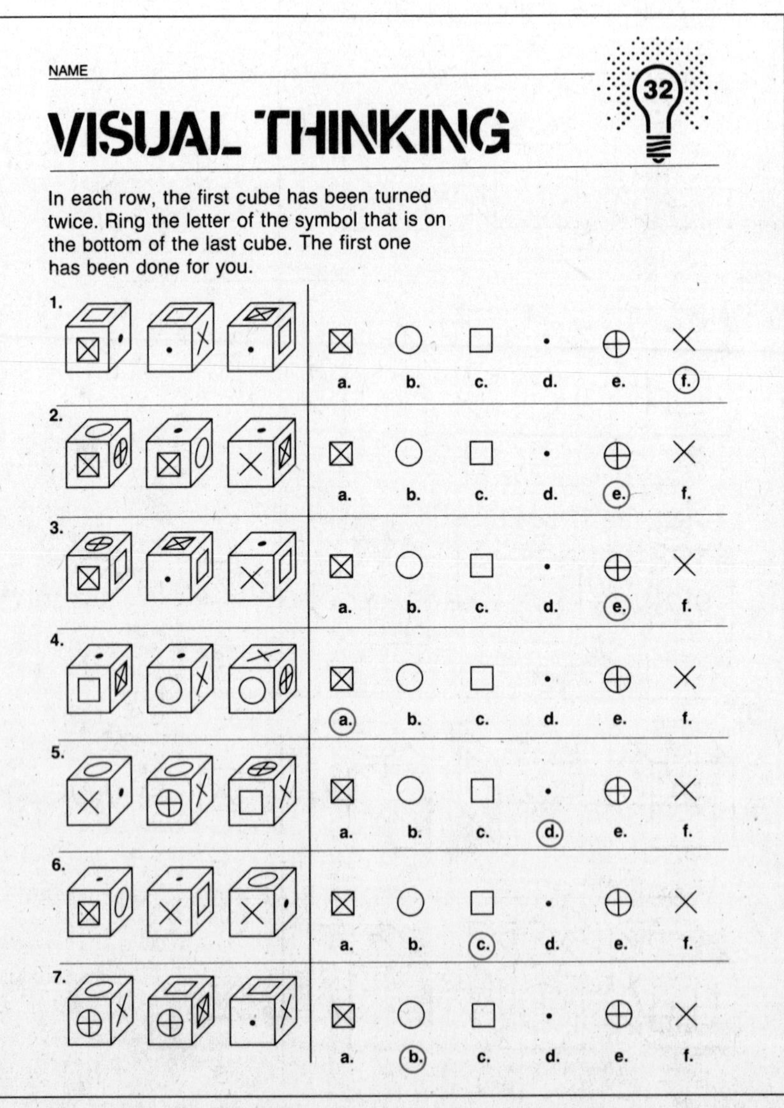

NAME ____________________

PROBLEM SOLVING

Yolanda works as an artist. Write an equation for each problem about Yolanda's art. Solve the problem.

1. Yolanda needs 27 pounds of clay to make a statue. She has 192 pounds of clay. How many statues can Yolanda make?

   ____

2. Yolanda ships her statues to the store only in full boxes of 6. If she has 39 statues ready, how many full boxes can she send to the store?

   ____

3. Yolanda also sells paintings. She made $145 selling paintings last week. If she sold 4 paintings last week, each for the same price, how much did she charge for each painting?

   ____

4. Yolanda found that her profit from the sale of her art equals one fourth of her sales. If she made $180 in profits for a week, what were her sales?

   ____

Teacher Notes

Use with
Objective 33
pages 106–107

Focus
Problem Solving
Write an Equation

Overview
Students *write equations* and decide how to interpret remainders as they solve problems.

Teaching Suggestions
Students will likely view the computations in Problems 1, 2, and 3 as division. Tell them that in giving the answers, they will have to decide how to use the remainder. ***Question:*** *Without solving Problems 1, 2, and 3, how will you treat the division in each case?* [Possible answers: Problem 1—divide only to the ones place and ignore any remainder (it will not be enough to make another statue); Problem 2—divide only to the ones place and ignore any remainder (it will not be enough to fill another box); Problem 3—divide to hundredths so the answer can be given in dollars and cents.]

NAME

33

PROBLEM SOLVING

Yolanda works as an artist. Write an equation for each problem about Yolanda's art. Solve the problem.

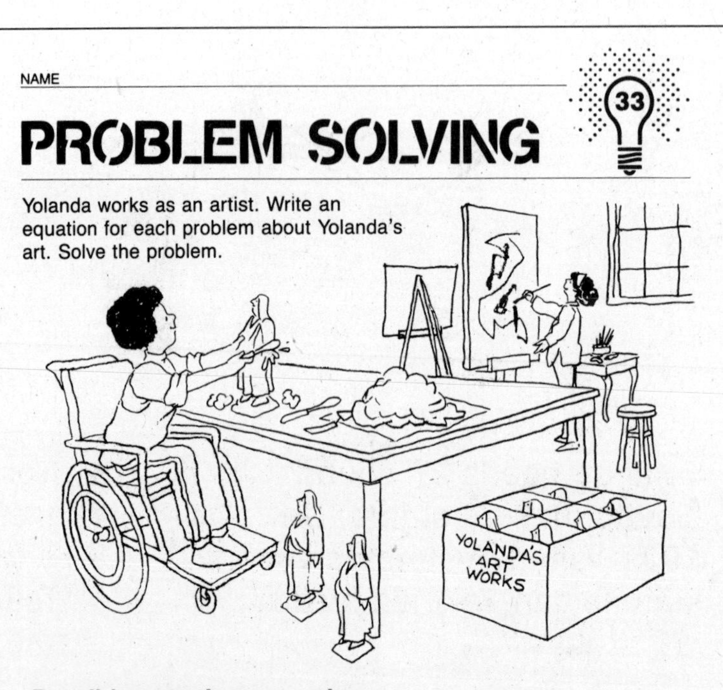

Possible equations are given.

1. Yolanda needs 27 pounds of clay to make a statue. She has 192 pounds of clay. How many statues can Yolanda make?

   $27 \times n = 192$; 7

2. Yolanda ships her statues to the store only in full boxes of 6. If she has 39 statues ready, how many full boxes can she send to the store?

   $6 \times n = 39$; 6

3. Yolanda also sells paintings. She made \$145 selling paintings last week. If she sold 4 paintings last week, each for the same price, how much did she charge for each painting?

   $4 \times n = \$145$; \$36.25

4. Yolanda found that her profit from the sale of her art equals one fourth of her sales. If she made \$180 in profits for a week, what were her sales?

   $\frac{1}{4}s = 180$; \$720

NAME ______________________________

PROBLEM SOLVING

Serena and five of her friends ordered pizza for a party. Each pizza was cut into ten slices of the same size.

Pablo took twice as much pizza as Serena did, and Jordan had as much as Pablo and Serena together. Tom and Barb each had half as much as Aimee did, while Aimee took the same amount that Jordan did. Serena had two slices of pizza.

1. Write five equations to show how much pizza each person in the group had.

____

____

____

2. How much pizza did each person have?

____

____

____

3. How many pizzas were ordered?

____

4. Was there any pizza left over? If so, how much?

____

Teacher Notes

Use with
Objective 34
pages 108–109

Focus
Problem Solving
Write an Equation
Use Logical Reasoning

Overview
Students write a group of related equations and solve them in the proper order to determine how many slices of pizza 6 friends had at a party.

Teaching Suggestions
For Problem 1, encourage students to use each person's initial to represent his or her amount of pizza in the equations. Help students translate the information into equations by discussing the meaning of the phrases "twice as much as," "together," "1/2 as much as," and "same amount as." Then discuss the mathematical symbols that can be substituted for these phrases when writing the equations. The equations students write for Problem 1 may vary slightly. For example, students may write $J = 3S$ or $B = T$.

For Problem 2, students can begin with the one known quantity of pizza eaten—Serena's amount. From this they can find Pablo's amount $(2 \times 2 = 4)$. This allows them to compute Jordan's and Aimee's amount $(4 + 2 = 6)$, which can then be used to find Tom's and Barb's amounts $(1/2(6) = 3)$.

For Problems 3 and 4, have students assume that there was not more than a whole pizza left over.

Extension
Have students suppose that they did not know how much Serena ate, but they knew that 5 pizzas were ordered.
Question: *What is the maximum number of pieces Serena could eat if the pizzas were each cut into ten slices, each person ate only whole slices, and the relationships of the amounts eaten by the six friends are the same as on the activity sheet?* [4; this gives a total of 48 slices eaten]

NAME

PROBLEM SOLVING

Serena and five of her friends ordered pizza for a party. Each pizza was cut into ten slices of the same size.

Pablo took twice as much pizza as Serena did, and Jordan had as much as Pablo and Serena together. Tom and Barb each had half as much as Aimee did, while Aimee took the same amount that Jordan did. Serena had two slices of pizza.

1. Write five equations to show how much pizza each person in the group had.
   $S = 2, P = 2 \times S,$
   $J = P + S, T = \frac{1}{2} \times A,$
   $B = \frac{1}{2} \times A, A = J$

2. How much pizza did each person have?
   Serena: 2, Pablo: 4,
   Jordan: 6, Tom: 3,
   Barb: 3, Aimee: 6

3. How many pizzas were ordered?
   3 pizzas

4. Was there any pizza left over? If so, how much?
   Yes; 6 slices

NAME ____________________

CRITICAL THINKING

A palindrome is a number or word that reads the same forward as backward.

1. Write a palindrome number with 3 digits. With 4 digits.

____

2. Is your age a palindrome number? If it is not, how old will you be on your next palindrome age?

____

3. Choose any 2-digit number that is not a palindrome. Reverse the digits and add this new number to your original number. Is the result a palindrome?

____

4. If your result in Problem 3 was not a palindrome, repeat the procedure of reversing digits and adding until you obtain a palindrome number. What is your palindrome number?

____

Teacher Notes

Use with
Objective 35
pages 110–111

Focus
Critical Thinking
Ordering and Sequencing
Using Number Sense

Overview
Students experiment with palindromic numbers and create some of their own.

Teaching Suggestions
Write 383, 67876, and 1000000001 on the chalkboard. ***Question:*** *What do you notice about the three groups of numbers?* [They read the same forward and backward.] Explain that a *palindrome* is a group of numbers or letters which reads the same forward and backward. Have students complete Problems 1 and 2.

If students get a palindrome in Problem 3, have them choose another number to try so that they can do Problem 4.

For Problem 4, some numbers will take longer than others to reach a palindrome.

Extension
Have students write words that are palindromes. [MOM, DAD, LEVEL] Challenge them to write a palindrome sentence. [MADAM, I'M ADAM.]

NAME ____________

CRITICAL THINKING

A palindrome is a number or word that reads the same forward as backward.

1. Write a palindrome number with 3 digits. With 4 digits.

   Possible answers: 171; 2442

2. Is your age a palindrome number? If it is not, how old will you be on your next palindrome age?

   Possible answer: No; 11

3. Choose any 2-digit number that is not a palindrome. Reverse the digits and add this new number to your original number. Is the result a palindrome?

   Possible answer: 57; 57 + 75 = 132; No

4. If your result in Problem 3 was not a palindrome, repeat the procedure of reversing digits and adding until you obtain a palindrome number. What is your palindrome number?

   Possible answer: 132 + 231 = 363

NAME ________________________________

VISUAL THINKING

Ring the letter of the figure on the right that completes the pattern shown on the left.

1.

a. b. c. d. e.

2.

a. b. c. d. e.

3.

a. b. c. d. e.

4.

a. b. c. d. e.

5.

a. b. c. d. e.

Teacher Notes

Use with
Objective 36
pages 112–113

Focus
Visual Thinking
Visual Patterns

Materials
Visual Thinking transparency (optional)

Overview
Students recognize the relationship in a *visual pattern* and use this same relationship to complete the pattern.

Teaching Suggestions
Have students study each pattern on the left until they can explain it in words. In Problem 1, each pair of rectangles contains line designs; there are 4 lines in each design in the first pair and three in the second. Therefore, the third pair will have two lines in each design.

In Problem 2, the rectangles are also paired with the number of vertical and horizontal lines switched. In the first rectangle of the first pair, there are 2 horizontal and 3 vertical lines; in the second rectangle there are 3 horizontal and 2 vertical lines. In Problem 3, the rectangles are alternating. In Problem 4, there are three kinds of alternating rectangles, and in Problem 5, there are four kinds of alternating rectangles.

Alternate Approach: Use the optional transparency to do the activity as a class.

Extension
Have students draw or describe the seventh rectangle in each problem. [Problem 1: A rectangle like the first one shown but with only one short line on each side. Problem 2: It should have 7 horizontal and 6 vertical lines. Problem 3: Identical to the first rectangle in the pattern. Problem 4: Identical to the first figure in the pattern. Problem 5: Identical to the third figure in the pattern.]

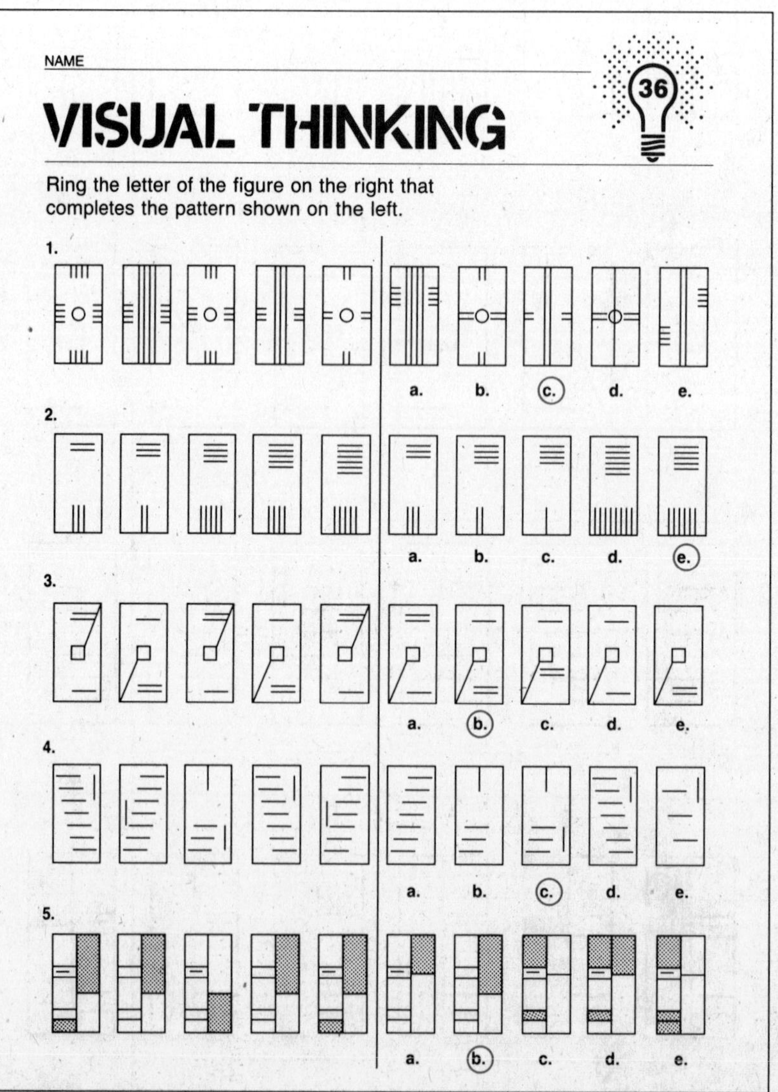

NAME ____

PROBLEM SOLVING

While at the museum on a field trip, the class saw jade statues that were made by an ancient civilization. Each statue had symbols that showed its weight. The names of the weight relationships were translated as shown below.

Translation:
The pug, dell, gore, and lum were units of weight.
1 dell weighs the same as the sum of 1 pug and 1 gore. 1 pug weighs as much as the sum of 1 gore and 1 lum. 2 gores weigh the same as 1 lum. 1 lum weighs 14 ounces.

1. Write each weight relationship given in the translation as an equation. The first equation is $D = P + G$.

   ____

   ____

   ____

2. Use the equations you wrote for Problem 1. How many ounces are in the following?

   lum: __________ gore: __________

   pug: __________ dell: __________

3. What is the weight of each statue in ounces?

   a. __________ b. __________

   c. __________ d. __________

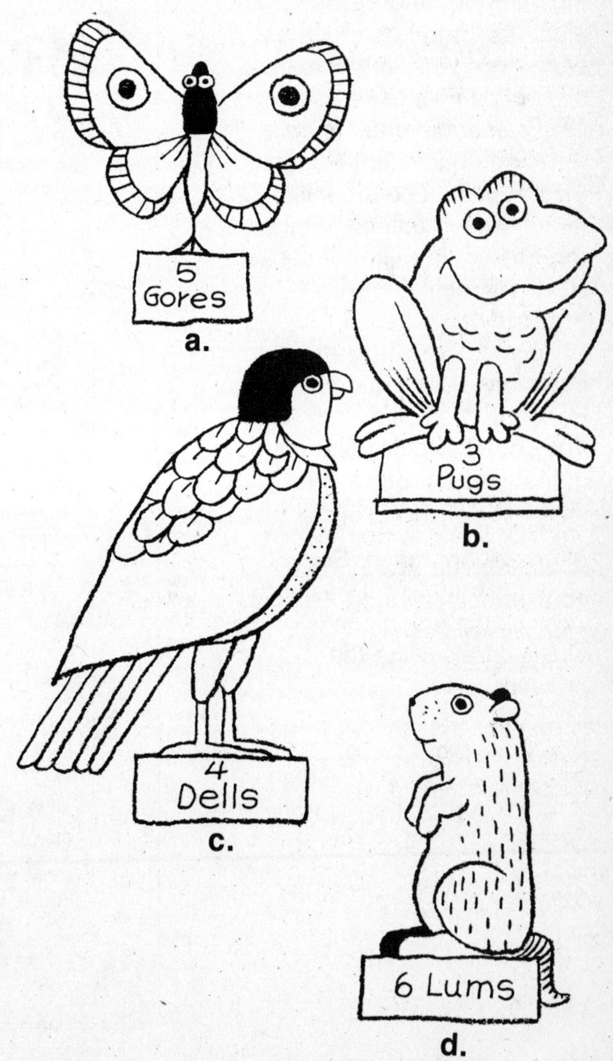

Teacher Notes

Use with
Objective 37
pages 114–115

Focus
Problem Solving
Write an Equation

Overview
Students translate unfamiliar units of measure into ounces and determine the weights of various objects.

Teaching Suggestions
Have students read the problem and discuss the translation. Discuss the meaning of the phrases "the same as" and "as much as." ***Question:*** *What mathematical symbol can we use to show "the same as" and "is equal to"?* [An equal sign] Suggest that students use the initial letter of each unit of weight to represent it in their equations. Have students complete Problem 1.

Have students use the equations they wrote for Problem 1 to solve Problem 2. They need to solve first for gores, then for pugs, then for dells.

Alternate Approach: Some students may find it easier to write all the equations in terms of L before solving the problem.

$L = 14$
$2 \times G = L$ or $G = 1/2L$
$P = L/2 + L$ or $P = 1\text{-}1/2\ L$
$D = 1\text{-}1/2\ L + 1/2\ L = 2L$

For Problem 3, students calculate the weight of each statue in ounces by multiplying the number on its base by the number of ounces in that unit of measure.

Extension
Have students convert each weight in Problem 3 to pounds.
[**a.** 2 lb 3 oz; **b.** 3 lb 15 oz; **c.** 7 lb; **d.** 5 lb 4 oz]

NAME ______________________

PROBLEM SOLVING

While at the museum on a field trip, the class saw jade statues that were made by an ancient civilization. Each statue had symbols that showed its weight. The names of the weight relationships were translated as shown below.

> Translation:
> The pug, dell, gore, and lum were units of weight.
> 1 dell weighs the same as the sum of 1 pug and 1 gore.
> 1 pug weighs as much as the sum of 1 gore and 1 lum.
> 2 gores weigh the same as 1 lum.
> 1 lum weighs 14 ounces.

1. Write each weight relationship given in the translation as an equation. The first equation is $D = P + G$.
   $P = G + L$,
   $2 \times G = L$,
   $L = 14$

2. Use the equations you wrote for Problem 1. How many ounces are in the following?
   lum: **14 oz** gore: **7 oz**
   pug: **21 oz** dell: **28 oz**

3. What is the weight of each statue in ounces?
   a. **35 oz** b. **63 oz**
   c. **112 oz** d. **84 oz**

NAME

VISUAL THINKING

The first picture in each row shows three views of a three-dimensional object. Ring the letter of the figure on the right which shows the object.

1.

a. b. c. d.

2.

a. b. c. d.

3.

a. b. c. d.

4.

a. b. c. d.

5.

a. b. c. d.

6.

a. b. c. d.

Use after pages 130–131.

Teacher Notes

Use with
Objective 38
pages 130–131

Focus
Visual Thinking
Spatial Perception

Materials
Visual Thinking transparency (optional)
Toothpick models of objects **a–d** in Problem 1
Various three-dimensional objects similar to those on the page
Grid paper

Overview
Students visualize a three-dimensional object when given two-dimensional views from three different sides.

Teaching Suggestions
Direct students' attention to Problem 1 and point out the small triangle. ***Question:*** *How could you use this shape to eliminate possibilities from the choices on the right?* [Choices **a** and **b** do not have a triangular side, and choice **d** has a triangle of a different shape.] Encourage students to use the side view of each object to help eliminate choices.

<u>Alternate Approach:</u> Use the toothpick models to help students visualize the objects in Problem 1. Students may turn the models to visualize each view. If students continue to have difficulty, they may work in groups to make additional models for the rest of the page.

Extension
Have students work in small groups. Tell each group to choose a three-dimensional object and work together to make a two-dimensional drawing of different sides of the object on grid paper. When all groups are finished, place all the objects and sets of drawings on a table. Have groups try to match the drawings to the objects.

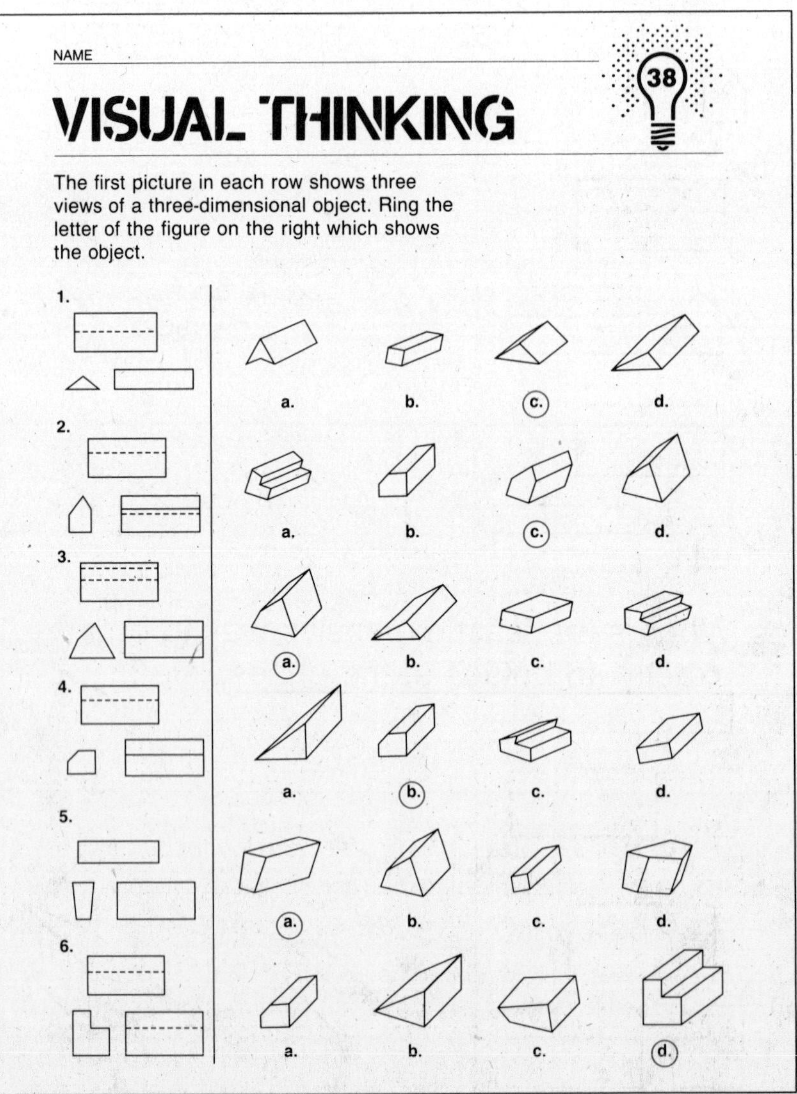
NAME

38

VISUAL THINKING

The first picture in each row shows three views of a three-dimensional object. Ring the letter of the figure on the right which shows the object.

1. a. b. (c.) d.

2. a. b. (c.) d.

3. (a.) b. c. d.

4. a. (b.) c. d.

5. (a.) b. c. d.

6. a. b. c. (d.)

NAME ________________________________

DECISION MAKING

Mr. Schumacher, the grocer, sells bottles of fruit juice for the prices shown.

6 Pack
100% Natural
Fruit Juices!
1 bottle $0.89
6-pack $4.79
12-pack $9.19
case of 24 $16.79

1. Ralph's class would like to buy exactly 46 bottles for a class picnic. Complete the table in order to find 6 different ways in which they can buy exactly 46 bottles.

	Combinations					
1 bottle						
6-pack						
12-pack						
Case of 24						

2. What is the least expensive way to buy exactly 46 bottles at the prices listed?

____

3. If the class has a 45¢ coupon for each six pack, how might they decide to buy the 46 bottles? Explain your answer.

____

____

Teacher Notes

Use with
Objective 39
pages 132–133

Focus
Decision Making

Overview
Students determine the least expensive way to make a purchase by using the fact that buying in larger quantities is usually more economical.

Teaching Suggestions
For Problem 1, help students begin to think about how to find combinations that make 46. ***Questions:*** *Can a combination make exactly 46 if there is 1 single bottle?* [No] *Why or why not?* [45 cannot be made from combinations of 6, 12, and 24.] Help students continue to explore whether 46 can be made with 2 or 3 single bottles.

Encourage students to list many different combinations. [Some combinations that are not shown are: 46 bottles; one 6-pack and 40 bottles; one 12-pack, one 6-pack, and 28 bottles.]

In Problem 2, have students examine the price list. ***Questions:*** *In which quantity is the juice least expensive?* [Case of 24] *What strategy might you use to find the least expensive combination?* [Possible answer: Use as many of each multiple-pack as possible.]

In Problem 3, students should consider the effect of the coupon. ***Question:*** *With the use of a coupon, which is more economical, two 6-packs or one 12-pack?* [Two 6-packs] Have students reassess their answers to Problem 2 using the coupon and decide if they would change their combination choice.

Extension
Have students reassess their answer to Problem 2 if the word "exactly" is taken out. [It would be cheaper to buy 2 cases of 24 and only use 46 bottles.]

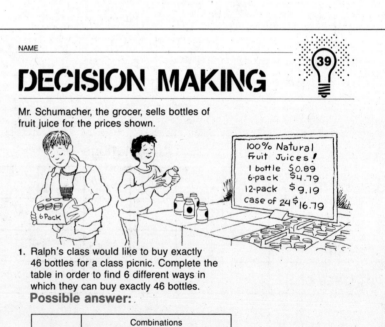

NAME ______________________

Mr. Schumacher, the grocer, sells bottles of fruit juice for the prices shown.

1. Ralph's class would like to buy exactly 46 bottles for a class picnic. Complete the table in order to find 6 different ways in which they can buy exactly 46 bottles.

Possible answer:

	Combinations					
1 bottle	4	4	4	4	4	4
6-pack	3	5	7	1	3	1
12-pack	2	1	0	1	0	3
Case of 24	0	0	0	1	1	0

2. What is the least expensive way to buy exactly 46 bottles at the prices listed?

1 case of 24, 1 12-pack, 1 6-pack, and 4 bottles

3. If the class has a 45¢ coupon for each six pack, how might they decide to buy the 46 bottles? Explain your answer.

Possible answer: 7 six-packs + 4 singles; The cost is about the same, and they would be easier to carry.

NAME ______________________________

VISUAL THINKING

An analogy is a statement that compares properties of two pairs of objects as in the following example. Draw the figure that will correctly complete the analogy.

Example: ↑ is to ↓ as ← is to __→__

1.

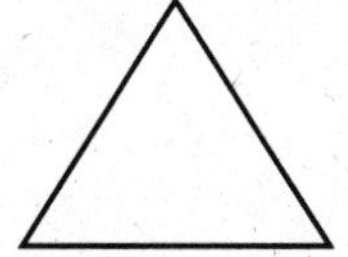 is to 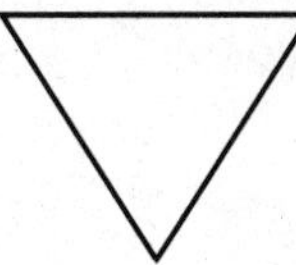 as 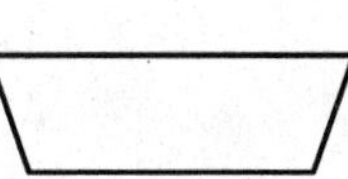 is to ______________

2.

 is to  as 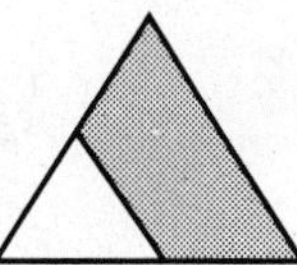 is to ______________

3.

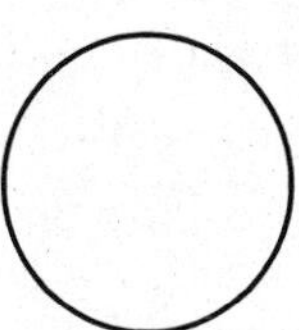 is to 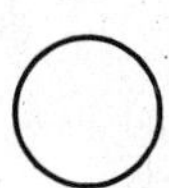 as  is to ______________

4.

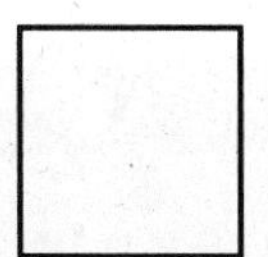 is to 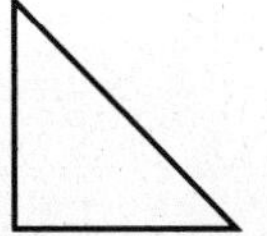 as  is to ______________

5.

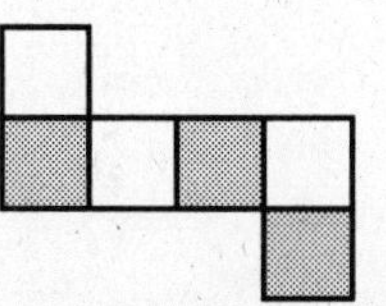 is to 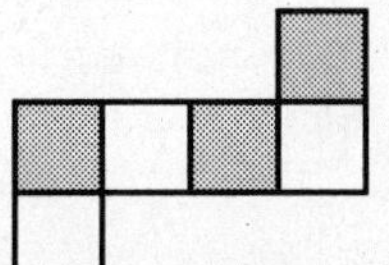 as 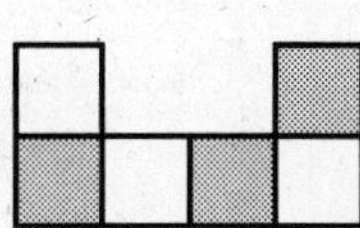 is to ______________

6.

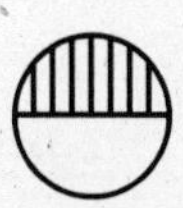 is to 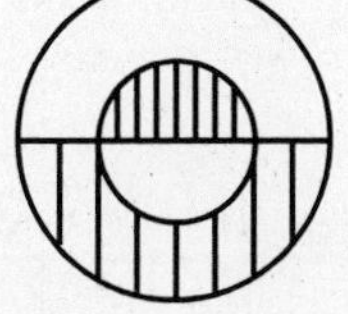 as  is to ______________

Use after pages 134–135.

Teacher Notes

Use with
Objective 40
pages 134–135

Focus
Visual Thinking
Visual Patterns

Materials
Visual Thinking transparency (optional)

Overview
Students recognize the relationship between two figures of a visual analogy and use the relationship to complete the analogy.

Teaching Suggestions
Question: *In the example, how do the first pair of arrows compare?* [They point in opposite directions.] Help students to see that the key is not that one points up and the other points down but that they point in opposite directions. Have students complete Problems 1 and 2. ***Question:*** *In Problem 3, how do the two objects compare?* [They have the same shape, but the second one is smaller.]

For students having difficulty with Problems 4–6, ask them to describe the change they observe from the first to the second object.

Extension
Divide students into groups of four. One student should draw a figure on paper. Have a second student make a drawing that shows a change in the first figure. A third student should draw a new figure. The fourth student should try to make a drawing that shows the same change that exists between the first two drawings. Have students take turns making the first drawing.

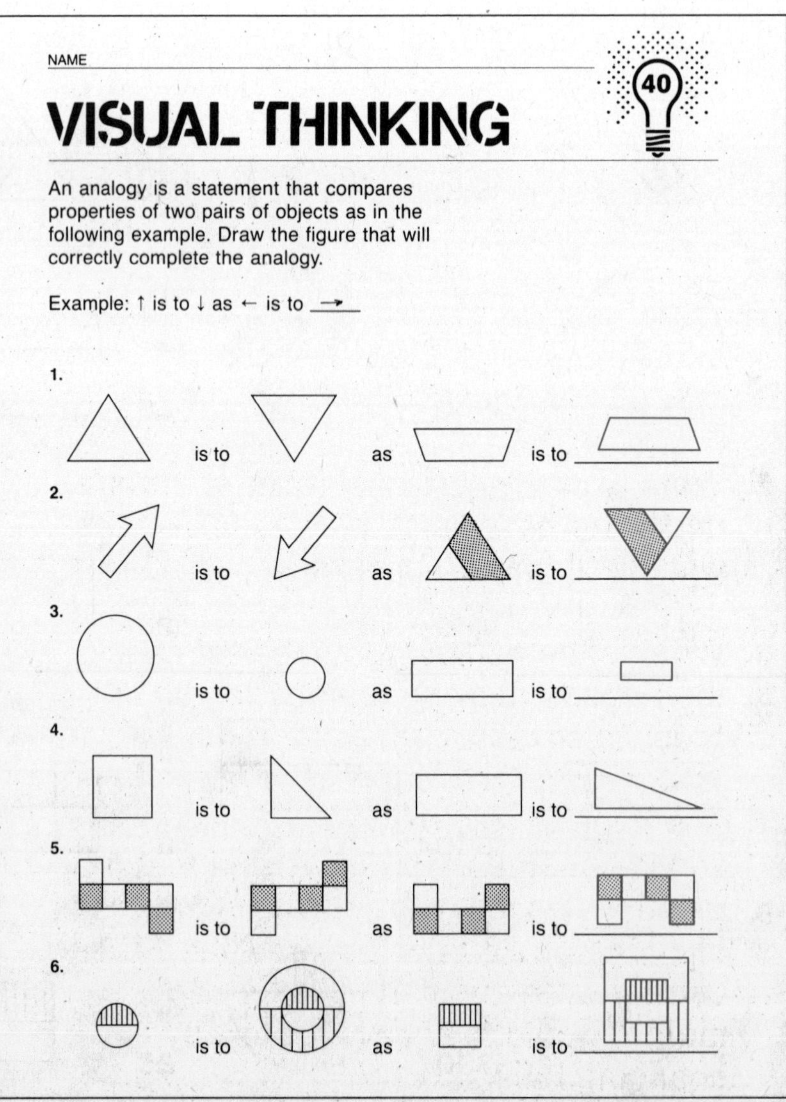
NAME

VISUAL THINKING

40

An analogy is a statement that compares properties of two pairs of objects as in the following example. Draw the figure that will correctly complete the analogy.

Example: ↑ is to ↓ as ← is to →

1. is to as is to

2. is to as is to

3. is to as is to

4. is to as is to

5. is to as is to

6. is to as is to

NAME ______________________________

PROBLEM SOLVING

One day the Filberts noticed a sign at the bank announcing new rates for checking accounts. Use the information from the drawing to answer the following questions. You may wish to make a table to help you.

1. What was the monthly charge under the old plan if only 1 check was written? If only 20 checks were written? ______________________

2. What would be the total monthly charge under the new plan if only 1 check were written? If only 20 checks were written? ______________________

3. What is the minimum number of checks the Filberts must write each month in order to save money under the new plan? ______________________

4. The Filberts asked another bank about service charges. The teller said that the monthly service charge was 90¢ and that they charge 25¢ per check. If the Filberts usually write about 20 checks each month, would they save money by changing banks? ______________________

Teacher Notes

Use with
Objective 41
pages 136–137

Focus
Problem Solving
Make a Table

Overview
Students *make a table* to determine the cost of writing checks under two plans.

Teaching Suggestions
Discuss with students ways banks charge their customers for the use of a checking account.

Have students complete Problems 1 and 2. Be sure they can explain how they arrive at their answers. [Old plan: 1 × 0.15 + 1.90 = $2.05; 20 × 0.15 + 1.90 = $4.90. New plan: 1 × 0.10 + 2.50 = $2.60; 20 × 0.10 + 2.50 = $4.50] ***Question:*** *At what number of checks do you think the new plan's charges will become cheaper?* Have students *make a table* like the one below.

Total Monthly Charge		
Number of checks	Old plan	New plan
1	$2.05	$2.60
2	$2.20	$2.70
3	$2.35	$2.80
4	$2.50	$2.90
5	$2.65	$3.00
6	$2.80	$3.10
7	$2.95	$3.20
8	$3.10	$3.30
9	$3.25	$3.40
10	$3.40	$3.50
11	$3.55	$3.60
12	$3.70	$3.70
13	$3.85	$3.80

Question: *At what point will you end your table?* [When the charges under the new plan are less than the charges under the old plan]

Extension
Have students find out what various local banks charge for checking accounts. By making tables similar to the one in the lesson, students could determine which bank offers a checking account plan at the lowest rate for a fixed number of checks written per month.

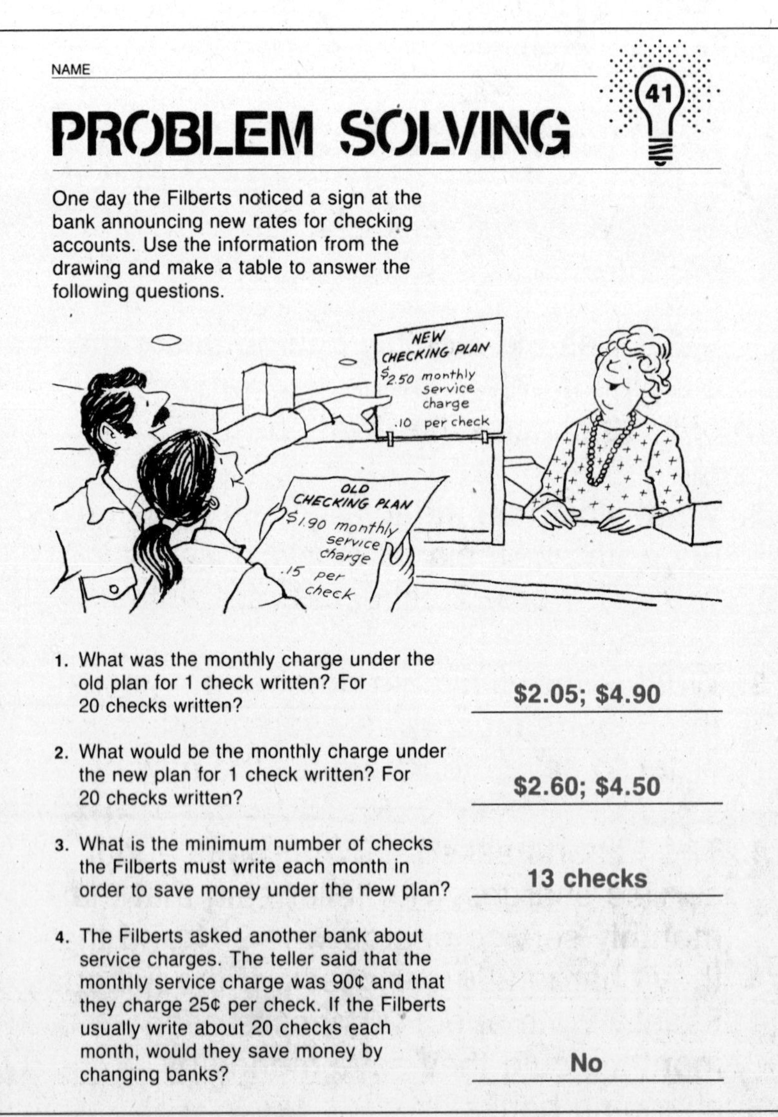

NAME

PROBLEM SOLVING 41

One day the Filberts noticed a sign at the bank announcing new rates for checking accounts. Use the information from the drawing and make a table to answer the following questions.

1. What was the monthly charge under the old plan for 1 check written? For 20 checks written? **$2.05; $4.90**
2. What would be the monthly charge under the new plan for 1 check written? For 20 checks written? **$2.60; $4.50**
3. What is the minimum number of checks the Filberts must write each month in order to save money under the new plan? **13 checks**
4. The Filberts asked another bank about service charges. The teller said that the monthly service charge was 90¢ and that they charge 25¢ per check. If the Filberts usually write about 20 checks each month, would they save money by changing banks? **No**

NAME ______________________________

DECISION MAKING

Oscar must buy meat and cheese for a picnic. He needs at least 2 pounds of each. Meat is $3 per pound and cheese is $2 per pound. Fill in the table below to find some of the combinations of meat and cheese he can buy for $18.

Pounds of meat	Cost	Pounds of cheese	Cost	Total
2				
2.5				
3				
3.5				
4				
4.5				

1. Twenty-eight people will be attending the picnic. One-fourth pound of food is planned per person. Each will eat various combinations of meat and cheese. Which combination of meat and cheese should Oscar buy? Explain your answer.

____

____

____

2. Which combination should he buy if he knows more guests prefer cheese? Explain your answer.

____

____

Teacher Notes

Use with
Objective 42
pages 138–139

Focus
Decision Making

Overview
Students find various combinations of meat and cheese that can be purchased for a fixed amount of money. They then *decide* which combination to buy based on consumption preferences.

Teaching Suggestions
Have students look at the table. ***Questions:*** *Which combination will have the greatest amount of cheese?* [The first] *Which will have the least?* [The last] Have students find the cost of 2 pounds of meat. [$6.00] ***Questions:*** *How much money is left to spend on cheese?* [$12.00] *How can you determine the amount of cheese that can be purchased for $12.00?* [Divide $12.00 by $2.00, the price of cheese per pound.]

Be sure students see that they actually need to establish the amount in the fourth column before finding the pounds of cheese that can be purchased.

For Problem 1, accept any answer that the student can reasonably justify.

For Problem 2, any of the first four combinations are acceptable answers.

Alternate Approach: If students are having difficulty completing the table, have them extend and rewrite the table using the following heads: Pounds of meat, × $3 (= Cost of meat), $18.00 – Cost of meat (= Cost of cheese), ÷ $2 (= Pounds of cheese).

Extension
Have small groups of students plan different parts of a picnic menu. Have them research prices for various foods or use newspaper ads. Assign each group a maximum amount that they can spend. Have students list factors that they might have to consider, such as whether they will have to buy ice for coolers or whether they will have to buy disposable forks and spoons.

NAME ____________________

DECISION MAKING

Oscar must buy meat and cheese for a picnic. He needs at least 2 pounds of each. Meat is $3 per pound and cheese is $2 per pound. Fill in the table below to find some of the combinations of meat and cheese he can buy for $18.

Pounds of meat	Cost	Pounds of cheese	Cost	Total
2	**$6.00**	**6**	**$12.00**	**$18.00**
2.5	**$7.50**	**5.25**	**$10.50**	**$18.00**
3	**$9.00**	**4.50**	**$9.00**	**$18.00**
3.5	**$10.50**	**3.75**	**$7.50**	**$18.00**
4	**$12.00**	**3**	**$6.00**	**$18.00**
4.5	**$13.50**	**2.25**	**$4.50**	**$18.00**

1. Twenty-eight people will be attending the picnic. One-fourth pound of food is planned per person. Each will eat various combinations of meat and cheese. Which combination of meat and cheese should Oscar buy? Explain your answer.

   Possible answer: 4 pounds of meat and 3 pounds of cheese; assumes most will have more meat on their sandwiches

2. Which combination should he buy if he knows more guests prefer cheese? Explain your answer.

   Possible answer: 3 pounds of meat and 4.50 pounds of cheese; allows more cheese in menu

NAME ______________________________

CRITICAL THINKING

Complete the chart below, and use it to answer the questions.

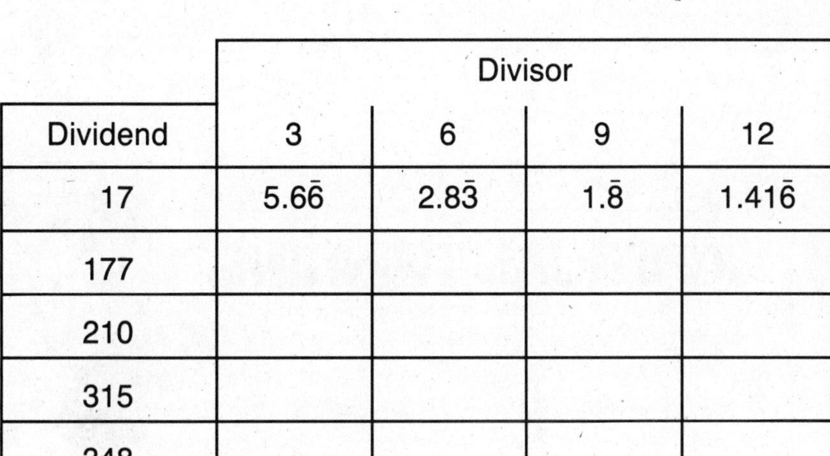

	Divisor			
Dividend	3	6	9	12
17	$5.6\bar{6}$	$2.8\bar{3}$	$1.\bar{8}$	$1.41\bar{6}$
177				
210				
315				
348				

1. If a number is divided by 3 and the quotient is a repeating decimal, what is true about the quotient when the same number is divided by 6, 9, or 12?

   ____

2. If a number is divisible by 9, then the number is also divisible by what other number(s)? ______________

3. If a number is divisible by 12, is it divisible by 3? By 6? ______________

4. If a number divided by 9 results in a repeating decimal, will a repeating decimal result if that number is divided by 18? By 27? ______________

Teacher Notes

Use with
Objective 43
pages 142–143

Focus
Critical Thinking
Making Generalizations

Materials
Calculators (optional)
2 pieces of paper,
90 cm square each

Overview
Students fill in a chart to show the quotient when various numbers are divided by 3, 6, 9, and 12. They then *make generalizations* about divisibility based on their results.

Teaching Suggestions
Have students complete the chart, using calculators if they are available. Direct their attention to the first row in the chart that has been completed. ***Question:*** *What does the bar above a digit mean?* [That the digit repeats forever]

Be sure students realize that a dividend is divisible by a divisor only if the quotient is a whole number. ***Question:*** *If the quotient is 16.5, is the dividend divisible by the divisor?* [No]

Alternate Approach: For students having difficulty understanding 1 ÷ 3 is a repeating decimal, have a demonstration using a 90 cm × 90 cm piece of paper. Point out that the paper is square. Cut the paper so one-third remains (30 cm × 90 cm). Cut the paper again so 1/3 remains (30 cm × 30 cm). Point out that the paper is square again.

Repeat 1/3 divisions of 10 cm × 30 cm and 10 cm × 10 cm. Point out that again a square remains. Use this never-ending pattern to help students visualize that 1 ÷ 3 is a repeating decimal. The same demonstration can be altered to show 2/3.

Extension
Have students use the chart to find a rule for telling whether a number is divisible by 6. [If the number is divisible by 3 and even]

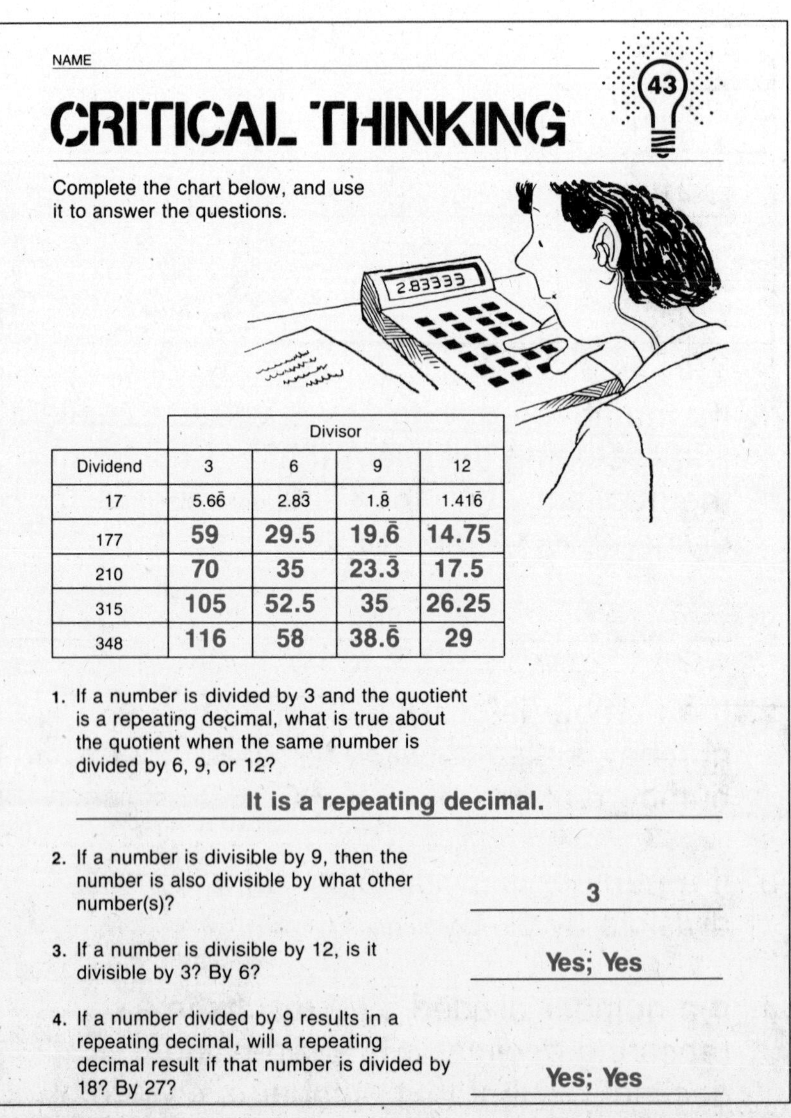

NAME

CRITICAL THINKING

Complete the chart below, and use it to answer the questions.

	Divisor			
Dividend	3	6	9	12
17	$5.6\bar{6}$	$2.8\bar{3}$	$1.\bar{8}$	$1.41\bar{6}$
177	59	29.5	$19.\bar{6}$	14.75
210	70	35	$23.\bar{3}$	17.5
315	105	52.5	35	26.25
348	116	58	$38.\bar{6}$	29

1. If a number is divided by 3 and the quotient is a repeating decimal, what is true about the quotient when the same number is divided by 6, 9, or 12?
   It is a repeating decimal.
2. If a number is divisible by 9, then the number is also divisible by what other number(s)? **3**
3. If a number is divisible by 12, is it divisible by 3? By 6? **Yes; Yes**
4. If a number divided by 9 results in a repeating decimal, will a repeating decimal result if that number is divided by 18? By 27? **Yes; Yes**

NAME ____________________

PROBLEM SOLVING

A change purse contains exactly nine coins which total 78¢. You want to find how many coins there are of each value.

Solve the problem above by completing the steps below.

1. Could there be 8 pennies? Why or why not?

____

____

2. How many pennies must there be?

____

3. Find all possibilities for the 9 coins. You may want to make a table to help you find the answer.

____

____

____

____

____

Teacher Notes

Use with
Objective 44
pages 144–145

Focus
Problem Solving
Make a Table

Overview
Students find the correct number of coins of each value to get a combination of nine coins that have a total value of 78¢.

Teaching Suggestions
Have students solve Problem 1. Write the following groups of numbers on the board: 5, 10, 25; 10, 25, 50; 5, 25, 50. ***Questions:*** *What is the sum of each group of numbers?* [40; 85; 80] *What digit will be in the ones place for the sum of any group of numbers using 5, 10, 25, and 50?* [0 or 5]

Have students use their answer to the previous problem to help them solve Problem 2.

For solving Problem 3, suggest that students set up a table showing various combinations of 9 coins, or 3 pennies and 6 nickels, dimes, quarters, and fifty-cent pieces.

Extension
Have students determine how exactly nine coins can make 57¢; 85¢; 99¢; $1.34; and $2.62. [Possible answers: 2 pennies, 3 nickels, 4 dimes; 1 nickel, 8 dimes; 4 pennies, 2 nickels, 1 dime, 1 quarter, 1 fifty-cent piece; 4 pennies, 1 nickel, 3 quarters, 1 fifty-cent piece; 2 pennies, 1 dime, 2 quarters, 4 fifty-cent pieces]

NAME

PROBLEM SOLVING

A change purse contains exactly nine coins which total 78¢. You want to find how many coins there are of each value.

Solve the problem above by completing the steps below.

1. Could there be 8 pennies? Why or why not?
   No; then the ninth coin would have to be a seventy-cent piece.

2. How many pennies must there be?
   3 pennies

3. Find all possibilities for the 9 coins. You may want to make a table to help you find the answer.
   There are three possibilities: 1 fifty-cent piece, 5 nickels, and 3 pennies; 2 quarters, 1 dime, 3 nickels, and 3 pennies; 1 quarter, 5 dimes, and 3 pennies.

NAME ______________________

CRITICAL THINKING

Clarissa wrote a song and sent it to W.E.B. Music to see if it could be a hit. She received this report.

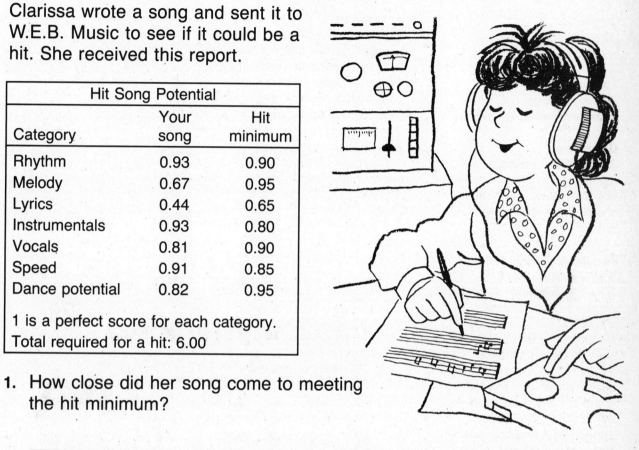

Hit Song Potential		
Category	Your song	Hit minimum
Rhythm	0.93	0.90
Melody	0.67	0.95
Lyrics	0.44	0.65
Instrumentals	0.93	0.80
Vocals	0.81	0.90
Speed	0.91	0.85
Dance potential	0.82	0.95

1 is a perfect score for each category.
Total required for a hit: 6.00

1. How close did her song come to meeting the hit minimum?

____

2. Could her song reach the hit minimum if only the vocals and the dance potential were improved? Explain.

____

____

3. Clarissa has time to improve only two categories of her song. Which two should she improve to reach the hit minimum? How many points does she need to improve each category?

____

____

Teacher Notes

Use with
Objective 45
pages 146–147

Focus
Critical Thinking
Developing Alternatives

Overview
Students are presented with several ways in which a score can be improved and must choose from among the alternatives.

Teaching Suggestions
Have students solve Problems 1 and 2. ***Question:*** *In which category is Clarissa short of the minimum?* [Melody, lyrics, vocals, and dance potential]

Have students look at Problem 3. ***Question:*** *Does Clarissa have to make the maximum improvement in the two areas she chooses? Explain.* [No, she only has to have the improvement total 0.49.]

In Problem 3, accept any answer where the improvement will total 0.49. Some students may notice that if Clarissa makes the maximum improvement possible in lyrics that she would not have to improve in a second category.

Alternate Approach: If students are having difficulty reading the report to answer Problems 2 and 3, have them add a third column labeled Difference. In this column students should take the difference between the values in Your Song and Hit Minimum, labeling it + if the song has a greater value than the hit minimum, – if it has less.

Extension
Suppose Clarissa's song had to score at least the minimum in each category to qualify as a hit. Have students determine how much her score would have to improve. [0.71]

NAME ______________________

CRITICAL THINKING

Clarissa wrote a song and sent it to W.E.B. Music to see if it could be a hit. She received this report.

Hit Song Potential		
Category	Your song	Hit minimum
Rhythm	.93	.90
Melody	.67	.95
Lyrics	.44	.65
Instrumentals	.93	.80
Vocals	.81	.90
Speed	.91	.85
Dance potential	.82	.95

1 is a perfect score for each category.
Total required for a hit: 6.00

1. How close did her song come to meeting the hit minimum?

   0.49 away

2. Could she get her song closer to the hit minumum by improving the vocals and the dance potential? Explain.

   No; she can add only 0.37 from those categories to her song's total.

3. Clarissa has time to improve only two categories of her song. Which two should she improve to reach the hit minimum? How many points does she need to improve each category?

   Possible answer: Melody 0.28; Lyrics 0.21

NAME ______________________________

PROBLEM SOLVING

Mrs. Nemo kept her gasoline sales slips for May. She started with a full tank of gasoline on May 1 and an odometer (an instrument that measures miles traveled) reading of 4,468.2 miles. She filled the tank each time she bought gas. Make a table to help solve the problems.

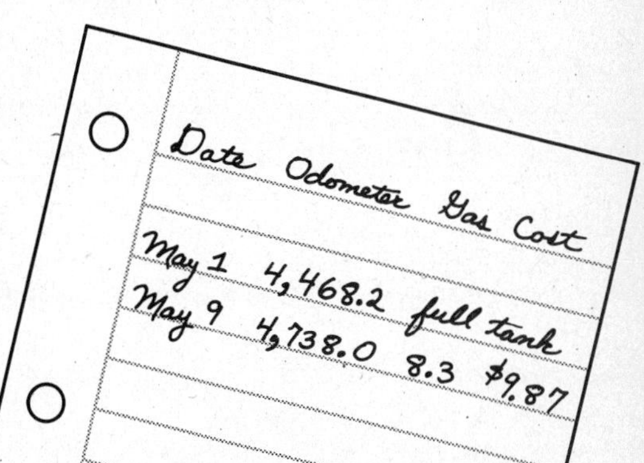

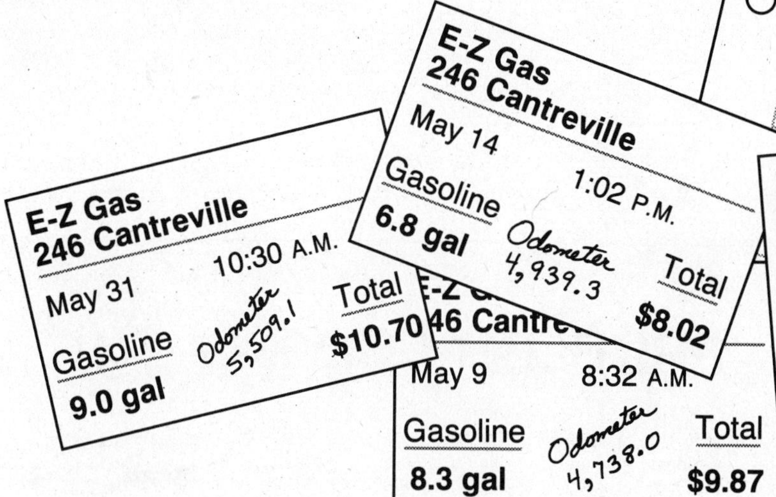

1. How many gallons of gasoline did Mrs. Nemo use between May 1 and May 9? How many miles did she drive? To the nearest tenth, how many miles per gallon did she get for this time period?

____

____

2. To the nearest tenth, how many miles per gallon did Mrs. Nemo get for May 9 to May 14? For May 14 to May 22? For May 22 to May 31?

____

____

____

3. To the nearest tenth, how many miles per gallon did she get for the month of May?

____

____

4. How much did she pay for gasoline for the month? To the nearest cent, what was the price per gallon for the gasoline she bought during May?

____

Teacher Notes

Use with
Objective 46
pages 148–149

Focus
Problem Solving
Make a Table

Overview
Students use given gasoline purchases and miles driven to find miles per gallon. Students *make a table* to help them determine gasoline costs.

Teaching Suggestions
To introduce the activity, explain that an odometer is a device used in cars to measure the distance a car has been driven. Tell students that to find the number of miles (or kilometers, depending on the odometer) driven, find the difference between two odometer readings.

Explain that "miles per gallon" tells the number of miles that were driven using one gallon of gas. For example, a car driven 180 miles on 9 gallons of gas got 180 ÷ 9, or 20, miles per gallon.

Students should *make a table* like Mrs. Nemo's record book from the information given on the receipts. ***Questions:** In what order should you record the gas purchases?* [By the dates on the receipts] *How would you find the number of gallons of gas used between May 1 and May 9?* [Since the tank was full on May 1, and 8.3 gallons had to be added on May 9, 8.3 gallons were used.]

Students should be instructed to round all computations to the nearest tenth.

To solve Problem 3, students should divide the total number of miles driven, 1,040.9, by the total number of gallons used, 33.7.

Extension
Have students investigate various factors that can affect gas mileage. [City driving, low tire pressure, or need for a tune-up can decrease gas mileage. Highway driving, proper tire pressure, and use of overdrive can increase gas mileage.]

NAME ____________________

PROBLEM SOLVING

46

Mrs. Nemo kept her gasoline sales slips for May. She started with a full tank of gasoline on May 1 and an odometer (an instrument that measures miles traveled) reading of 4,468.2 miles. She filled the tank each time she bought gas. Make a table to help solve the problems.

Date	Odometer	Gas	Cost
May 1	4,468.2	full tank	
May 9	4,738.0	8.3	$9.87

E-Z Gas, 246 Cantreville — May 9, 8:32 A.M. — Gasoline 8.3 gal — Odometer 4,738.0 — Total $9.87

E-Z Gas, 246 Cantreville — May 14, 1:02 P.M. — Gasoline 6.8 gal — Odometer 4,939.3 — Total $8.02

E-Z Gas, 246 Cantreville — May 22, 5:55 P.M. — Gasoline 9.6 gal — Odometer 5,228.3 — Total $11.13

E-Z Gas, 246 Cantreville — May 31, 10:30 A.M. — Gasoline 9.0 gal — Odometer 5,509.1 — Total $10.70

1. How many gallons of gasoline did Mrs. Nemo use between May 1 and May 9? How many miles did she drive? To the nearest tenth, how many miles per gallon did she get for this time period?
   8.3 gallons; 269.8 miles;
   32.5 miles per gallon

2. To the nearest tenth, how many miles per gallon did Mrs. Nemo get for May 9 to May 14? For May 14 to May 22? For May 22 to May 31?
   29.6 miles per gallon;
   30.1 miles per gallon;
   31.2 miles per gallon

3. To the nearest tenth, how many miles per gallon did she get for the month of May?
   30.9 miles per gallon

4. How much did she pay for gasoline for the month? To the nearest cent, what was the price per gallon for the gasoline she bought during May?
   $39.72; $1.18 per gallon

NAME ____________________

CRITICAL THINKING

The Dougal family lives in Schaumburg, Illinois. Below is a table which shows the direct-dial charges from their area to some major cities in the United States.

Dial-direct Sample rates from-Schaumburg	Miles	Weekday full rate: First minute	Weekday full rate: Each additional minute	Evening rate: First minute	Evening rate: Each additional minute	Weekend rate: First minute	Weekend rate: Each additional minute
Atlanta, GA	622	$0.62	$0.43	$0.38	$0.26	$0.25	$0.18
Boston, MA	866	0.62	0.43	0.38	0.26	0.25	0.18
Detroit, MI	258	0.58	0.39	0.35	0.24	0.24	0.16
Los Angeles, CA	1710	0.64	0.44	0.39	0.27	0.26	0.18
Miami, FL	1205	0.64	0.44	0.39	0.27	0.26	0.18
Milwaukee, WI	70	0.57	0.37	0.35	0.23	0.23	0.15
Minn, MN	322	0.59	0.42	0.36	0.26	0.24	0.17
New York, NY	738	0.62	0.43	0.38	0.26	0.25	0.18
Wash. D.C.	631	0.62	0.43	0.38	0.26	0.25	0.18

1. The Dougals were charged $2.82 for a Tuesday evening call to Los Angeles. How many minutes long was the call? ____________________

2. Monica Dougal placed a 12-minute call to a friend in Miami on Friday at noon. How many minutes could she have talked on Sunday for the same amount of money? ____________________

3. Joe Dougal called his brother, Ken, who lives in one of the cities listed in the table. The Saturday morning call lasted 20 minutes and the charge was $3.08. Use the rate table above to find the city where Ken lives. ____________________

Teacher Notes

Use with
Objective 47
pages 150–151

Focus
Critical Thinking
Reasoning with Graphs and Charts

Overview
Students analyze a table of telephone rates to answer questions about charges for telephone calls.

Teaching Suggestions
Explain that dial-direct calls are interstate calls, excluding Alaska and Hawaii, which are made from a residential or business phone without assistance from an operator. ***Question:*** *How many rates are in the table, and what are they?* [3; weekday, evening, and weekend]

Point out that you pay for the number of minutes that you talk. ***Question:*** *In the table, how does the first-minute rate compare with the additional-minute rate?* [It is higher.]

In Problem 1, students must use the table rates for an evening call to Los Angeles. ***Questions:*** *What would you do first to solve Problem 1?* [Subtract the first-minute rate ($0.39) from the total charge.] *How would you find the number of additional minutes?* [Divide the difference, $2.43, by the additional-minute rate, $0.27; to get 9 minutes.] Be sure students remember to add the first minute to get a total of 10 minutes for the call.

In Problem 2, have students first find the charge for the Friday call, then work backward as in Problem 1 to find the length of the Sunday call for the same charge. In Problem 3, suggest that students check the charge for a 20-minute call to Atlanta. Once they find that this is too much, they can eliminate all other cities with the same weekend rate.

Extension
Have students find the rates for dial-direct calls for your area. How do your rates compare to the rates in the table? [Rates will vary depending on location.]

NAME ______________________________ 47

CRITICAL THINKING

The Dougal family lives in Schaumburg, Illinois. Below is a table which shows the direct-dial charges from their area to some major cities in the United States.

Dial-direct Sample rates from-Schaumburg	Miles	Weekday full rate: First minute	Weekday full rate: Each additional minute	Evening rate: First minute	Evening rate: Each additional minute	Weekend rate: First minute	Weekend rate: Each additional minute
Atlanta, GA	622	$0.62	$0.43	$0.38	$0.26	$0.25	$0.18
Boston, MA	866	0.62	0.43	0.38	0.26	0.25	0.18
Detroit, MI	258	0.58	0.39	0.35	0.24	0.24	0.16
Los Angeles, CA	1710	0.64	0.44	0.39	0.27	0.26	0.18
Miami, FL	1205	0.64	0.44	0.39	0.27	0.26	0.18
Milwaukee, WI	70	0.57	0.37	0.35	0.23	0.23	0.15
Minn, MN	322	0.59	0.42	0.36	0.26	0.24	0.17
New York, NY	738	0.62	0.43	0.38	0.26	0.25	0.18
Wash. D.C.	631	0.62	0.43	0.38	0.26	0.25	0.18

1. The Dougals were charged $2.82 for a Tuesday evening call to Los Angeles. How many minutes long was the call? **10 minutes**

2. Monica Dougal placed a 12-minute call to a friend in Miami on Friday at noon. How many minutes could she have talked on Sunday for the same amount of money? **30 minutes**

3. Joe Dougal called his brother, Ken, who lives in one of the cities listed in the table. The Saturday morning call lasted 20 minutes and the charge was $3.08. Use the rate table above to find the city where Ken lives. **Milwaukee, WI**

NAME ______________________________

VISUAL THINKING

Think about how the capital letter is formed for each letter in the alphabet.

1. Which letters can be written using *only* line segments?

____

____

2. Of the letters using only line segments, which contain parallel line segments?

____

3. Of the letters using only line segments, which letters contain right angles?

____

4. Which capital letters fit into all three of the previous categories?

____

5. How many lowercase letters will satisfy all three categories? Make a prediction, then repeat Questions 1 to 3.

____

Teacher Notes

Use with
Objective 48
pages 162–163

Focus
Visual Thinking
Spatial Perception

Materials
Visual Thinking transparency (optional)

Overview
Students use uppercase letters of the alphabet to learn about line segments, parallel lines, and perpendicular lines.

Teaching Suggestions
Review the definitions of the terms *line segment, parallel lines,* and *right angle.* A line segment is a part of a line that joins two points. Parallel lines are lines within a plane that will not intersect no matter how far they are extended. A right angle is an angle that measures 90°. Right angles are formed by perpendicular lines. Then have students complete Problems 1–4.

After students make their predictions for Problem 5, have them print the lowercase letters on the bottom of the page. The lowercase *k, l, t, v, w, x, y,* and *z* can be written using only line segments. Only the lowercase letter *z* contains parallel segments. Only the lowercase letters *t, k,* and *x* contain line segments at right angles.

Alternate Approach: If students need more practice, have them answer Problems 1–3 using the numbers 1–10. Answers will vary slightly depending upon how students write the numbers.

Extension
Provide students with copies of the uppercase letters of the Greek alphabet.

Α, Β, Γ, Δ, Ε, Ζ, Η, Θ, Ι, Κ, Λ, Μ, Ν, Ξ, Ο, Π, Ρ, Σ, Τ, Υ, Φ, Χ, Ψ, Ω

Have them repeat Problems 1–3. Point out the many similarities between the two alphabets.

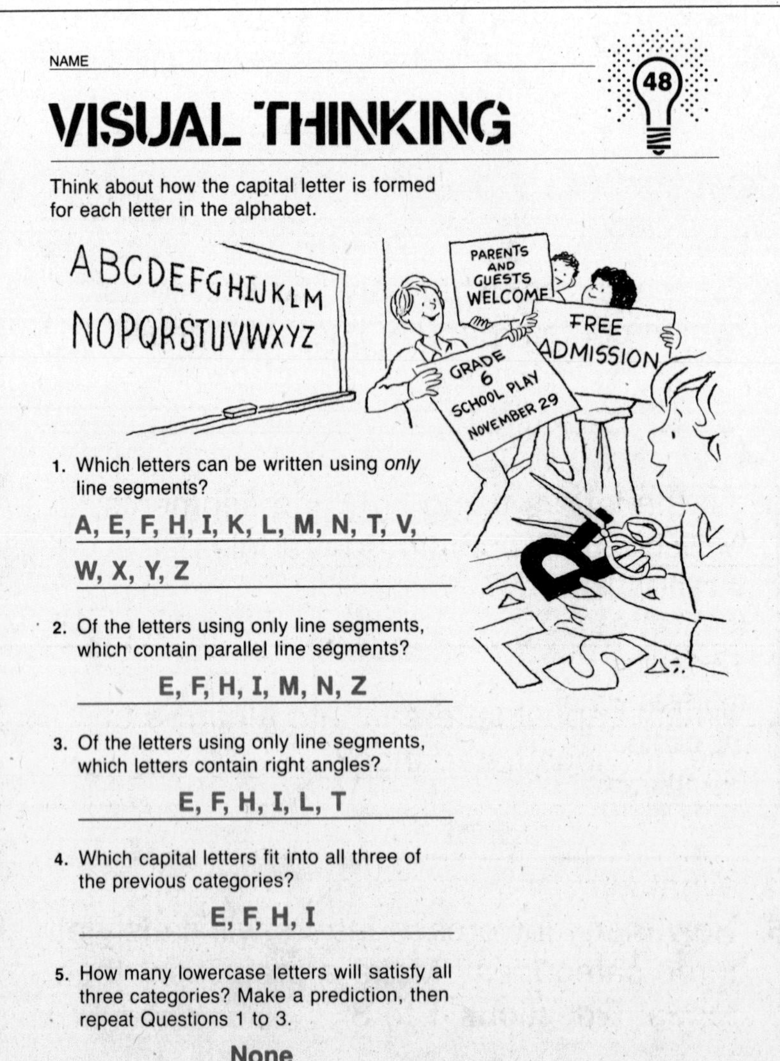
NAME

48

VISUAL THINKING

Think about how the capital letter is formed for each letter in the alphabet.

1. Which letters can be written using *only* line segments?
   A, E, F, H, I, K, L, M, N, T, V, W, X, Y, Z
2. Of the letters using only line segments, which contain parallel line segments?
   E, F, H, I, M, N, Z
3. Of the letters using only line segments, which letters contain right angles?
   E, F, H, I, L, T
4. Which capital letters fit into all three of the previous categories?
   E, F, H, I
5. How many lowercase letters will satisfy all three categories? Make a prediction, then repeat Questions 1 to 3.
   None

NAME ______________________________

DECISION MAKING

The Bingo O'Malley Aerial circus needs to order support cables for their new tent. They want to choose one of the four types below.

Cable	Quality	Cost per Foot
Steel Alloy	Excellent	$20
Steel	Good	$16
Nylon	Good	$12
Rope	Fair	$ 8

The tent can be supported by either 8, 12, or 16 cables. The fewer cables used, the longer each one must be, but the less time it will take to set up and take down the tent. Eight cables must be 64 feet each, 12 cables must be 50 feet each, and 16 cables must be 40 feet each. There is $10,500 left in the circus budget for the cables.

1. Complete the following table by computing and listing the cost of each option.

	Type of cable			
Number of cables	Steel Alloy	Steel	Nylon	Rope
8 cables (64 feet each)	$10,240	$8,192	$6,144	$4,096
12 cables (50 feet each)				
16 cables (40 feet each)				

2. What kind of cables do you think the circus should buy? Explain your answer.

____

____

Teacher Notes

Use with
Objective 49
pages 164–167

Focus
Decision Making

Overview
Students analyze the costs of different kinds of circus tent cables and decide which to purchase.

Teaching Suggestions
To complete the table, students must multiply the number of cables by the number of feet needed by the cost per foot for each type of cable. Remind students to use units to avoid confusion. For example, to compute the cost of 12 steel alloy cables, multiply 12 cables by 50 feet by $20 per foot. Thus, the cost of 12 steel alloy cables is $12,000.

In answering Problem 2, some students may feel that a compromise on quality or time might be better than using up the remaining money in the budget.

NAME ______________________

DECISION MAKING

The Bingo O'Malley Aerial circus needs to order support cables for their new tent. They want to choose one of the four types below.

Cable	Quality	Cost per Foot
Steel Alloy	Excellent	$20
Steel	Good	$16
Nylon	Good	$12
Rope	Fair	$ 8

The tent can be supported by either 8, 12, or 16 cables. The fewer cables used, the longer each one must be, but the less time it will take to set up and take down the tent. Eight cables must be 64 feet each, 12 cables must be 50 feet each, and 16 cables must be 40 feet each. There is $10,500 left in the circus budget for the cables.

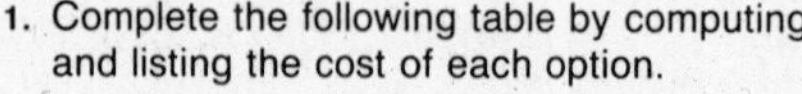

1. Complete the following table by computing and listing the cost of each option.

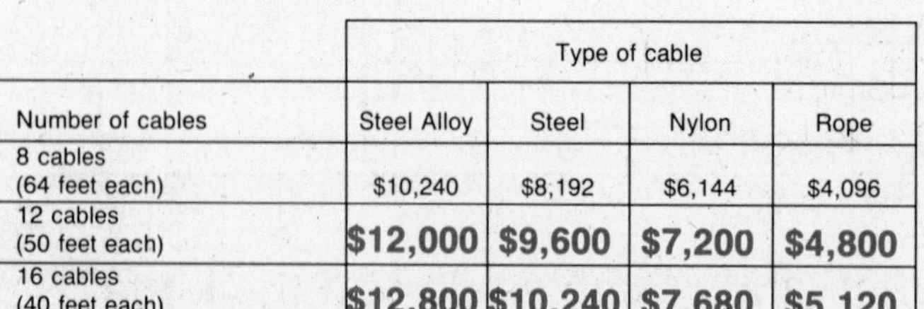

	Type of cable			
Number of cables	Steel Alloy	Steel	Nylon	Rope
8 cables (64 feet each)	$10,240	$8,192	$6,144	$4,096
12 cables (50 feet each)	**$12,000**	**$9,600**	**$7,200**	**$4,800**
16 cables (40 feet each)	**$12,800**	**$10,240**	**$7,680**	**$5,120**

2. What kind of cables do you think the circus should buy? Explain your answer.
   Possible answer: 8 steel alloy cables; excellent quality, fewest number, and is within budget

NAME ______________________________

VISUAL THINKING

For each row, circle the letter of the figure that does not fit with the others. Explain your answer.

Example:

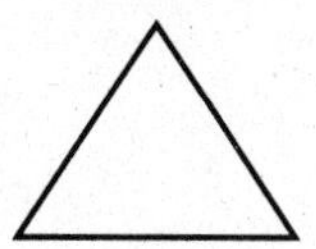 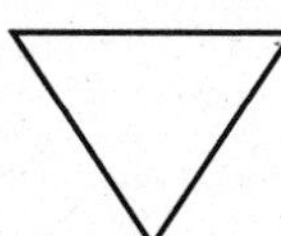 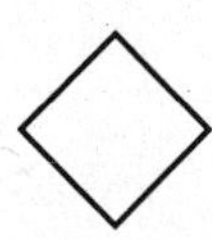 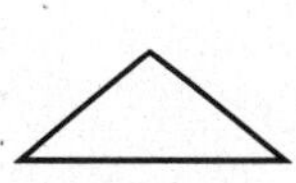

a. b.  c. d.

Why? Not a triangle

1.

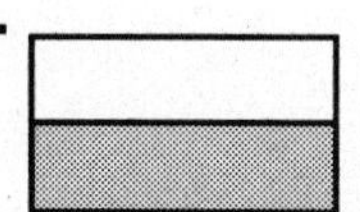 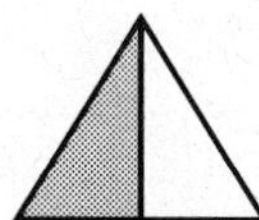 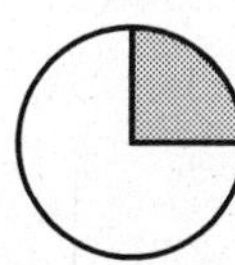 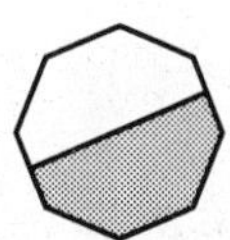

a. b. c. d.

Why? ______________________________

2.

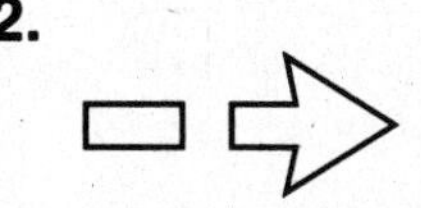 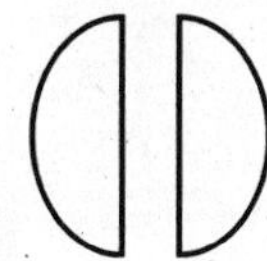 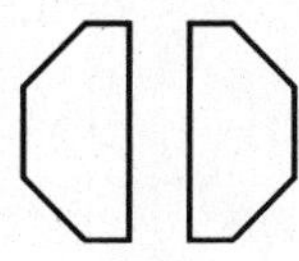 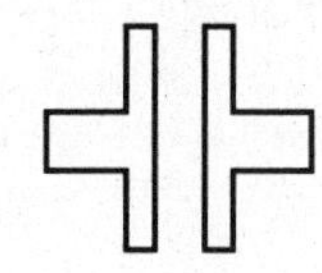

a. b. c. d.

Why? ______________________________

3.

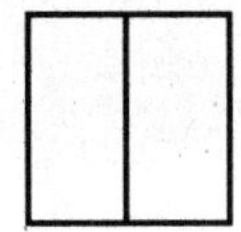 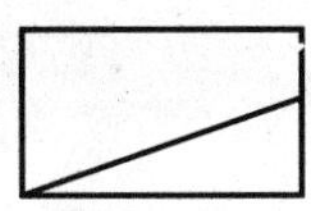 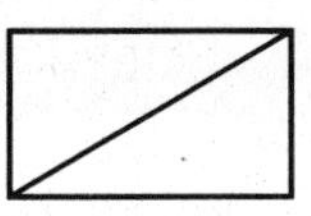 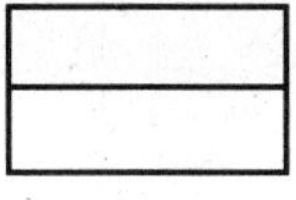

a. b. c. d.

Why? ______________________________

4.

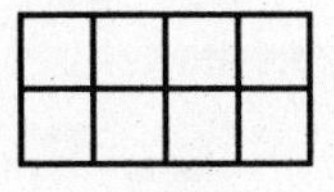 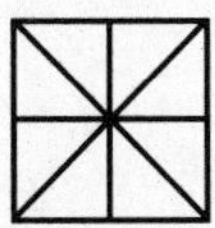 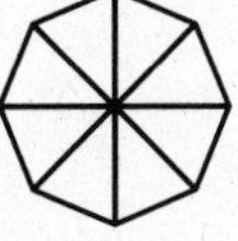 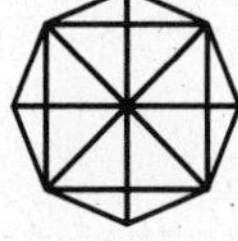

a. b. c. d.

Why? ______________________________

5.

 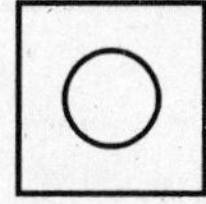  

a. b. c. d.

Why? ______________________________

Use after pages 168–169.

Teacher Notes

Use with
Objective 50
pages 168–169

Focus
Visual Thinking
Visual Patterns

Overview
Students study a group of items to determine how they are similar and dissimilar.

Teaching Suggestions
Introduce this concept through a simple example using three circles and a square. Have students list more than one criterion explaining why the square does not belong to the group.

If necessary, review the concept of symmetry for Problem 2. Discuss the definition of *polygon* with students. Remind them that a polygon is a closed plane figure bounded by line segments that meet at their endpoints. The line segments do not cross and enclose only one region.

Alternate Approach: Have students first list the ways in which the figures are similar, if they have difficulty determining which figure does not belong.

Extension
Show students a penny, a nickel, a dime, and a quarter. Have them determine how the penny differs from the others. [It is made from different metals and therefore is a different color.] Now show only the silver-colored coins, and have students determine which coin is different. [The nickel is the only coin with a smooth edge.]

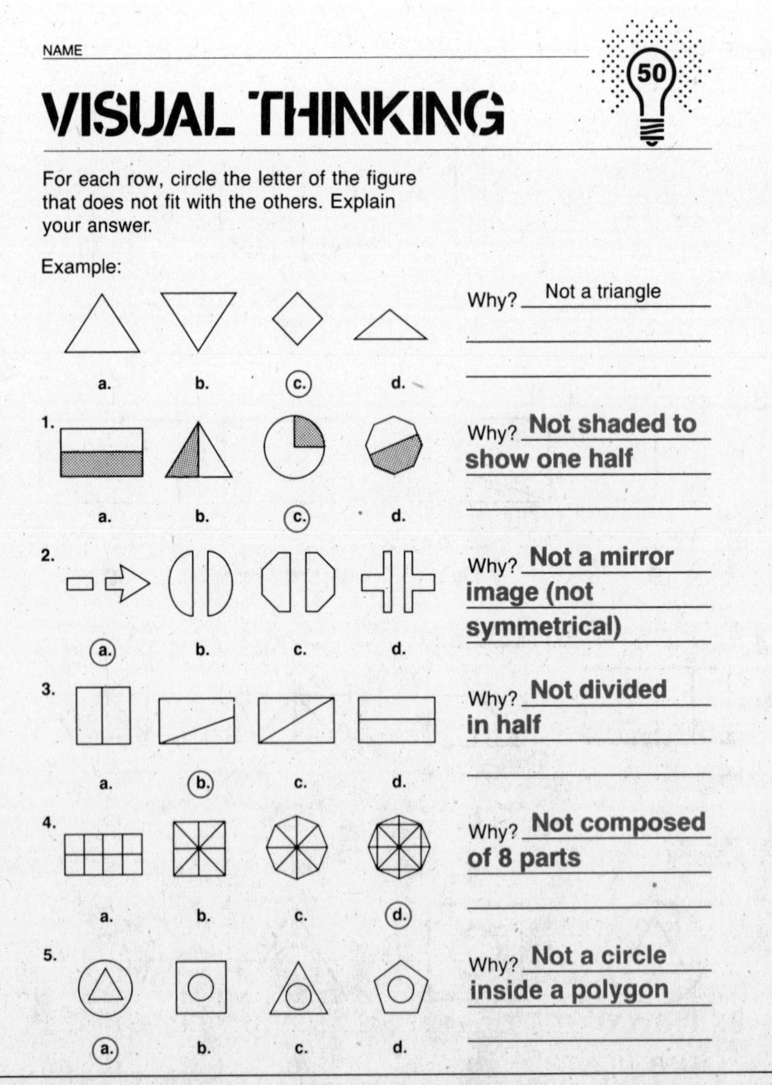

NAME

VISUAL THINKING

50

For each row, circle the letter of the figure that does not fit with the others. Explain your answer.

Example: a. b. (c.) d. Why? Not a triangle

1. a. b. (c.) d. Why? **Not shaded to show one half**

2. (a.) b. c. d. Why? **Not a mirror image (not symmetrical)**

3. a. (b.) c. d. Why? **Not divided in half**

4. a. b. c. (d.) Why? **Not composed of 8 parts**

5. (a.) b. c. d. Why? **Not a circle inside a polygon**

NAME ______________________

VISUAL THINKING

The following large triangle has three sides of equal length. Use it to answer the questions below. The triangles may overlap.

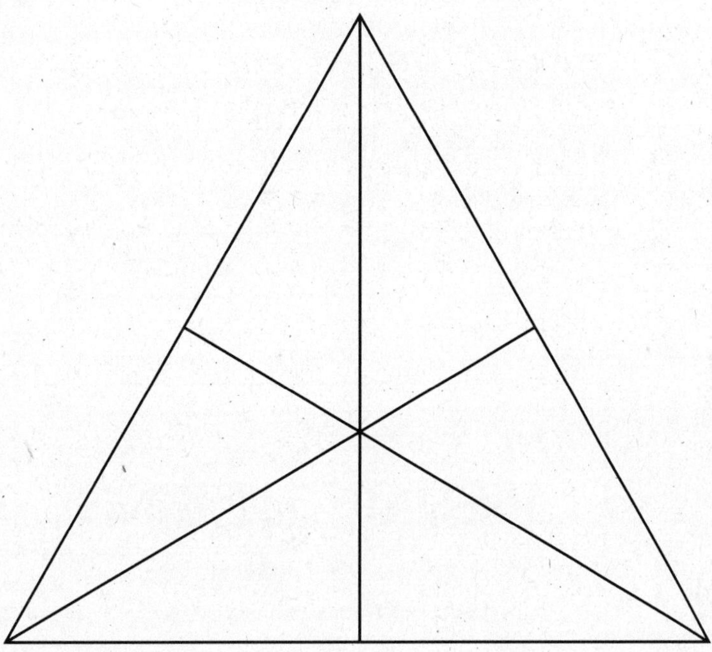

1. How many triangles can be found in the figure above? ______
2. How many equilateral triangles are there? ______
3. How many isosceles triangles are there? ______
4. How many scalene triangles are there? ______
5. How many right triangles are there? ______
6. How many obtuse triangles are there? ______
7. How many acute triangles are there? ______
8. How many quadrilaterals can be found in the figure? ______

Teacher Notes

Use with
Objective 51
pages 170–171

Focus
Visual Thinking
Spatial Perception

Overview
Students determine the number and kinds of triangles that make up a figure.

Teaching Suggestions
Review the following definitions. A triangle is a polygon with three sides. An equilateral triangle has three equal sides and each of its angles measures 60°. An isosceles triangle has at least two equal sides and two equal angles. A scalene triangle has no equal sides. A right triangle has one right angle. An obtuse triangle has one obtuse (greater than 90° but less than 180°) angle. An acute triangle has angles that measure less than 90°. A quadrilateral is a polygon of four sides.

Alternate Approach: Have students use three different colored markers to trace the acute, obtuse, and right angles.

Extension
Have students discuss the following questions. Could a right triangle be equilateral? [No] isosceles? [Yes] scalene? [Yes] Could an acute triangle be equilateral? [Yes] isosceles? [Yes] scalene? [Yes] Could an obtuse triangle be equilateral? [No] isosceles? [Yes] scalene? [Yes]

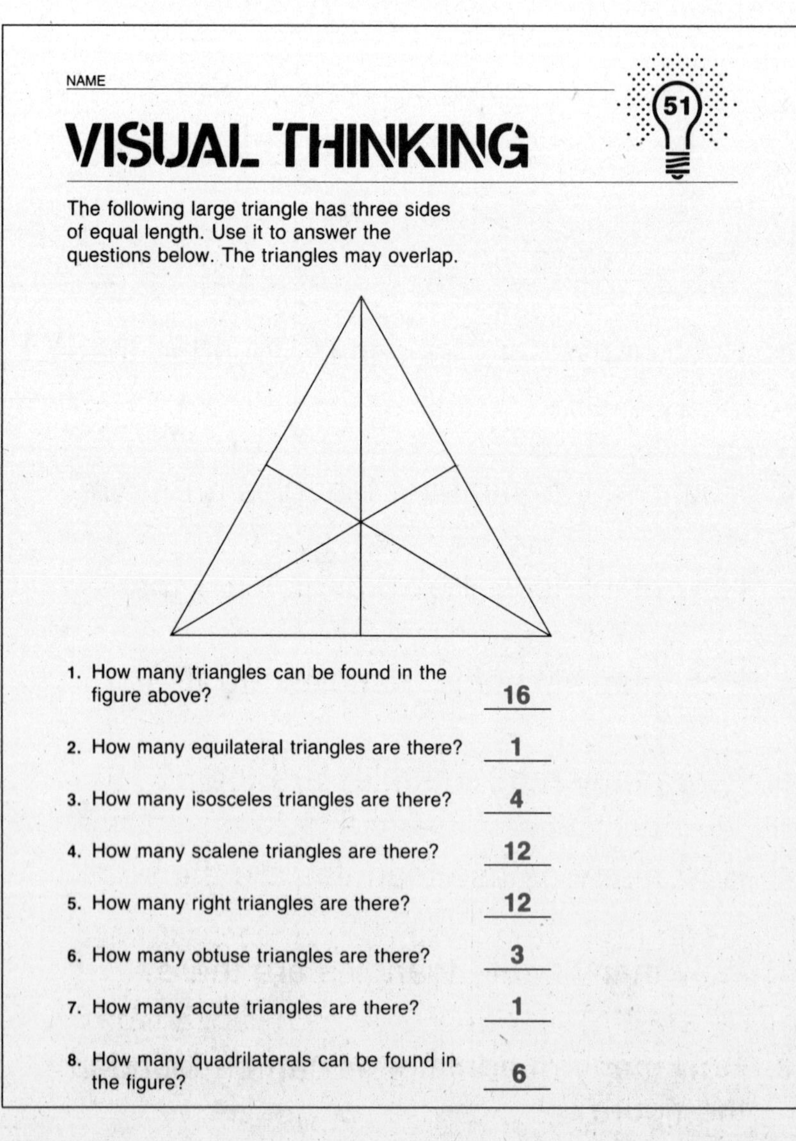

NAME

VISUAL THINKING

51

The following large triangle has three sides of equal length. Use it to answer the questions below. The triangles may overlap.

1. How many triangles can be found in the figure above? **16**
2. How many equilateral triangles are there? **1**
3. How many isosceles triangles are there? **4**
4. How many scalene triangles are there? **12**
5. How many right triangles are there? **12**
6. How many obtuse triangles are there? **3**
7. How many acute triangles are there? **1**
8. How many quadrilaterals can be found in the figure? **6**

NAME ______________________

PROBLEM SOLVING

Susan and George are boating on a lake. They want to contact their friend Dave by using signal flags. Each flag stands for a different letter of the alphabet. They have the four flags that spell Dave's name set aside from a previous voyage, but they have forgotten which flag stands for each letter.

1. How many possible ways of arranging the 4 flags on the pole are there? (If necessary, solve a simpler problem using only 2 or 3 flags to find a pattern.) ______________________

2. To display each arrangement of flags takes 6 minutes. If Susan and George have to try all possible arrangements before they spell Dave's name, how long will it take? ______________________

3. Susan and George now want to contact their friend Joyce. If they have to try all the arrangements of 5 flags to spell her name, how many arrangements will they have to try? ______________________

Teacher Notes

Use with
Objective 52
pages 172–173

Focus
Problem Solving
Solve a Simpler Problem
Make a Table

Overview
Students find the number of possible arrangements of four flags on a pole.

Teaching Suggestions
Students can make pictures of each flag or indicate 1, 2, 3, and 4 on separate pieces of paper and arrange them vertically on their desks. If students choose to number the flags, the list below shows all of the 24 possible arrangements.

1234	2341	3412	4123
1243	2314	3421	4132
1324	2431	3142	4213
1342	2413	3124	4231
1423	2134	3241	4312
1432	2143	3214	4321

Students may notice that two flags have $2 \times 1 = 2$ choices; three flags have $3 \times 2 = 6$ choices; four flags have $4 \times 3 \times 2 = 24$ choices; five flags have $5 \times 4 \times 3 \times 2 = 120$ choices. ***Question:** How many possibilities exist with seven flags?* [5,040]

Extension
If it takes Susan and George 8.5 minutes to arrange the flags to spell Joyce's name, have students compute the time needed to try all possible arrangements. [1,020 minutes or 17 hours]

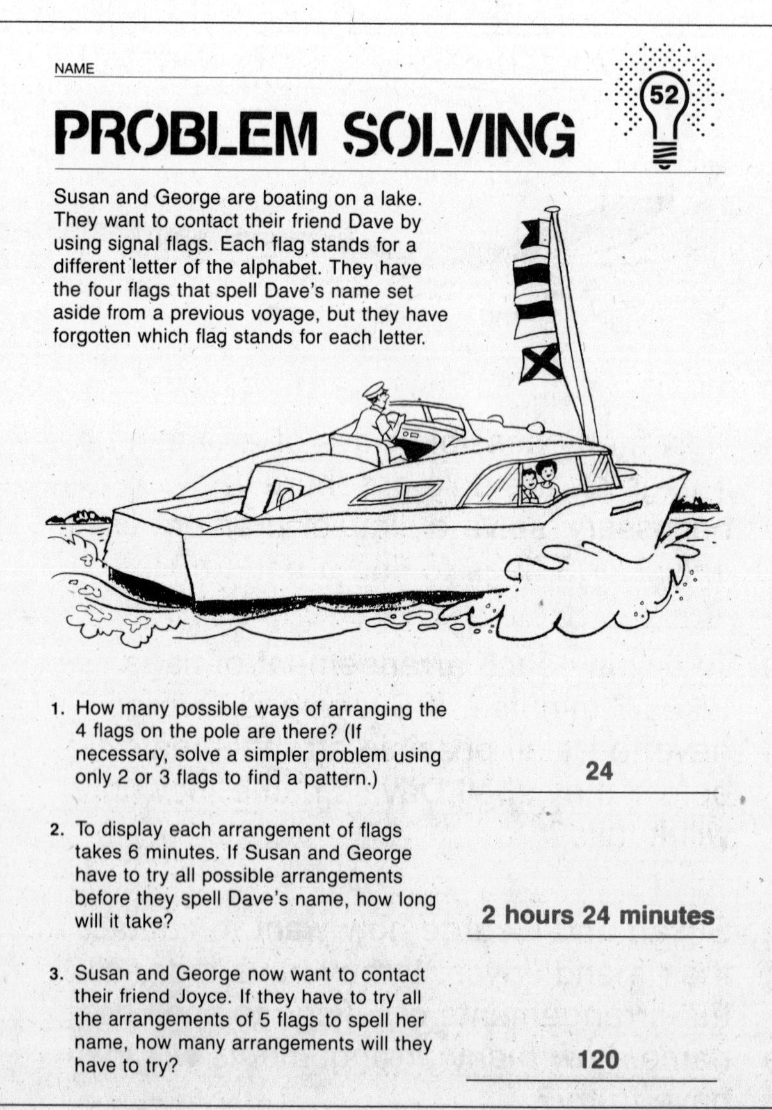
NAME

52

PROBLEM SOLVING

Susan and George are boating on a lake. They want to contact their friend Dave by using signal flags. Each flag stands for a different letter of the alphabet. They have the four flags that spell Dave's name set aside from a previous voyage, but they have forgotten which flag stands for each letter.

1. How many possible ways of arranging the 4 flags on the pole are there? (If necessary, solve a simpler problem using only 2 or 3 flags to find a pattern.) **24**
2. To display each arrangement of flags takes 6 minutes. If Susan and George have to try all possible arrangements before they spell Dave's name, how long will it take? **2 hours 24 minutes**
3. Susan and George now want to contact their friend Joyce. If they have to try all the arrangements of 5 flags to spell her name, how many arrangements will they have to try? **120**

NAME

CRITICAL THINKING

A carpenter cut a 4-foot by 3-foot board into two pieces and glued them together to make a 6-foot by 2-foot board.

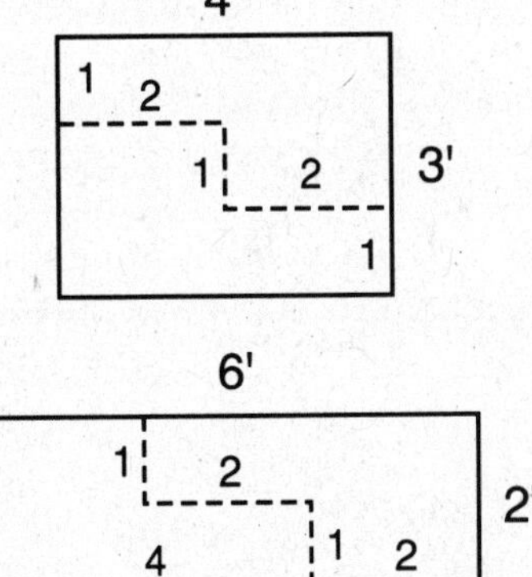

For each of Exercises 1–3, he made the cuts shown in the first board and glued them together to make the second board. Label the lengths of each piece of board as shown in the example.

1.

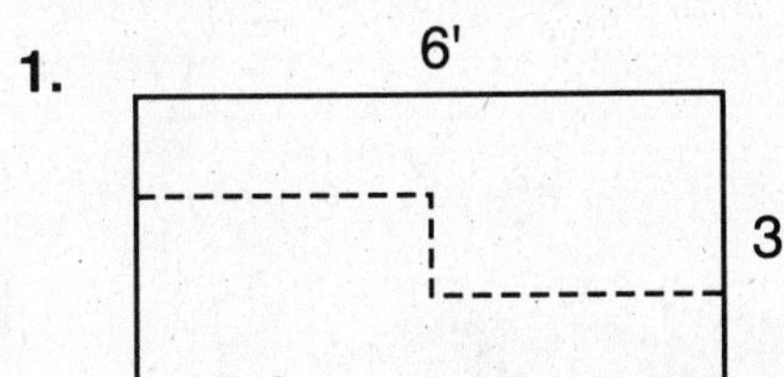

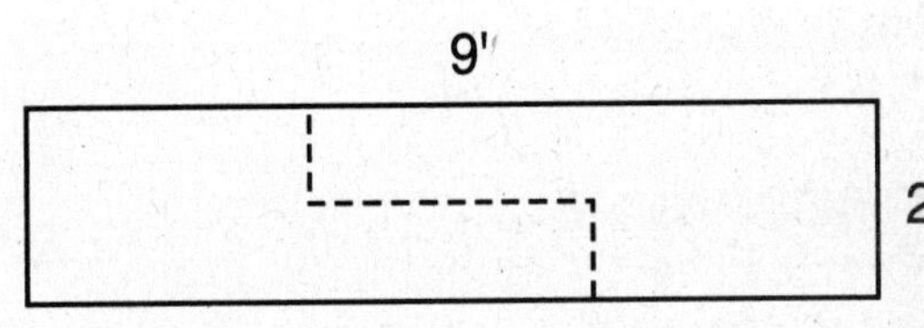

2.

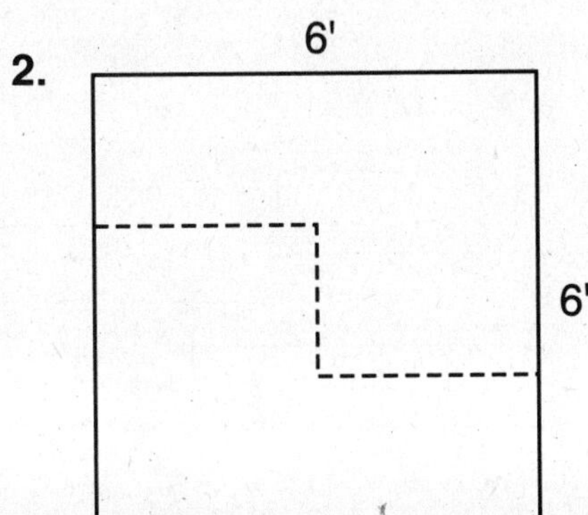

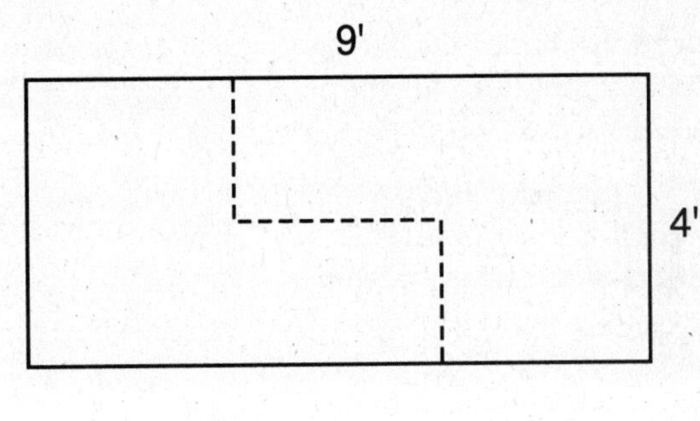

3.

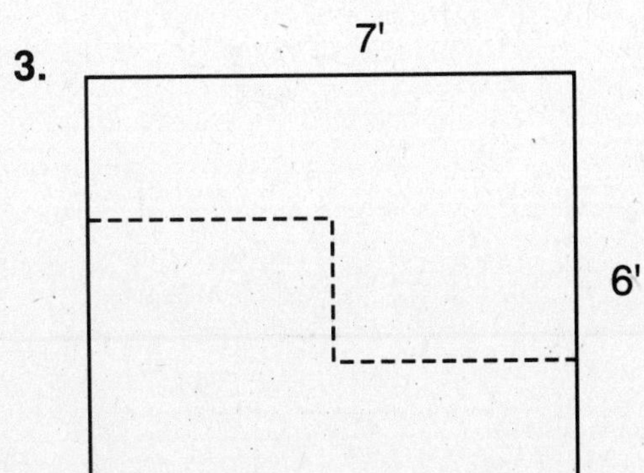

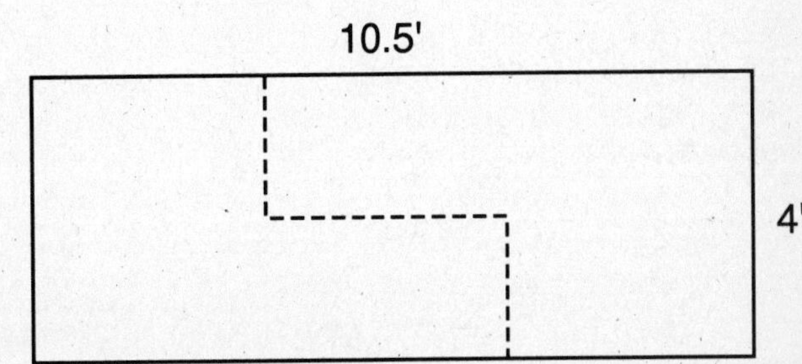

Teacher Notes

Use with
Objective 53
pages 174–177

Focus
Critical Thinking
Using Number Sense

Materials
Tracing paper

Overview
Students recognize the relationship in a visual pattern and use this same relationship to complete the pattern.

Teaching Suggestions
Make sure students understand that, in each problem, the sum of the vertical edges of the pieces must equal the vertical measure of the board on the right. The same is true for the horizontal edges of the pieces.

Alternate Approach: Provide tracing paper to students who are having difficulties with this activity. Have them trace the top portion of each board. Explain how to shift the tracing to the right until it aligns with the bottom portion to make the wooden board on the right.

Extension
Have students suggest other possible ways to cut each board on the left to make the corresponding board on the right. For example, the 4′ × 3′ board can be cut down the middle into two 2′ × 3′ boards to produce the 6′ × 2′ board.

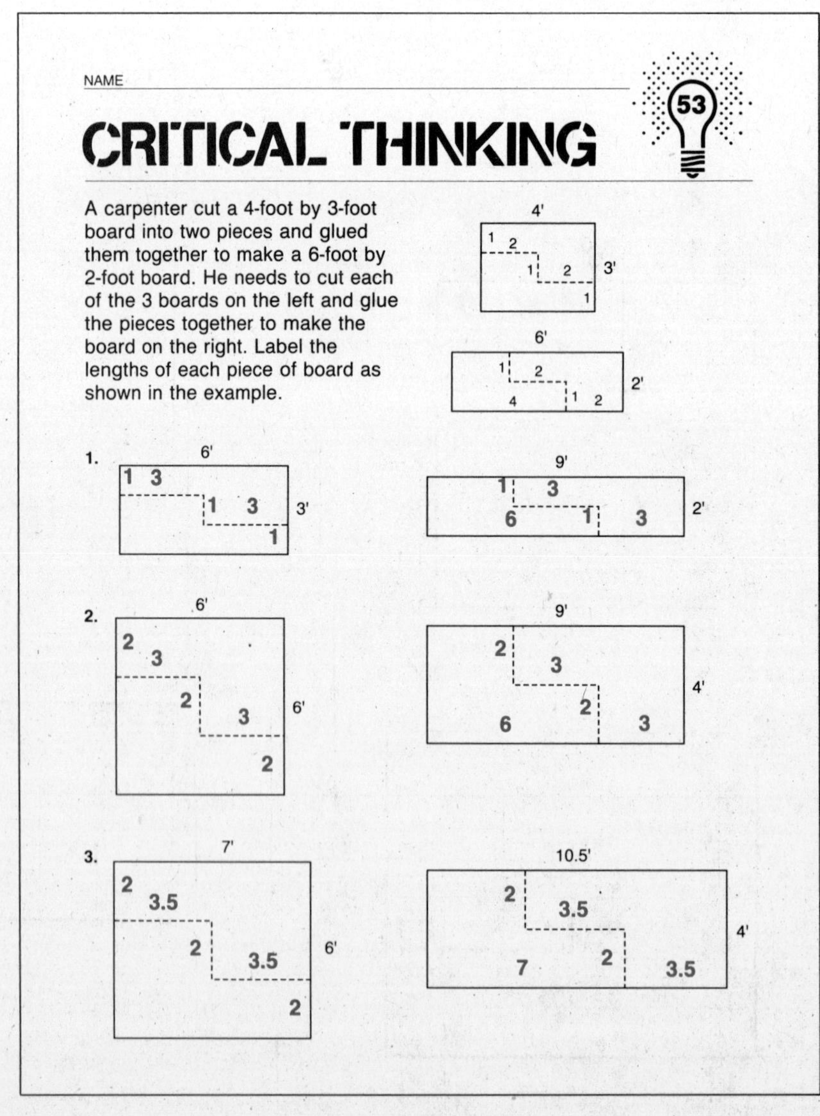

NAME ______

PROBLEM SOLVING

Maria wants to hold a meeting that all the salespeople in her company can attend. The salespeople are in the office only on certain work days.

Arthur is at the office every work day. Bernie is there every second work day, Candice every third work day, Debra every fourth work day, and Ellen every fifth work day.

Complete the table below to solve the following problems:

Salesperson	Work days in the office												
	1	2	3	4	5	6	7	8	9	10	11	12	13
Arthur	X	X	X	X	X	X	X	X	X	X	X	X	X
Bernie		X		X		X		X		X		X	
Candice													
Debra													
Ellen													

1. When are Arthur and Bernie in the office together?

______

2. Which salespeople are always in the office with Debra?

______

3. How often can the first 3 salespeople meet together?

______

4. Extend the table to find when all the salespeople are present in the office.

______

Teacher Notes

Use with
Objective 54
pages 180–181

Focus
Problem Solving
Solve a Simpler Problem
Make a Table
Find a Pattern

Overview
Students use least common multiples to determine when five salespeople, who are in the office only on certain days, can meet.

Teaching Suggestions
Make sure students realize that they are dealing with least common multiples in this activity.

Have students determine that Arthur and Bernie are in the office on days that are multiples of two. Candice is in on days that are multiples of three. ***Question:*** *On what days can the three meet?* [only on days that are multiples of both 2 and 3, or a multiple of 6]

In Problem 4, students need to detemine that Debra is in the office on days that are multiples of four and that Ellen is in on days that are multiples of five. Some students may discover that the least common multiple of 1, 2, 3, 4, and 5 is 60. Thus, all five people could meet every 60 work days.

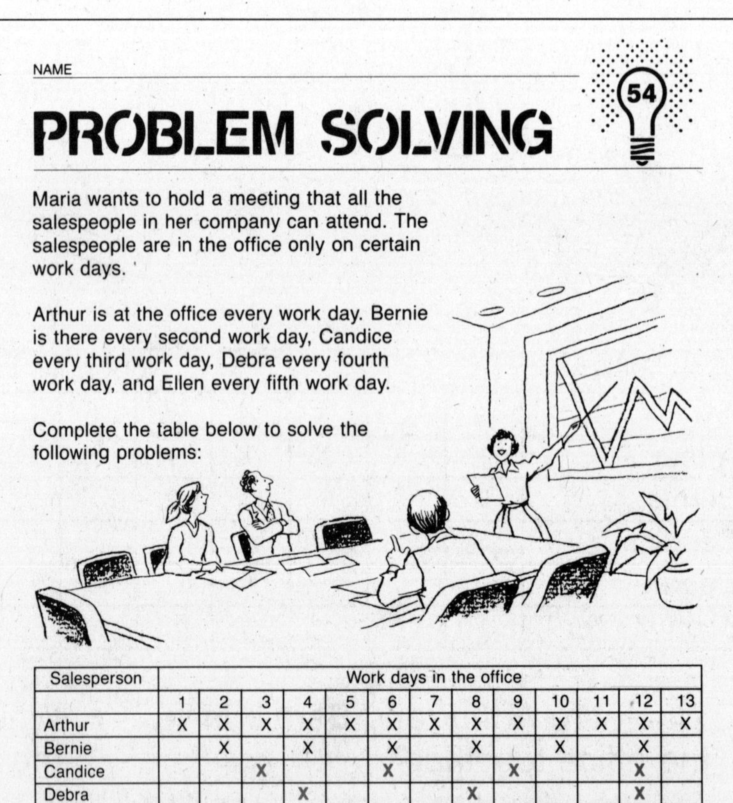
NAME ______

PROBLEM SOLVING

54

Maria wants to hold a meeting that all the salespeople in her company can attend. The salespeople are in the office only on certain work days.

Arthur is at the office every work day. Bernie is there every second work day, Candice every third work day, Debra every fourth work day, and Ellen every fifth work day.

Complete the table below to solve the following problems:

Salesperson	Work days in the office												
	1	2	3	4	5	6	7	8	9	10	11	12	13
Arthur	X	X	X	X	X	X	X	X	X	X	X	X	X
Bernie		X		X		X		X		X		X	
Candice			X			X			X			X	
Debra				X				X				X	
Ellen					X					X			

1. When are Arthur and Bernie in the office together?
Every other work day

2. Which salespeople are always in the office with Debra?
Arthur and Bernie

3. How often can the first 3 salespeople meet together?
Every 6th work day

4. Extend the table to find when all the salespeople are present in the office.
Every 60th work day

NAME ______

PROBLEM SOLVING

Color the figure below so that on each level 3 squares are blue, 3 squares are yellow, and 3 squares are red. Squares with a common side may not be the same color, nor may squares immediately above or below each other be the same color. The three center squares are already done. Color them yellow, blue, and red.

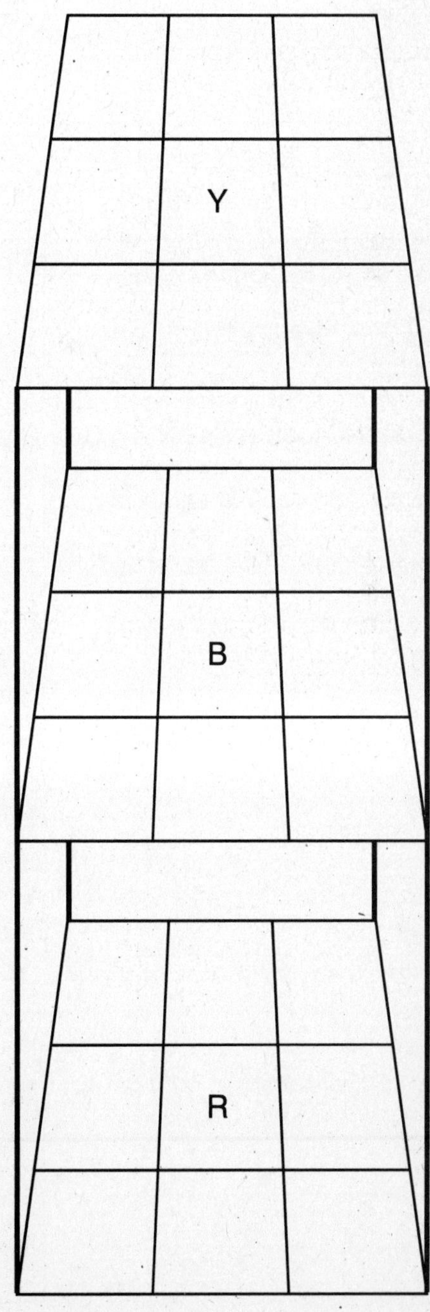

Teacher Notes

Use with
Objective 55
pages 182–183

Focus
Problem Solving
Try and Check
Find a Pattern

Materials
Yellow, red, and blue colored pencils

Overview
Students recognize the relationship in a visual pattern and use this same relationship to complete the pattern.

Teaching Suggestions
Have students work on each level of the figure on the activity sheet from the center column outward.

Alternate Approach: If students have difficulty, have them work in small groups to solve the problem.

Extension
Have pairs of students play tic-tac-toe. Have students discuss the advantage of obtaining the center square and being able to go first.

NAME ______________________

PROBLEM SOLVING

Color the figure below so that on each level 3 squares are blue, 3 squares are yellow, and 3 squares are red. Squares with a common side may not be the same color, nor may squares immediately above or below each other be the same color. The three center squares are already done. Color them yellow, blue, and red.

Possible answer:

B	R	B
R	Y	R
Y	B	Y

R	Y	R
Y	B	Y
B	R	B

Y	B	Y
B	R	B
R	Y	R

NAME ____________________

VISUAL THINKING

The diagram below shows a layout for a model train system. The numbered switches allow trains to go from one track to another track. Use this diagram to answer the questions.

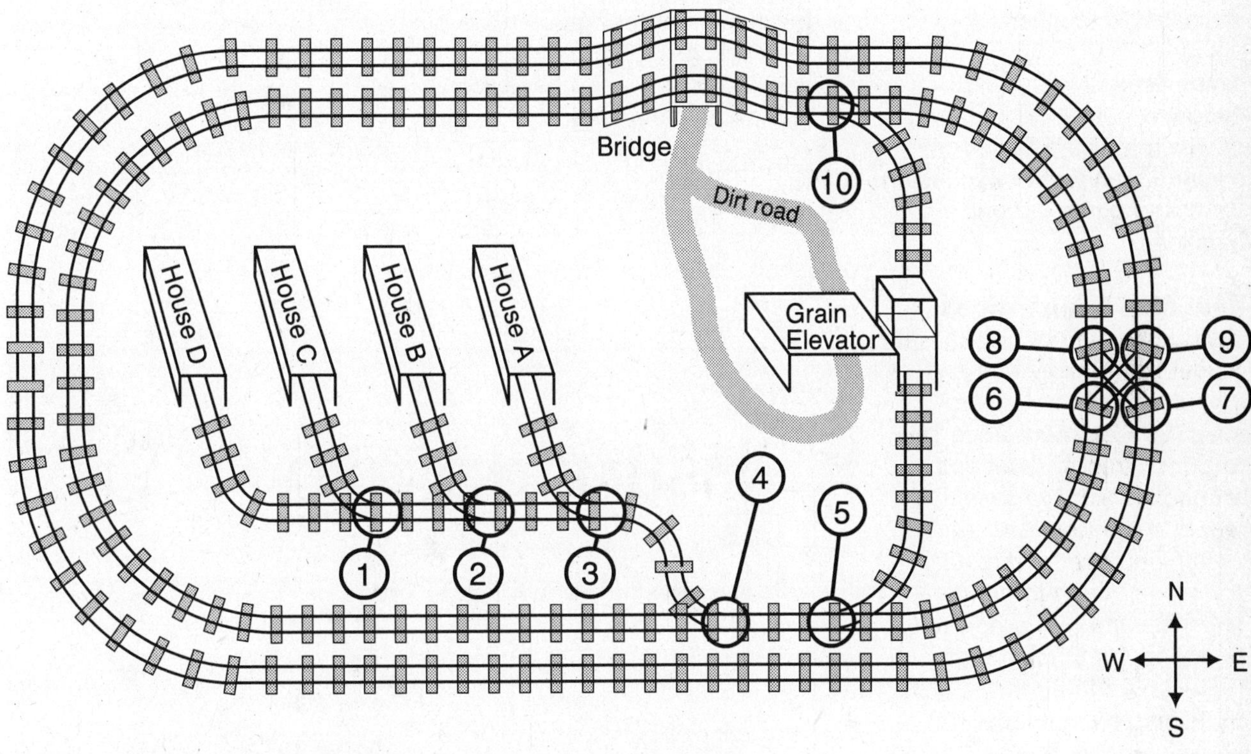

1. A train going east from the bridge on the outer track must go through 5 switches to reach Railway House A. Write them in order. ____________________

2. Can a train going west from the bridge on the outer track reach the grain elevator without reversing? If so, which switches must it go through? ____________________

3. Which switches would a train leaving Railway House D pass through to reach the outer track of the bridge without going in reverse? ____________________

Teacher Notes

Use with
Objective 56
pages 184–185

Focus
Visual Thinking
Spatial Perception

Overview
Students determine the order in which a model train goes through numbered switches on a track to get to various locations.

Teaching Suggestions
If students are not familiar with model trains, explain that at junctions such as those at switches 6–9, the train is able to switch tracks. ***Question:*** *Through which five switches would a train traveling east from the bridge on the outer track go through to get to the grain elevator?* [In order: 9, 6, 5, 4, and 10] Explain that a train can go through a switch, remaining on the same track, and then go in reverse through the switch to change tracks and continue in the opposite direction. ***Question:*** *What are two possible routes to the grain elevator, with reversing, for a train traveling east from the bridge on the outer track?* [The train can pass through switches 9, 6, and 5 and then reverse to get to the elevator, or it can pass through switches 9, 6, reverse, 8, 10, and reverse.]

Extension
Have a volunteer bring in a model train track. Divide students into two groups. Have one group set up a small town with various routes to different buildings. Let that group quiz the other group about the various routes. Then have the groups reverse roles.

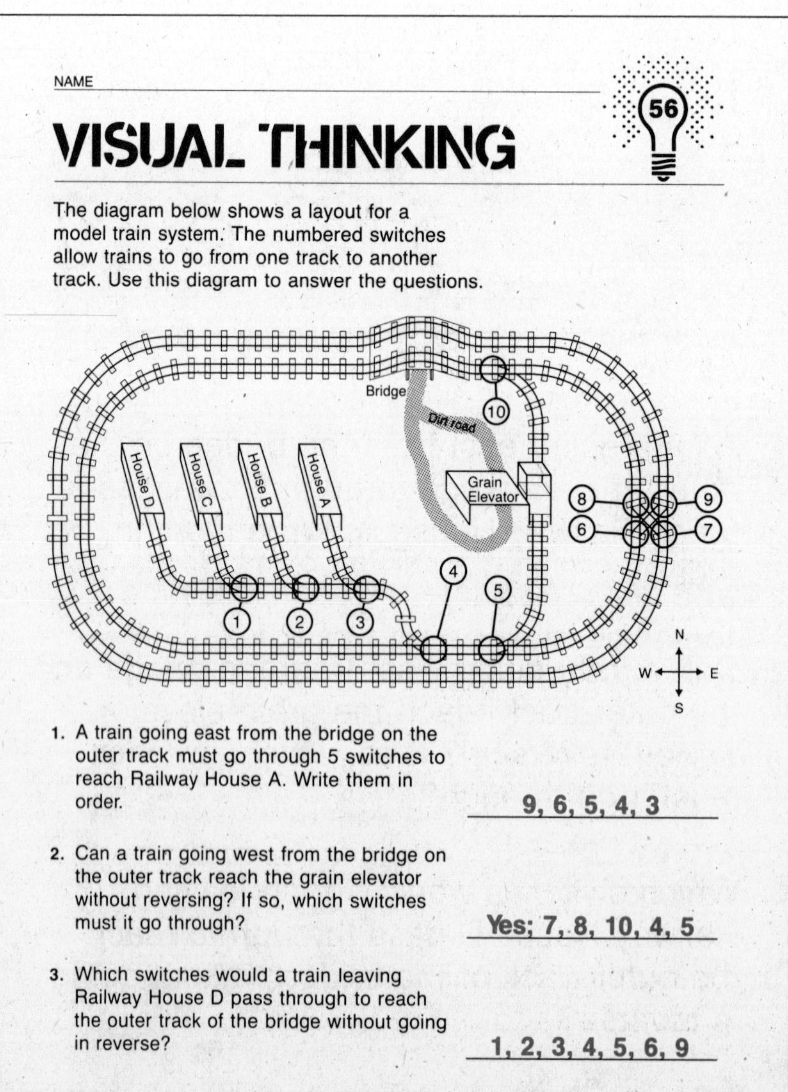

NAME

VISUAL THINKING

56

The diagram below shows a layout for a model train system. The numbered switches allow trains to go from one track to another track. Use this diagram to answer the questions.

1. A train going east from the bridge on the outer track must go through 5 switches to reach Railway House A. Write them in order. **9, 6, 5, 4, 3**

2. Can a train going west from the bridge on the outer track reach the grain elevator without reversing? If so, which switches must it go through? **Yes; 7, 8, 10, 4, 5**

3. Which switches would a train leaving Railway House D pass through to reach the outer track of the bridge without going in reverse? **1, 2, 3, 4, 5, 6, 9**

NAME ______________________________

VISUAL THINKING

The figure below is made of 24 toothpicks and shows 14 squares of different sizes. Some of the squares overlap.

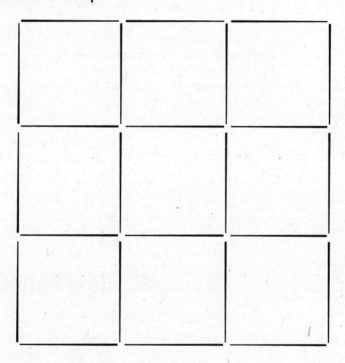

Answer the following questions, using toothpicks to find your answers. Be sure to count all the squares you see. Draw your solutions to the right of each question.

1. Remove 8 toothpicks from the figure and leave 4 squares. Each remaining toothpick must be part of at least one square.

2. Using the original figure, remove 4 toothpicks to leave 5 squares. (There are two possible solutions. Can you find both?)

3. Using the original figure, remove 4 toothpicks to make 9 squares.

Teacher Notes

Use with
Objective 57
pages 186–187

Focus
Visual Thinking
Spatial Perception

Materials
24 toothpicks for each student
Visual Thinking transparency (optional)

Overview
Students manipulate toothpicks to construct various figures according to given instructions.

Teaching Suggestions
Introduce this activity by having students make the figure below with 12 toothpicks.

Ask students to remove two toothpicks so that the remaining ones will form two squares. Also add that each of the remaining toothpicks must be a part of at least one of the squares. A solution is shown below.

Explain that the instructions did not specify that the squares had to be the same size.

Extension
Have students create their own toothpick problems. The original figures and instructions can be numbered and put on small index cards that can be hung on the bulletin board. A key of solutions can be kept by a volunteer.

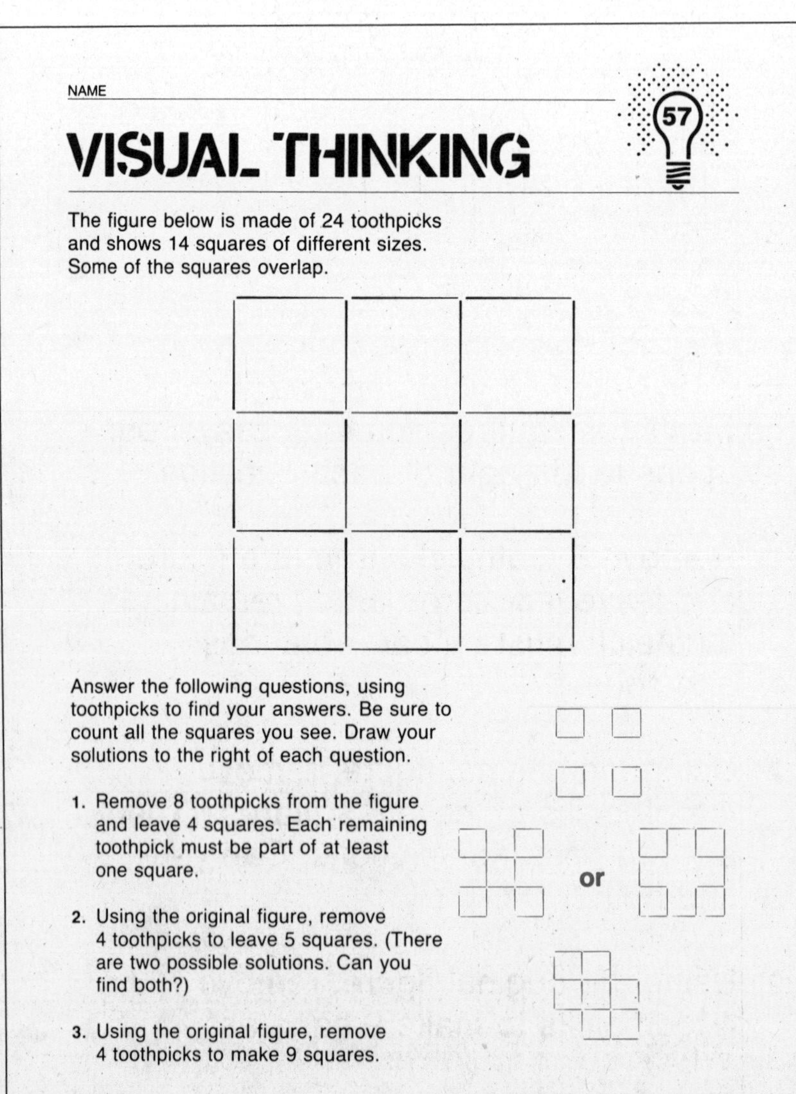

NAME ______________________

57

VISUAL THINKING

The figure below is made of 24 toothpicks and shows 14 squares of different sizes. Some of the squares overlap.

Answer the following questions, using toothpicks to find your answers. Be sure to count all the squares you see. Draw your solutions to the right of each question.

1. Remove 8 toothpicks from the figure and leave 4 squares. Each remaining toothpick must be part of at least one square.
2. Using the original figure, remove 4 toothpicks to leave 5 squares. (There are two possible solutions. Can you find both?)

   or

3. Using the original figure, remove 4 toothpicks to make 9 squares.

NAME

PROBLEM SOLVING

Secret Agent Pierre has been captured and locked in a 24-room castle. Agent Monique, his rescuer, has copies of the 24 castle keys, which are numbered to match the room numbers. She has time to pick only one key before the guards find her.

Use the clues below to fill in the room numbers for each section of the castle. Note that some sections of the castle share common areas.

- The rooms in the castle are numbered from 1 to 24.
- All rooms with numbers less than 15 are in the main hall.
- Rooms 17, 19, 22, and 23 are also in the main hall.
- All rooms with numbers that are multiples of 3 are in the tower.
- All rooms with numbers that are multiples of 4 are in the wing.
- Agent Pierre is in a castle room where the main hall, the tower, and the wing, share a common area.

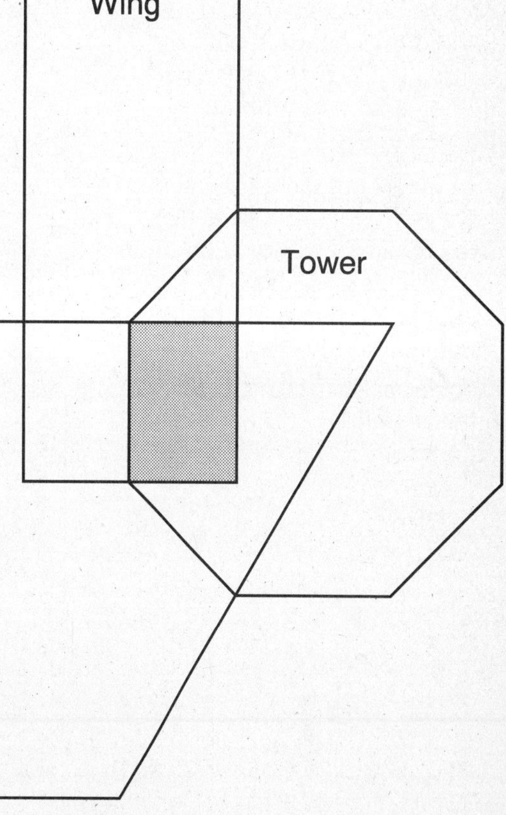

1. Which key should Agent Monique pick to free Agent Pierre? ______

Teacher Notes

Use with
Objective 58
pages 188–189

Focus
Problem Solving
Use Logical Reasoning

Overview
Students use their knowledge of multiples and a Venn diagram to identify a certain number with particular attributes.

Teaching Suggestions
Review the following definition of a *Venn diagram.* A Venn diagram is a diagram that uses geometric figures to show relationships among sets. For the diagram on the page, be sure students understand that the rooms that are in both the Wing and the Main Hall must fit the conditions for both of these areas.

Alternate Approach: If students have difficulty with this activity, use the simple Venn diagram of multiples of 4 and 6 that are less than 40 shown in the next column to demonstrate the skill needed to solve the problem.

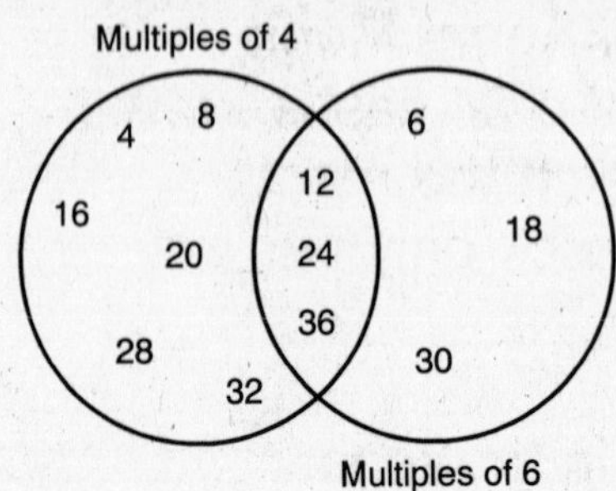

Multiples of 4
4
8
16
20
28
32
12
24
36
6
18
30
Multiples of 6

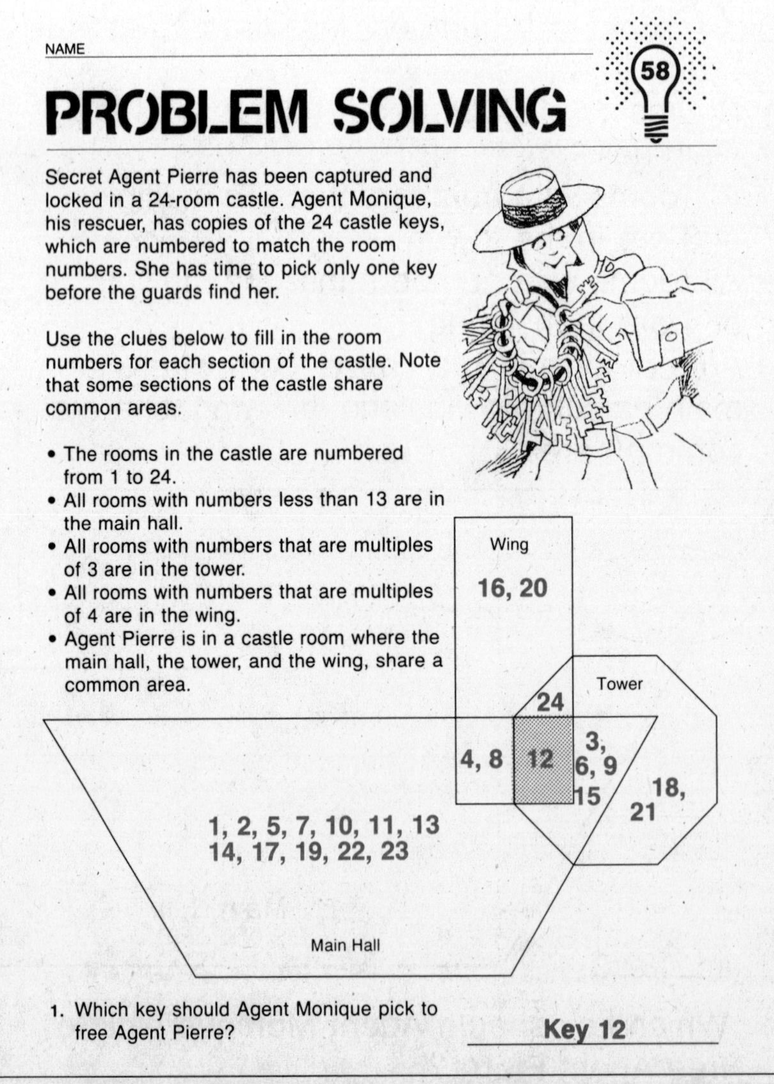

NAME
58
PROBLEM SOLVING
Secret Agent Pierre has been captured and locked in a 24-room castle. Agent Monique, his rescuer, has copies of the 24 castle keys, which are numbered to match the room numbers. She has time to pick only one key before the guards find her.
Use the clues below to fill in the room numbers for each section of the castle. Note that some sections of the castle share common areas.
• The rooms in the castle are numbered from 1 to 24.
• All rooms with numbers less than 13 are in the main hall.
• All rooms with numbers that are multiples of 3 are in the tower.
• All rooms with numbers that are multiples of 4 are in the wing.
• Agent Pierre is in a castle room where the main hall, the tower, and the wing, share a common area.
Wing
16, 20
Tower
24
4, 8
12
3, 6, 9
15
18, 21
1, 2, 5, 7, 10, 11, 13
14, 17, 19, 22, 23
Main Hall
1. Which key should Agent Monique pick to free Agent Pierre?
Key 12

NAME ____________________

VISUAL THINKING

Ring the letters of the two figures on the right that will form the figure on the left when joined. The figures may be flipped or turned, but they cannot overlap and there cannot be gaps.

1.

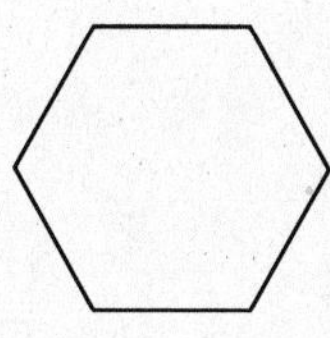

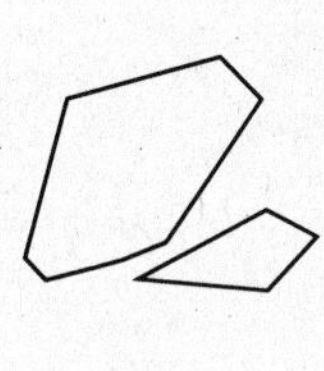

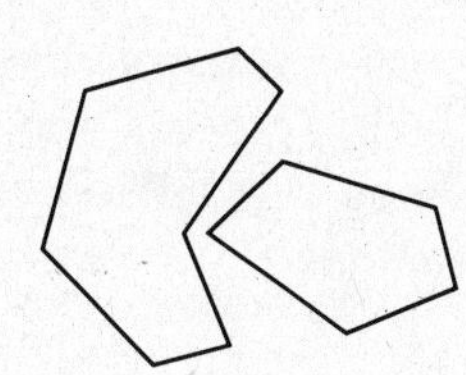

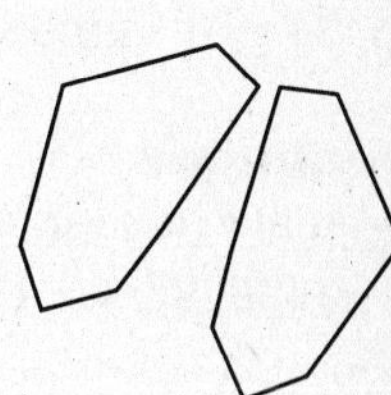

a. b. c. d.

2.

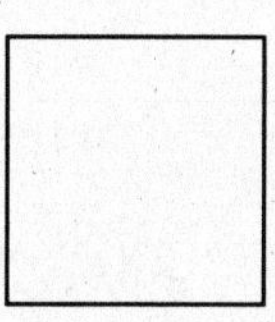

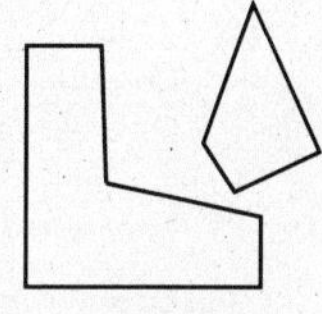

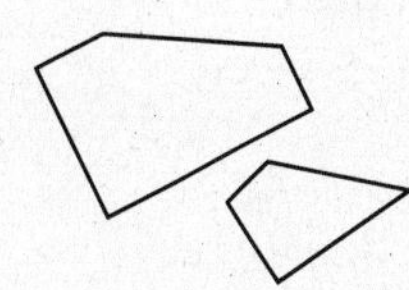

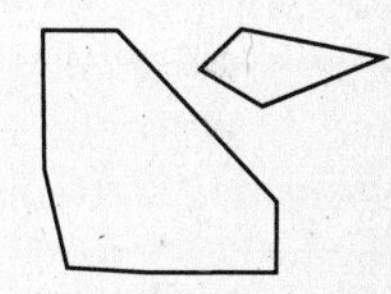

a. b. c. d.

3.

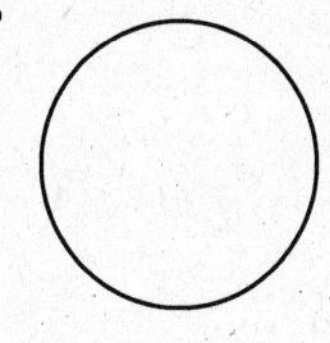

a. b. c. d.

4.

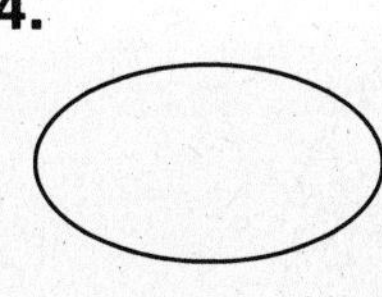

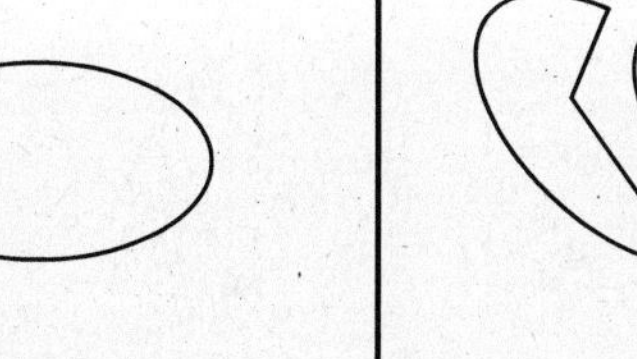

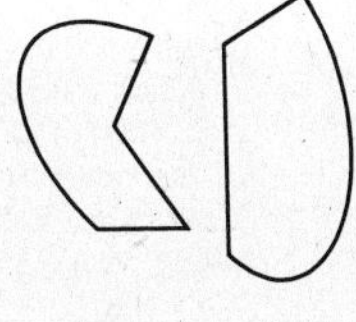

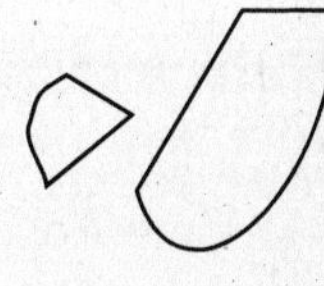

a. b. c. d.

5.

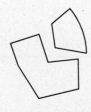

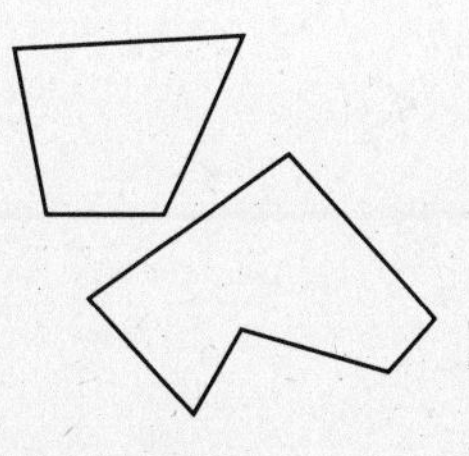

a. b. c. d.

Teacher Notes

Use with
Objective 59
pages 200–201

Focus
Visual Thinking
Spatial Perception

Materials
Visual Thinking transparency (optional)

Overview
Students study shapes to determine which pair, when put together, forms the given shape.

Teaching Suggestions
If students have difficulty, tell them that this activity is very much like working a jigsaw puzzle. In working a puzzle, pieces must be studied to see if they fit together. Tell students that, as with a puzzle, pieces may have to be turned over and moved around before they fit together.

Suggest that students eliminate pairs that obviously do not work. Tell students that some pieces are not large enough to form the desired figure. Also, some pieces are obviously the wrong shape.

Alternate Approach: Suggest that students copy the shapes and actually try to put them together. This could be a final step after eliminating the obvious wrong pairs.

Extension
Have students tell about activities they may have done at home that involve putting pieces together to form a whole object. Besides puzzles, possible answers include building models and gluing pieces of a broken object together.

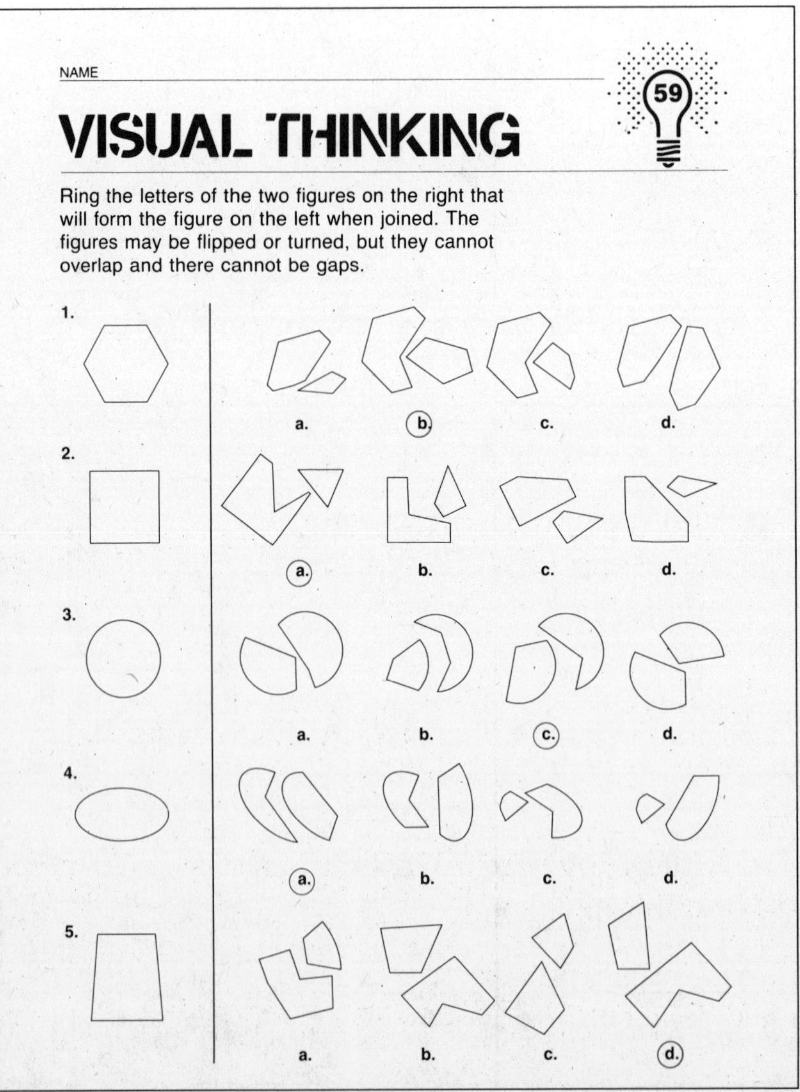

NAME
59
VISUAL THINKING
Ring the letters of the two figures on the right that will form the figure on the left when joined. The figures may be flipped or turned, but they cannot overlap and there cannot be gaps.
1.
a. (b.) c. d.
2.
(a.) b. c. d.
3.
a. b. (c.) d.
4.
(a.) b. c. d.
5.
a. b. c. (d.)

NAME ______________________________

CRITICAL THINKING

When Mai wrote the date for June 15, 1990, she wrote 6/15/90. She noticed that the month (6) times the day (15) equaled the year. Mai wondered how often that happens in 1990.

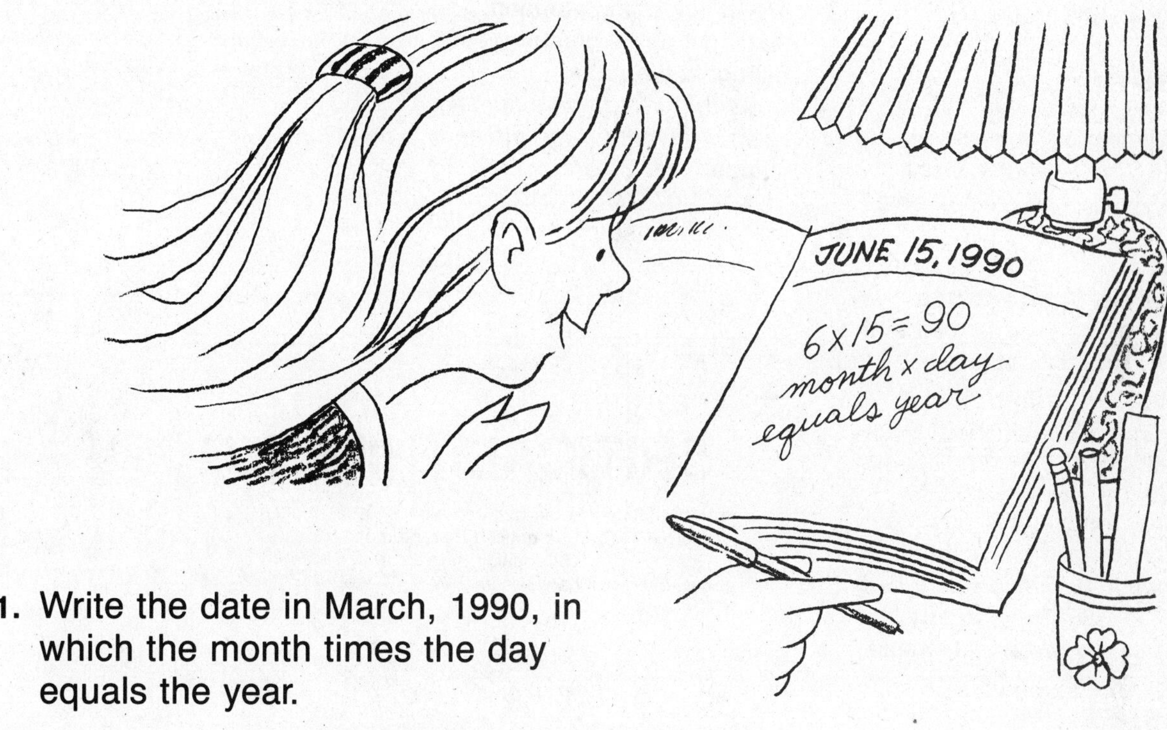

1. Write the date in March, 1990, in which the month times the day equals the year.

____

2. There are three other dates in 1990 that fit this equation. List all of them.

____

____

3. Is there a date in 1997 that fits this equation? Why or why not?

____

____

4. Write a date in 1992 that fits this equation.

____

____

5. Choose a year greater than 2000 and write a date that fits this equation.

____

Teacher Notes

Use with
Objective 60
pages 202–205

Focus
Critical Thinking
Using Logic

Overview
Students look at the relationship between the day, month, and year of several dates when they are written as numbers.

Teaching Suggestions
Ask students to write their birth dates using only numbers. Some students may be unfamiliar with this method. Explain the procedure if necessary. Ask students to multiply the month times the day. ***Question:** Did anyone get a product that equals your birth year?* [It is unlikely, as few dates in any given year would yield that product.]

***Question:** How can you determine the dates in a given year that have this pattern?* [Allow students to brainstorm. It should not take them very long to conclude that the easiest way is to divide the year by the numbers 1 through 12.] As practice, have students determine dates for a few years both past and future. Some dates to use are 1960 [3/20/60, 4/15/60, 5/12/60, 6/10/60, 10/6/60, 12/5/60]; 1988 [4/22/88, 8/11/88, 11/8/88]; and 1996 [4/24/96, 6/16/96, 8/12/96, 12/8/96].

Make sure students understand that for answers to Problem 2, 6/15/90 and 3/30/90 should not be included.

Discuss Problem 3 with students. Explain that numbers like 97 are prime numbers and that most prime number years will not fit the pattern. ***Question:** What prime number years will work?* [Any prime number year 31 and lower—1/07/07, 1/13/13, 1/31/31, and so on.]

Extension
Have students determine which year from 1990–2000 has the most dates that fit the relationship [1996].

Have students develop other relationships with dates or other groups of numbers. For each relationship developed, several examples should be given.

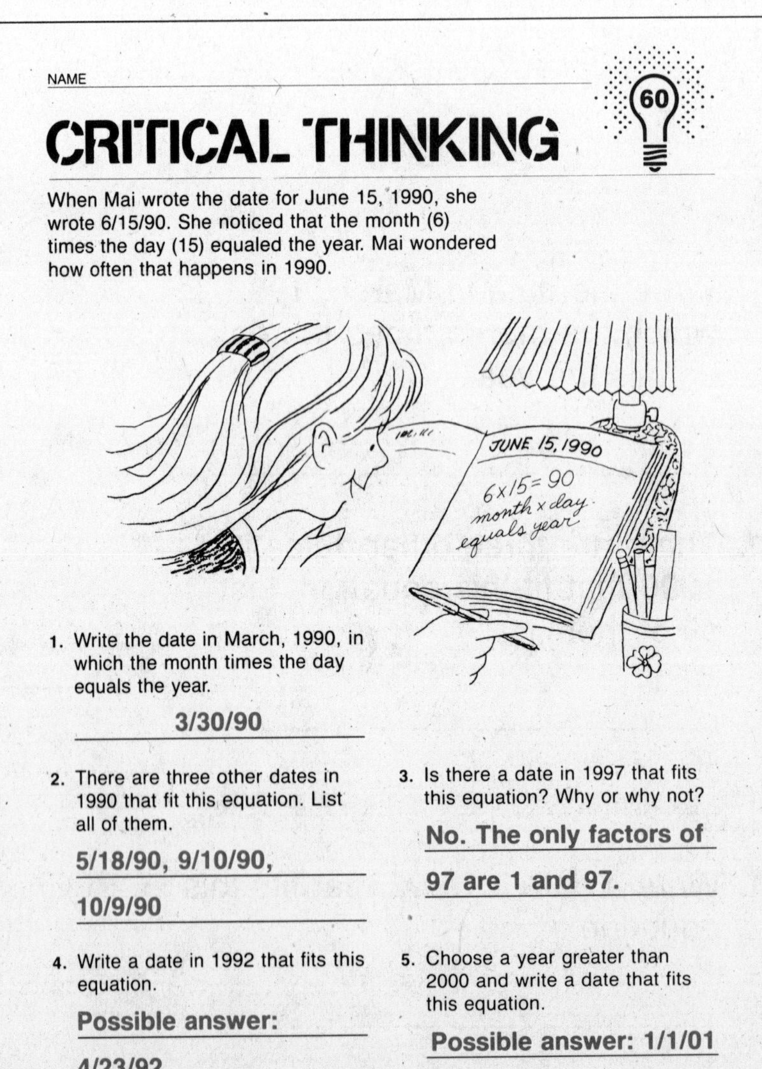

NAME ______

CRITICAL THINKING

60

When Mai wrote the date for June 15, 1990, she wrote 6/15/90. She noticed that the month (6) times the day (15) equaled the year. Mai wondered how often that happens in 1990.

1. Write the date in March, 1990, in which the month times the day equals the year.

   3/30/90

2. There are three other dates in 1990 that fit this equation. List all of them.

   5/18/90, 9/10/90, 10/9/90

3. Is there a date in 1997 that fits this equation? Why or why not?

   No. The only factors of 97 are 1 and 97.

4. Write a date in 1992 that fits this equation.

   Possible answer: 4/23/92

5. Choose a year greater than 2000 and write a date that fits this equation.

   Possible answer: 1/1/01

NAME ____________________

DECISION MAKING

The cheerleaders from Baker School and Dewey School are organizing a combined field trip to a baseball game. Transportation needs to be arranged. The cheerleaders can choose only one of the following kinds of vehicles. They want an easy way to transport students and they want to spend their money economically. There are 60 students from Baker and 84 from Dewey.

Vehicle	Capacity	Cost
Car	4 students	$10
Van	6 students	$12
Minibus	12 students	$24
Bus	24 students	$65

1. What is the most economical and easiest way to get the students to the game? Hint:

____

2. Explain your answer.

____

____

____

Use after pages 206–207.

Teacher Notes

Use with
Objective 61
pages 206–207

Focus
Decision Making

Overview
Students analyze data to make the best decision about transporting groups of students based on the given criteria.

Teaching Suggestions
Guide students to prepare a table for organizing data. Discuss with students what information is needed for the table. In the discussion, students should decide to find the total number of students, how many of each type of vehicle would be needed to transport all the students, and how much each type of vehicle would cost.

A student table might resemble the following. [Arrangement may vary.]

Vehicle	Number needed	Total cost
Car	36	$360
Van	24	288
Minibus	12	288
Bus	6	390

Once students have determined the total cost for each type of vehicle, they must decide which is the easiest and most economical vehicle. Because the costs of the van and the minibus are equal, answers will be based on how each student interprets "easiest."

After all students have completed the activity sheet, have a class discussion on Problem 2 in which each student gives his or her reasons for picking the vehicle chosen.

Alternate Approach: Instead of finding the total cost for each type of vehicle, students can find the cost per person for each vehicle. [Car—$2.50; Van—$2.00; Minibus—$2.00; Bus—$2.71]

Extension
Assume that the costs for cars, vans, and minibuses also require an additional charge of $1.00 per person to help pay for gasoline. However, there is no additional charge for the buses. Which vehicle is now the most economical? [Bus]

NAME ____________________

DECISION MAKING

The cheerleaders from Baker School and Dewey School are organizing a combined field trip to a baseball game. Transportation needs to be arranged. The cheerleaders can choose only one of the following kinds of vehicles. They want an easy way to transport students and they want to spend their money economically. There are 60 students from Baker and 84 from Dewey.

Vehicle	Capacity	Cost
Car	4 students	$10
Van	6 students	$12
Minibus	12 students	$24
Bus	24 students	$65

Possible answers:

1. What is the most economical and easiest way to get the students to the game? Hint: Make a chart of the costs for each kind of vehicle.
   Use 12 minibuses.
2. Explain your answer.
   Total cost is $288; equal to the van costs, but with fewer vehicles.

NAME ______________________________

PROBLEM SOLVING

Suppose you are an engineer hired to build a road between the towns of Hampstead and Manchester. It costs $3,000 per kilometer to build a road across the prairie and $12,000 per kilometer to build a road across the swamp.

1. Cut out the ruler that is given. Measure to the nearest kilometer the shortest route between Hampstead and Manchester. How many kilometers is it? What is the cost for this route?

____

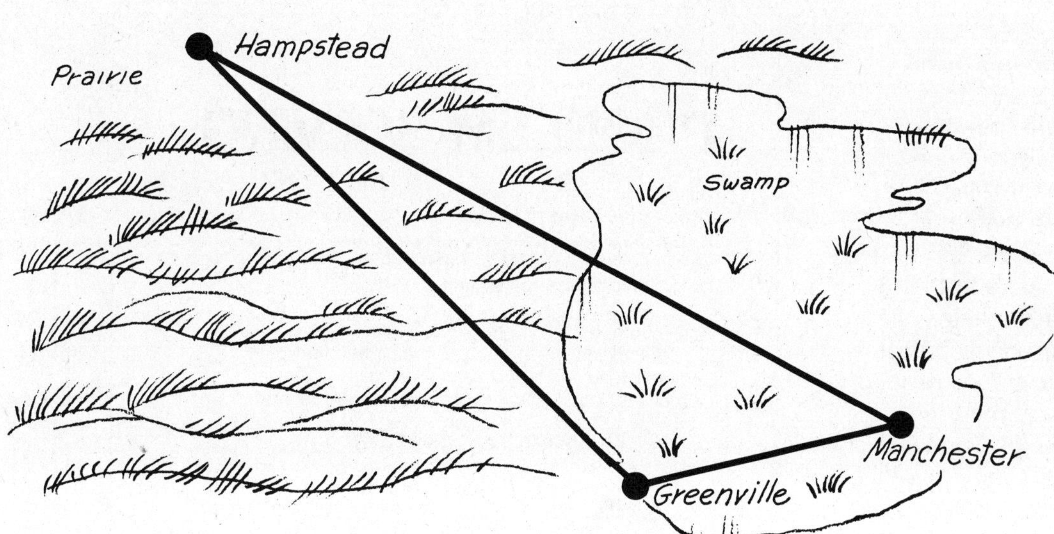

1 2 3 4 5 6 7 8 9 10 11 12 13 14 15 16 17 18 19 20 21 22 23

1 Unit represents 1 Kilometer

2. Measure to the nearest kilometer the route between Hampstead and Manchester that goes through Greenville. How many kilometers is it? What is the cost for this route?

____

3. Which route between Hampstead and Manchester is the least expensive?

____

Teacher Notes

Use with
Objective 62
pages 208–209

Focus
Problem Solving
Try and Check

Materials
Scissors

Overview
Students determine the distance and cost of roads between two cities using different routes to find which is less expensive.

Teaching Suggestions
Inform students that they should measure from the center of each dot. Since one unit on the paper ruler represents one kilometer, students should be able to determine distance to the nearest whole kilometer.
Questions: *Are distances other than the total distance needed to answer Problem 1?* [Yes] *What distances?* [Distances across the prairie and over the swamp are also needed.] Point out that the total cost of constructing the road equals the cost across the prairie plus the cost over the swamp. Thus, the cost of the shorter road to Manchester is 11 km × $3000 + 9 km × $12,000 = $33,000 + $108,000 or $141,000.

The cost of the longer road through Greenville is 15 km × $3000 + 7 km × $12,000 = $45,000 + $84,000 or $129,000.

Extension
There is a less expensive route than the road from Hampstead to Greenville to Manchester. Have students find this route and how much would it cost. [15 km to Greenville, then 3 km beyond Greenville, then 7 km across the prairie along the swamp, then 2 km over the swamp to Manchester. Cost = 25 km × $3000 + 2 km × $12,000 = $75,000 + $24,000 or $99,000.]

NAME ____________________

PROBLEM SOLVING

Suppose you are an engineer hired to build a road between the towns of Hampstead and Manchester. It costs $3,000 per kilometer to build a road across the prairie and $12,000 per kilometer to build a road across the swamp.

1. Cut out the ruler that is given. Measure to the nearest kilometer the shortest route between Hampstead and Manchester. How many kilometers is it? What is the cost for this route?

   20 kilometers; $141,000

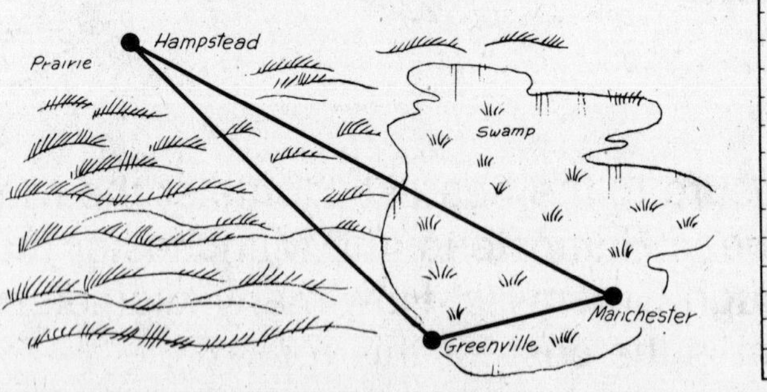

1 2 3 4 5 6 7 8 9 10 11 12 13 14 15 16 17 18 19 20 21 22 23
1 Unit represents 1 Kilometer

2. Measure to the nearest kilometer the route between Hampstead and Manchester that goes through Greenville. How many kilometers is it? What is the cost for this route?

   22 kilometers; $129,000

3. Which route between Hampstead and Manchester is the least expensive?

   The route through Greenville

NAME ________________________________

VISUAL THINKING

Ring the letter of the figure on the right that is formed by folding the figure on the left.

1.

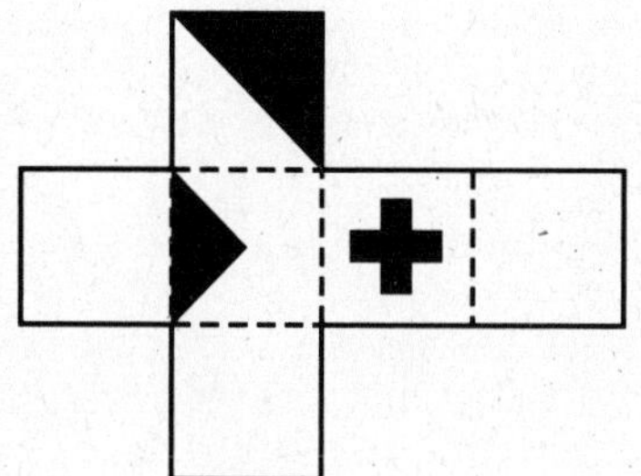

a. b. c. d.

2.

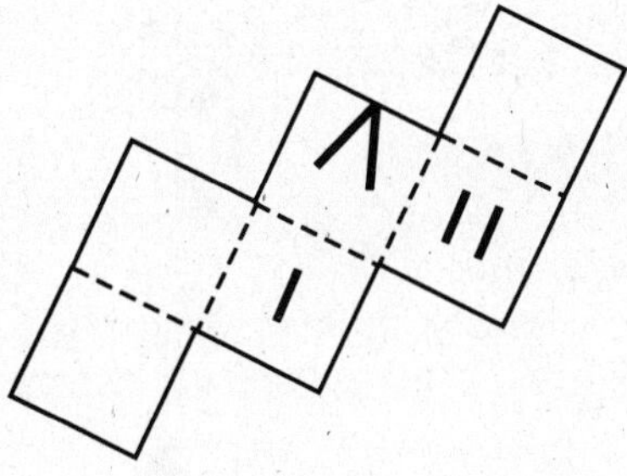

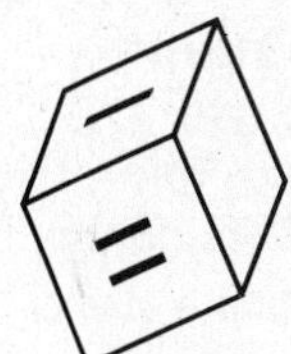

a. b. c. d.

3.

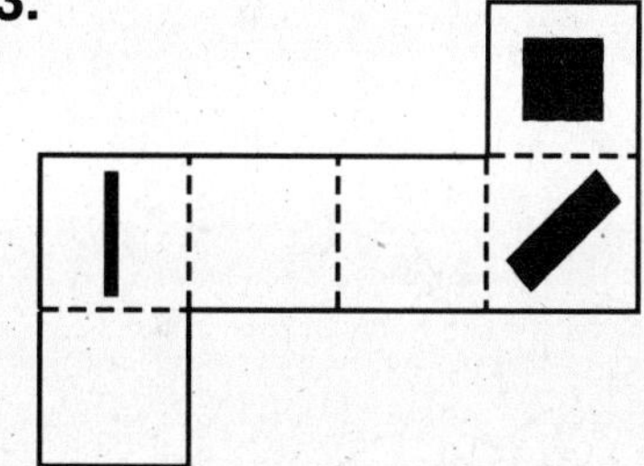

a. b. c. d.

4.

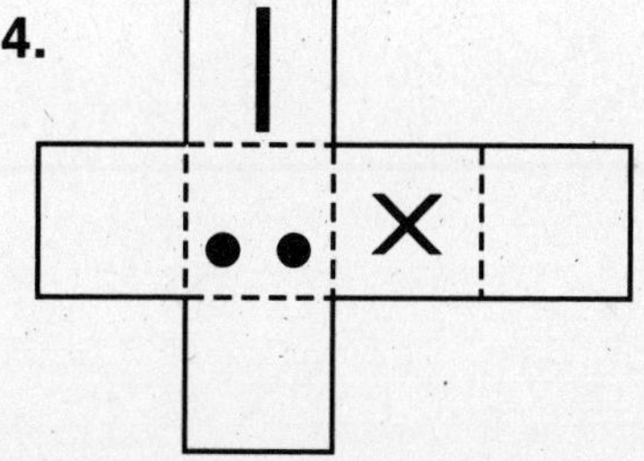

a. b. c. d.

Teacher Notes

Use with
Objective 63
pages 210–213

Focus
Visual Thinking
Visual Patterns

Materials
Visual Thinking transparency (optional)

Overview
Students study cubes to determine which one of four choices is formed from the unfolded cube pattern given.

Teaching Suggestions
Discuss how the joined squares are folded to form cubes. Explain that students should imagine that the paper is folded 90° at each dashed line to form a cube.

Point out that it is not necessary to visualize exactly how the entire pattern folds. It is important to notice how two or three sides appear relative to each other when folded. For Problem 1, point out that the small black triangle "points" to the plus sign. Therefore, students should look for a cube with the same pattern.

Another suggestion is to have students eliminate any cubes that do not match the given pattern. For example, choice **c** of Problem 3 has a cube with one face that is not found in the cube pattern given.

Alternate Approach: Suggest that students copy, cut out, and fold cubes to see which choice matches.

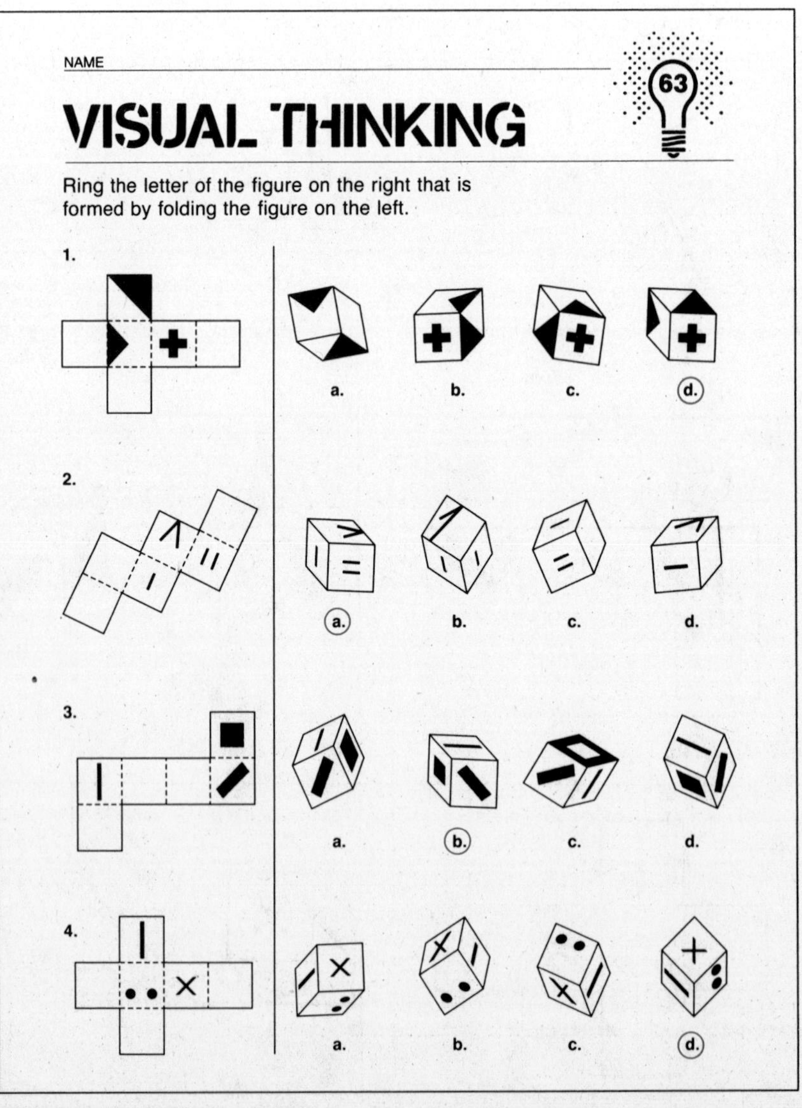

NAME

PROBLEM SOLVING

Jana is moving into a new apartment. The hallway leading to her apartment is 4 feet wide with a right angle turn as shown in the grid below. Each square centimeter on the grid represents one square foot of the hallway. On moving day, Jana has a rectangular carton with a base that is 2 feet by 4 feet. The carton contains fragile items and cannot be turned on its side or tilted. Jana wonders if the carton will pass through the turn in the hallway.

1. Will the carton with the 2-foot by 4-foot base pass through the turn in the hallway? One way to figure this out is to make a model. Cut out a 2-cm by 4-cm rectangle to represent the base of the carton and see if it will pass through the turn in the hallway.

____

2. Find the area of that rectangular base.

____

3. Experiment with different-size "rectangular cartons." Which rectangular base has the greatest area that will still pass through the turn in the hallway?

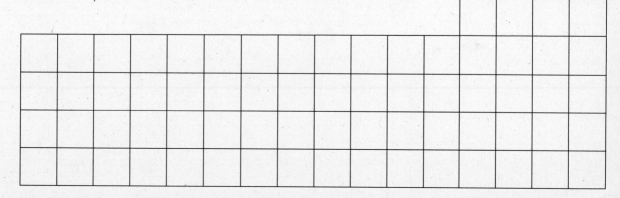

____

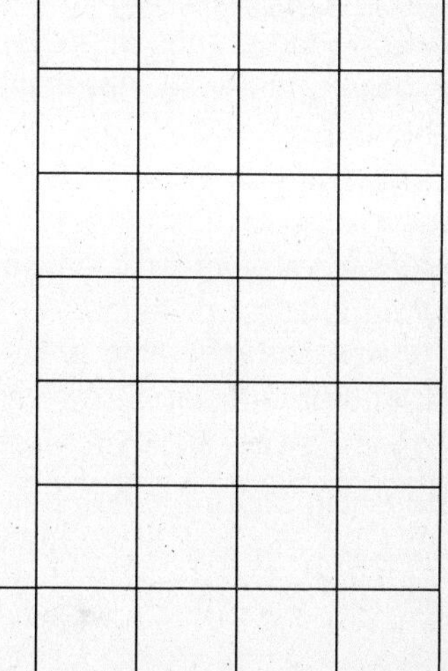

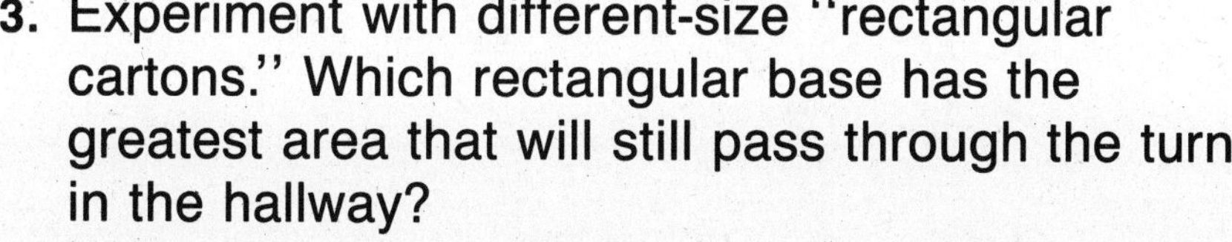

Teacher Notes

Use with
Objective 64
pages 216–217

Focus
Problem Solving
Try and Check

Materials
Scissors
Centimeter grid paper

Overview
Students use models to determine which rectangular shapes will pass through a corner of a hallway. Then they determine which of these rectangles has the greatest area.

Teaching Suggestions
For Problem 1, students can cut out a rectangle 2 cm by 4 cm from centimeter grid paper to represent the base of the carton. Using this rectangle, they can see that the rectangle can be turned around the corner without crossing the lines representing the walls.

Questions: *What formula can you use to determine the area of the base of the carton?* [$A = \ell \times w$.] *What is this area?* [$A = 4$ feet $\times$ 2 feet = 8 square feet.]

Alternate Approach: Students can also count the number of squares in the 4 × 2 grid to get the answer.

For Problem 3, students *try and check* several dimensions of rectangles. They can determine the largest rectangle that can go through the hallway by using each width from 1 to 4 feet. They then should determine the area of each rectangle to find which one has the largest area. Students may think that a carton with a base of 4 feet by 4 feet will not fit. Point out that it can go through if it is not turned at the corner.

Extension
Challenge students to find the radius of the largest semicircle that will fit through the hallway and around the corner. [The largest semicircle has a radius of 4 feet and an area of about 25 square feet.]

NAME

PROBLEM SOLVING

64

Jana is moving into a new apartment. The hallway leading to her apartment is 4 feet wide with a right angle turn as shown in the grid below. Each square centimeter on the grid represents one square foot of the hallway. On moving day, Jana has a rectangular carton with a base that is 2 feet by 4 feet. The carton contains fragile items and cannot be turned on its side or tilted. Jana wonders if the carton will pass through the turn in the hallway.

1. Will the carton with the 2-foot by 4-foot base pass through the turn in the hallway? One way to figure this out is to make a model. Cut out a 2-cm by 4-cm rectangle to represent the base of the carton and see if it will pass through the turn in the hallway.

   Yes

2. Find the area of that rectangular base.

   8 square feet

3. Experiment with different-size "rectangular cartons." Which rectangular base has the greatest area that will still pass through the turn in the hallway?

   4 by 4

NAME

DECISION MAKING

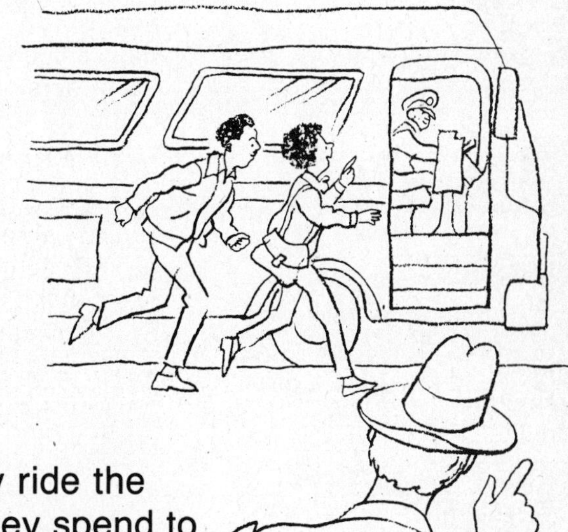

Mr. and Mrs. Wakefield both take the bus to and from work. Each ride costs $.80 and they both work five days a week. They also sometimes take the bus to shop, run errands, and so on. The City Bus Company offers weekly and monthly bus passes for unlimited rides. A weekly pass costs $7 and a monthly pass costs $35.

1. If the Wakefields pay each time they ride the bus, what is the total amount that they spend to go to work each day? Each week? Each month (4 weeks)?

2. In order to spend the least on their travel, should the Wakefields pay each time they ride the bus, buy weekly passes, or buy monthly passes? Why?

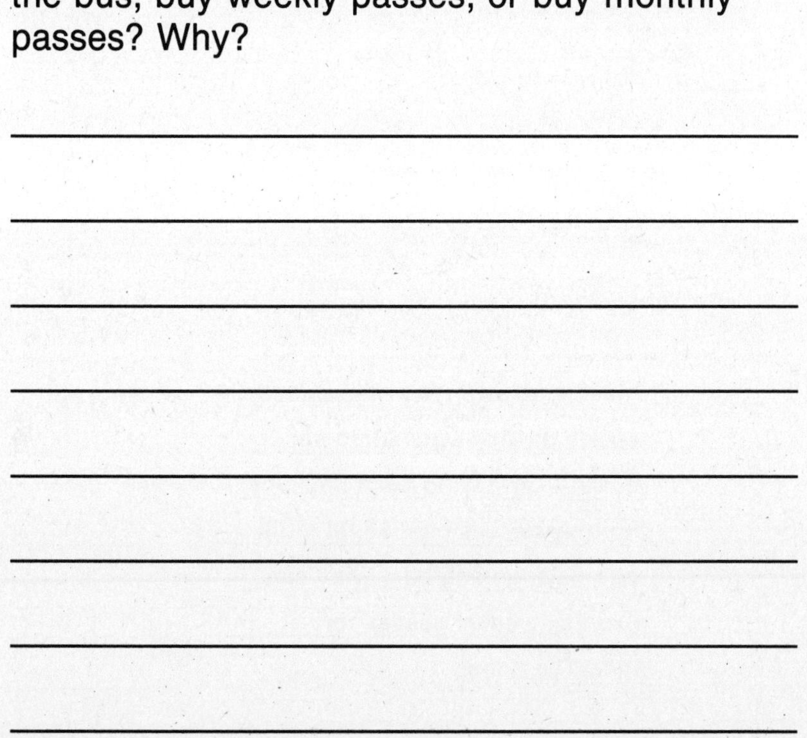

Teacher Notes

Use with
Objective 65
pages 218–219

Focus
Decision Making

Overview
Students analyze various payment options to determine the most economical way to ride a bus to and from a given destination.

Teaching Suggestions
Some students may forget to consider the cost of two people making two trips each day. To help them avoid this mistake, encourage students to set up a table. They should read the activity, then go back and reread it carefully as they make the table. A table to find the cost of buying single-ride tickets might look like this.

	Cost ($)		
	Day	Week	Month
Mr. W.	1.60	8.00	32.00
Mrs. W.	1.60	8.00	32.00
Both	3.20	16.00	64.00
1 pass	—	7.00	35.00
2 passes	—	14.00	70.00

Questions: *How many weekly passes would they need for a month?* [8] *What is the cost?* [$56] If a student's table is complete, he or she should be able to find the costs for Problem 1. Also, it is easier to see which option is best and to calculate the savings to answer Problem 2.

Extension
Have students pretend they are the owners of City Bus Company. A study shows that very few people buy monthly passes. You decide to change the pass costs to increase sales of the monthly pass while still giving your customers money-saving options. Propose new prices to accomplish these goals. [Possible answer: Change monthly pass cost to $25]

NAME ______________________

DECISION MAKING

Mr. and Mrs. Wakefield both take the bus to and from work. Each ride costs $.80 and they both work five days a week. They also sometimes take the bus to shop, run errands, and so on. The City Bus Company offers weekly and monthly bus passes for unlimited rides. A weekly pass costs $7 and a monthly pass costs $35.

1. If the Wakefields pay each time they ride the bus, what is the total amount that they spend to go to work each day? Each week? Each month (4 weeks)?

   $3.20; $16.00; $64.00

2. In order to spend the least on their travel, should the Wakefields pay each time they ride the bus, buy weekly passes, or buy monthly passes? Why?

   Possible answer: Weekly passes; weekly passes save $8.00 per month over paying each day, but monthly passes cost $6.00 more than paying each day. They can also use weekly passes for unlimited rides.

NAME ____________________

VISUAL THINKING

Ella's older brothers are hanging her new basketball goal and backboard that came with the diagram below. Use it to answer the questions.

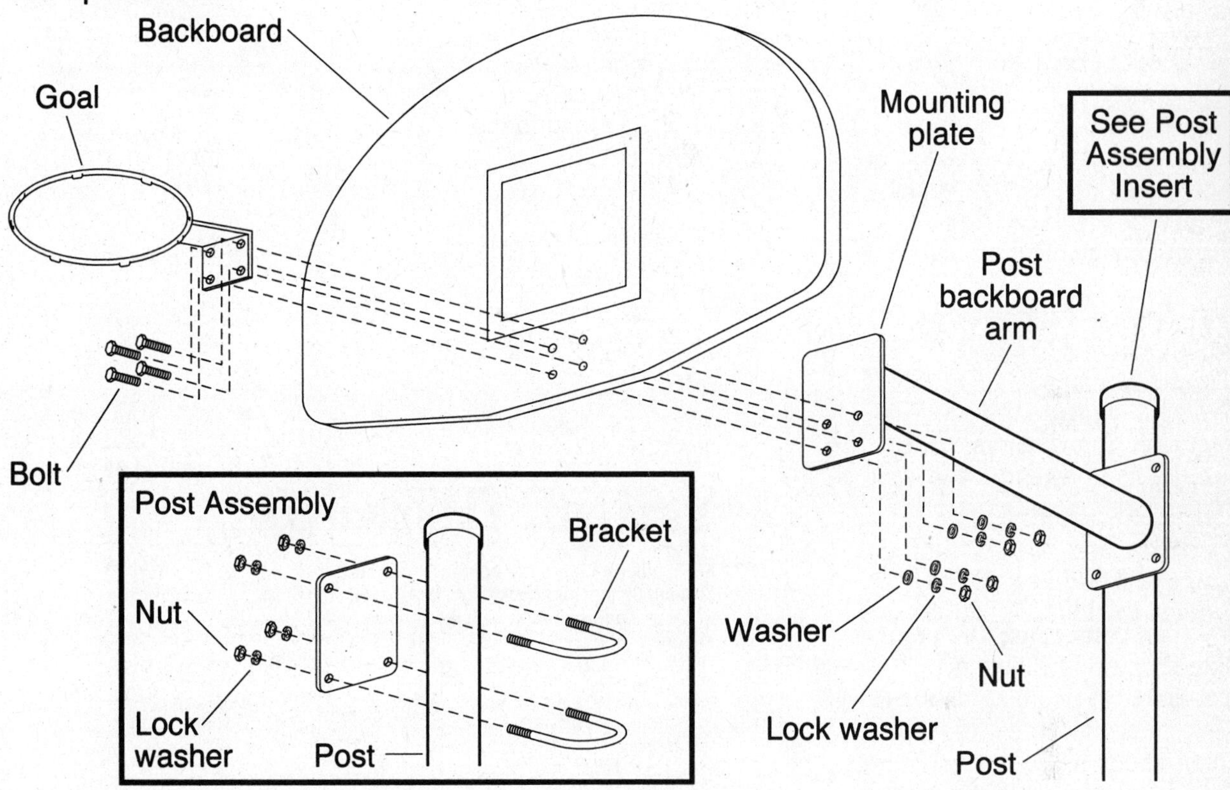

1. How many bolts are used to assemble the goal and backboard? ____________________

2. In the complete assembly, how many lock washers are used? How many washers are used?

____

3. How many brackets are used in the complete assembly? ____________________

4. List in order the parts through which each bolt is threaded.

____

Teacher Notes

Use with
Objective 66
pages 220–221

Focus
Visual Thinking
Spatial Perception

Overview
Students use a schematic diagram and interpret visual clues to answer questions about assembling an object.

Teaching Suggestions
Students must be able to follow a schematic diagram. Even if students are not familiar with washers, bolts, and nuts, they can answer the questions by referring to the labels.

For Problems 1–3, students must count the number of certain parts using the labels and drawings. Caution students to use diagrams and labels since some parts look very much alike.

For Problem 4, point out that the dashed lines represent how the various parts fit together. Dashed lines also show where bolts and brackets go through, and the order of washers and nuts on the bolts and brackets.

Alternate Approach: This activity may be an opportunity to involve students who are mechanically minded. These students may be able to help other students who experience difficulty with the activity.

Extension
Items that require assembly usually have printed instructions to accompany the diagrams like the one used in the activity. Have students write possible instructions for assembling the goal to the backboard, and then to the post.

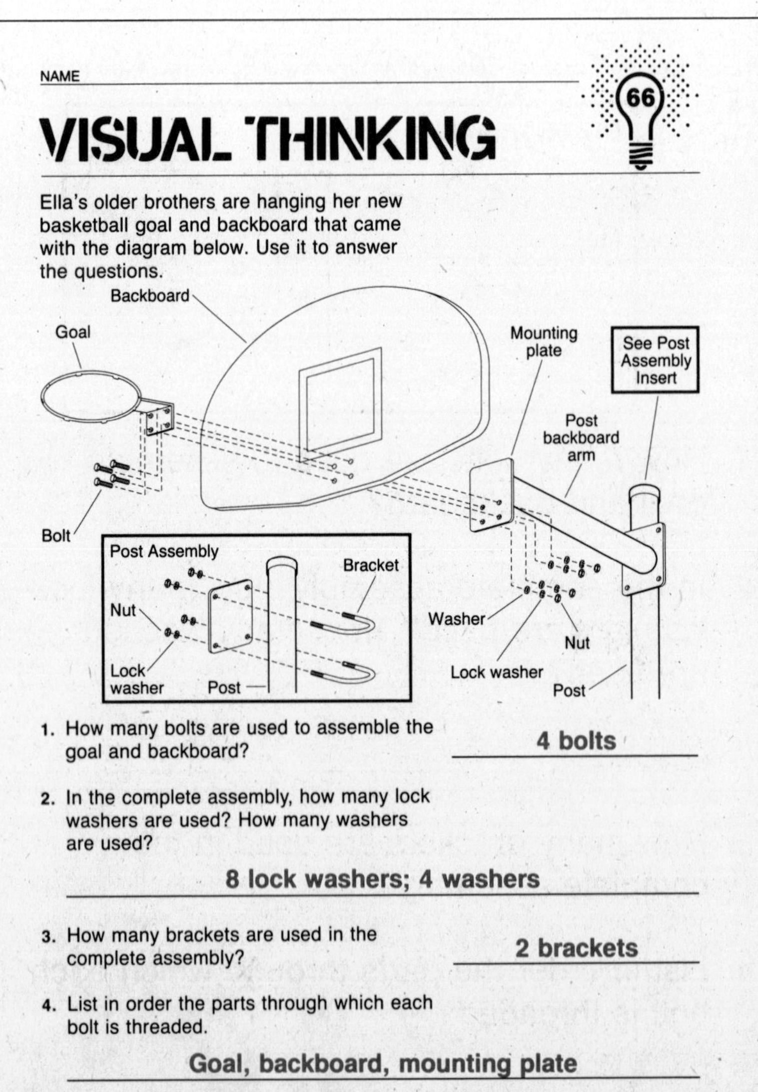

NAME ______________________ 66

VISUAL THINKING

Ella's older brothers are hanging her new basketball goal and backboard that came with the diagram below. Use it to answer the questions.

1. How many bolts are used to assemble the goal and backboard? **4 bolts**

2. In the complete assembly, how many lock washers are used? How many washers are used?
8 lock washers; 4 washers

3. How many brackets are used in the complete assembly? **2 brackets**

4. List in order the parts through which each bolt is threaded.
Goal, backboard, mounting plate

NAME ______________________

CRITICAL THINKING

Ring the letter of the figure on the right that completes the pattern shown on the left.

1.

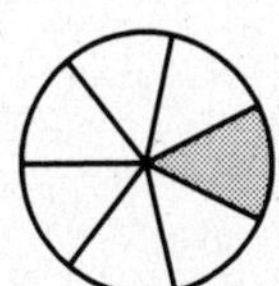 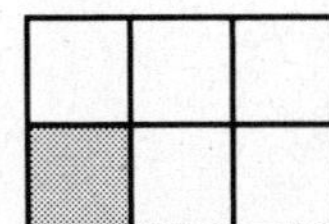 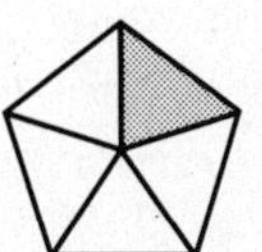

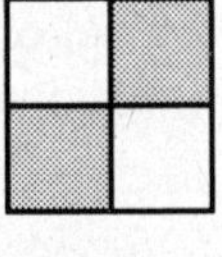 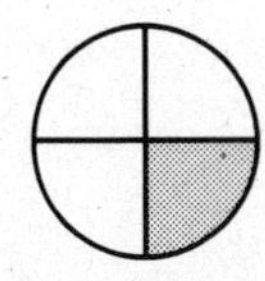 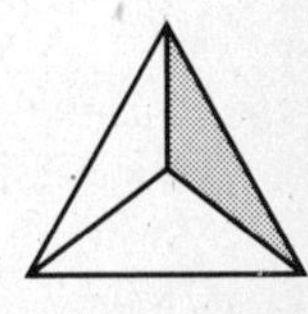

a. **b.** **c.**

2.

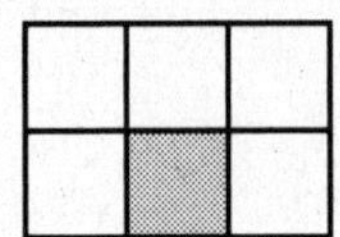 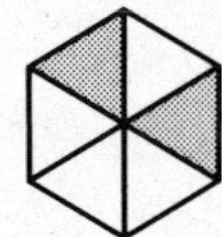 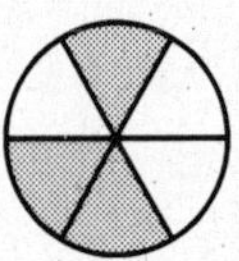

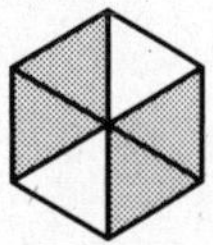 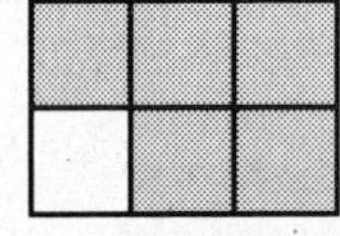 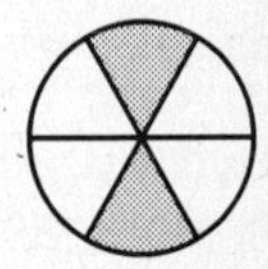

a. **b.** **c.**

3.

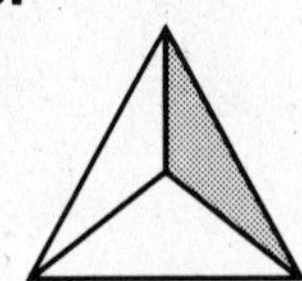 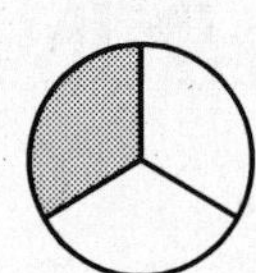 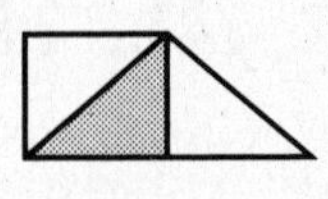

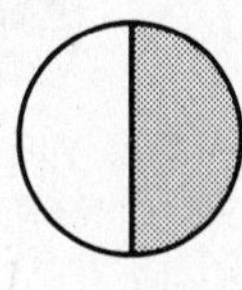 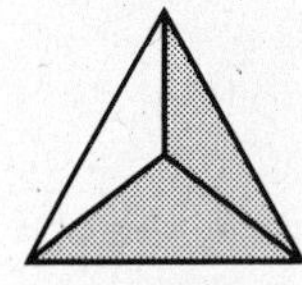 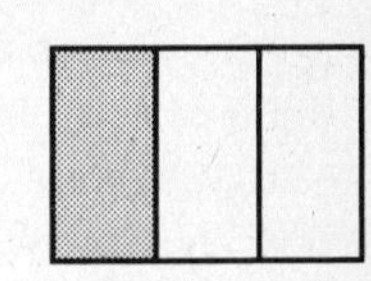

a. **b.** **c.**

4.

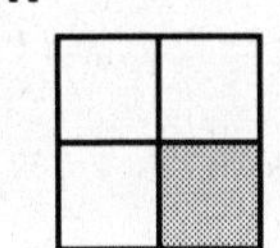 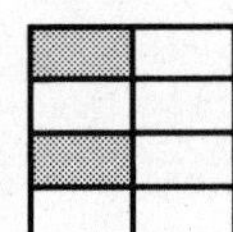 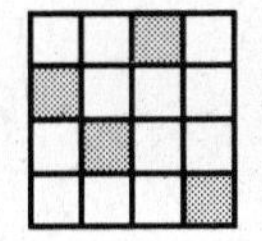

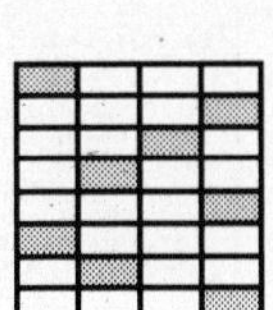 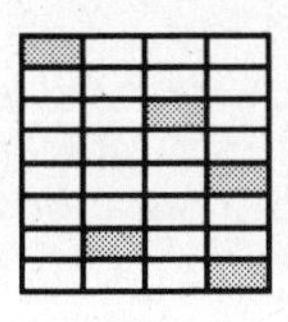 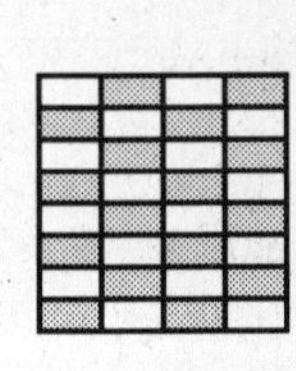

a. **b.** **c.**

5.

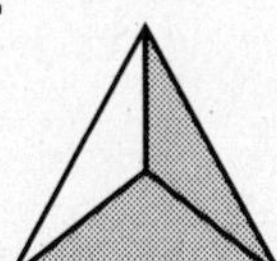 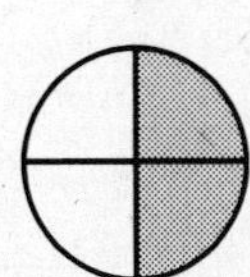 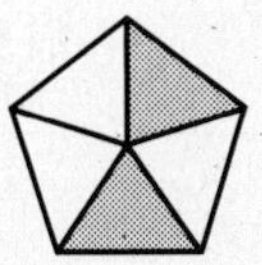

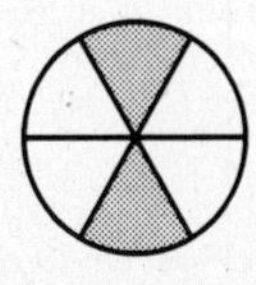 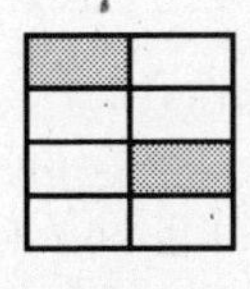 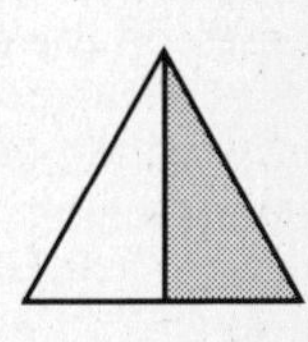

a. **b.** **c.**

6.

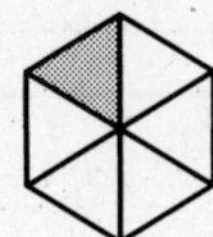 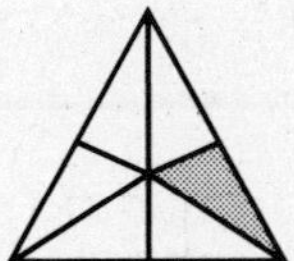 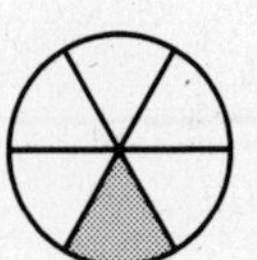

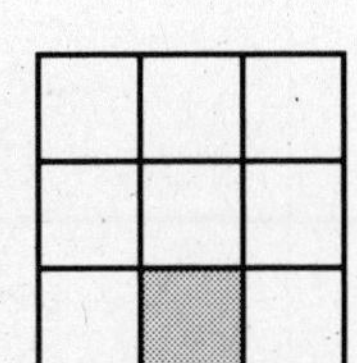  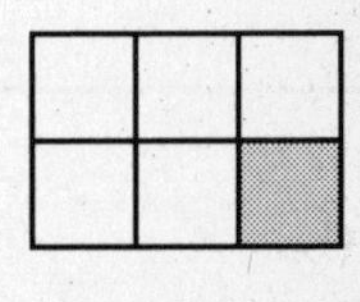

a. **b.** **c.**

Use after pages 222–223.

Teacher Notes

Use with
Objective 67
pages 222–223

Focus
Critical Thinking
Finding/Extending/Using Patterns

Overview
Students recognize the relationship in a pattern and use this same relationship to complete the pattern.

Teaching Suggestions
Each of the patterns in the activity has two possible variables—the number of total parts in each shape and the number of shaded parts in each shape. In addition, students must realize that overall shape is not a factor.

If students need help, have them list common features and differences between the figures.

If students need additional help, encourage them to count and write down the number of total parts and the number of shaded parts in each shape. With the numbers written down, students may be able to see the pattern more easily. For example, Problem 1 can be written as 7-6-5 for total parts and 1-1-1 for shaded parts. Thus, students should be able to see that the next figure should have a total of 4 parts with 1 part shaded.

If students have difficulty with Problem 4, point out that the previous number patterns were based on adding or subtracting, but this pattern is based on a different operation (multiplying).

Extension
Have students devise their own series of patterns. Encourage them to use a number of variables.

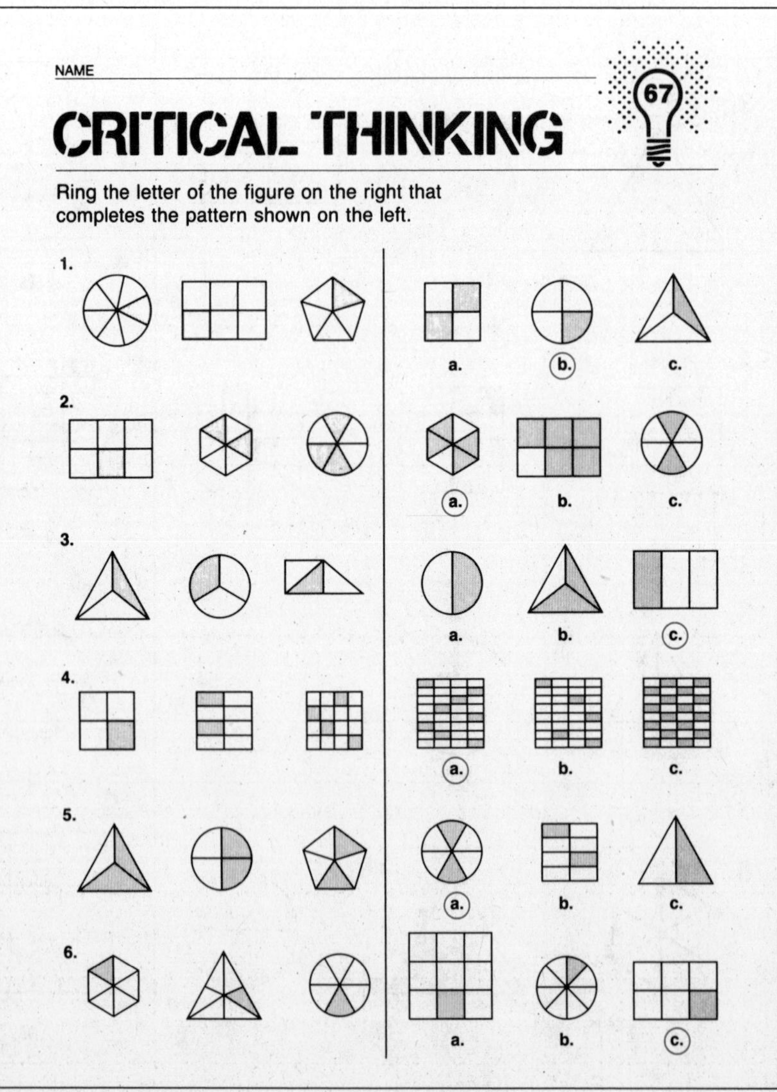

NAME ____________________

CRITICAL THINKING

Many years ago in a distant land there were two villages. All people from Lance Village always told the truth. All people from Fib Village always lied.

One day a stranger met three men from this land on the road. The stranger asked the men what village each was from.

- The first man whispered his answer to the second man.
- The second man repeated the first man's answer: "He said that he is from Fib Village."
- The third man said that the second man was lying.

Is the third man from Lance Village or Fib Village? Explain.

Teacher Notes

Use with
Objective 68
pages 234–237

Focus
Critical Thinking
Using Logic

Overview
Students *use logic* to determine whether given statements are true or false.

Teaching Suggestions
Have students read the problem carefully.

Help students see that they first need to establish what the first man said. ***Questions:*** *If the first man was from Lance Village, what would he have said?* [That he was from Lance Village, because he would have told the truth] *If the first man was from Fib Village, what would he have said?* [That he was from Lance Village, because he would have lied] *What did the first man say?* [That he was from Lance Village] *Now that you know what the first man said, was the second man telling the truth or lying? How do you know?* [He was lying because he said that the first man was from Fib Village] *Since the second man was lying, was the third man telling the truth or lying? How do you know?* [He was telling the truth because it had been established that the second man was lying] *Where is the third man from?* [Lance Village]

Extension
Have students work in small groups of three or four to make up their own logic problems. Then have groups exchange papers and solve each other's problems.

NAME ____________________

CRITICAL THINKING

Many years ago in a distant land there were two villages. All people from Lance Village always told the truth. All people from Fib Village always lied.

One day a stranger met three men from this land on the road. The stranger asked the men what village each was from.

- The first man whispered his answer to the second man.
- The second man repeated the first man's answer: "He said that he is from Fib Village."
- The third man said that the second man was lying.

Is the third man from Lance Village or Fib Village? Explain.

The first man had to have said he was from Lance Village because all citizens of this land would say that they are from Lance Village—the Lance Village residents because it is true, the Fib Village residents because it is false. Therefore, the second man must be lying, and the third man must be telling the truth—thus proving himself to be from Lance Village.

NAME ______________________________

VISUAL THINKING

Ring the letter of the figure on the right that matches the figure on the left. The figures may be flipped or turned.

1. 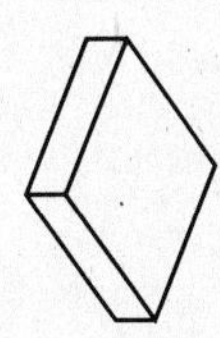

a. b. 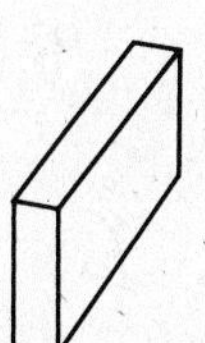 c. 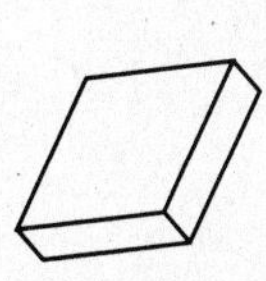 d. 

2. 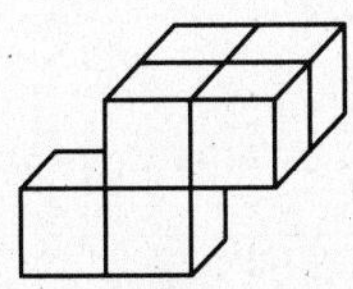

a. b.  c. 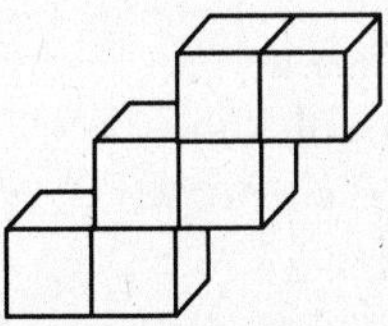 d. 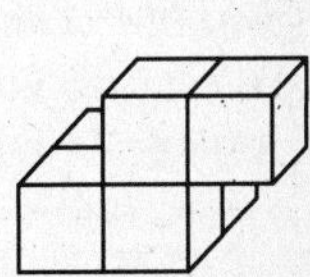

3. 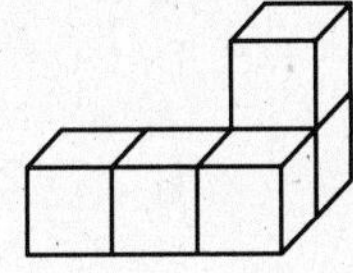

a. b. 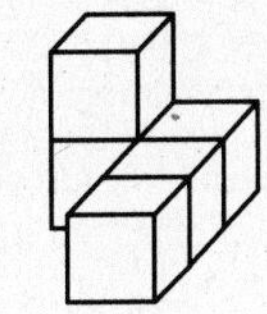 c. 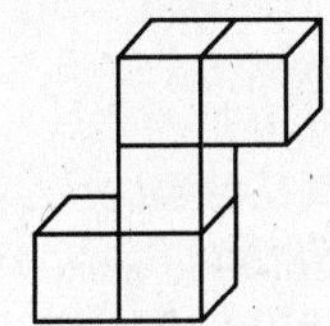 d. 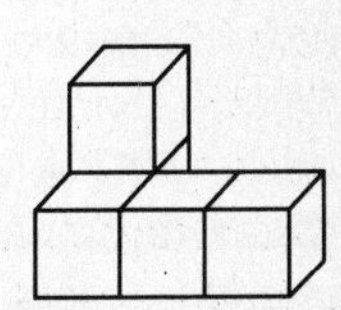

4. 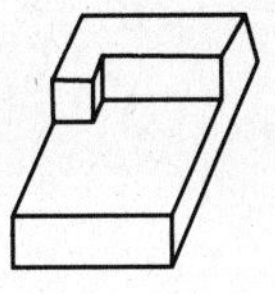

a. 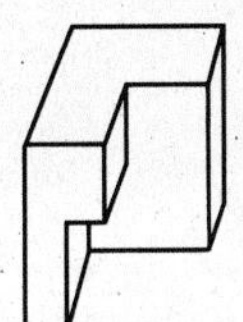 b. 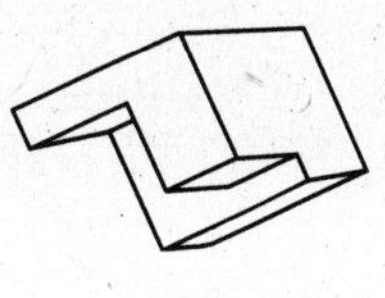 c. 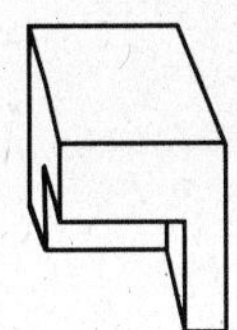 d. 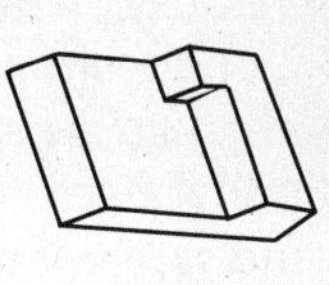

5. 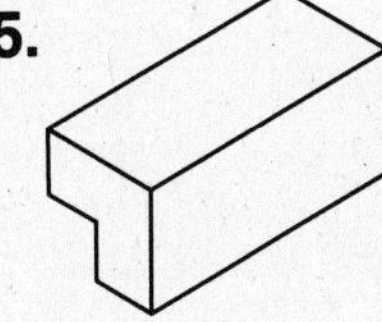

a. b. 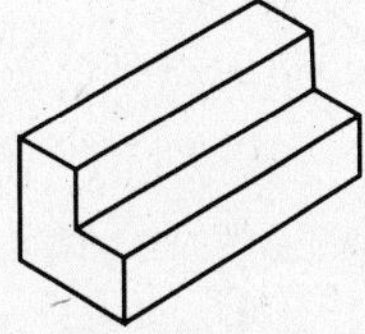 c. 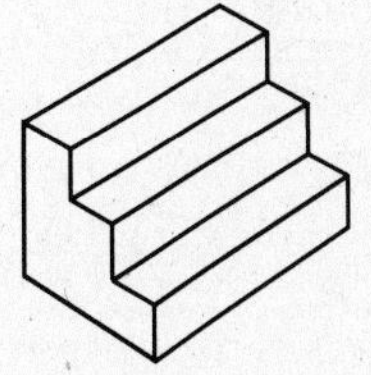 d.

6. 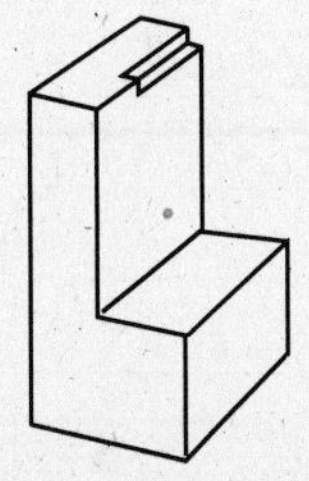

a. 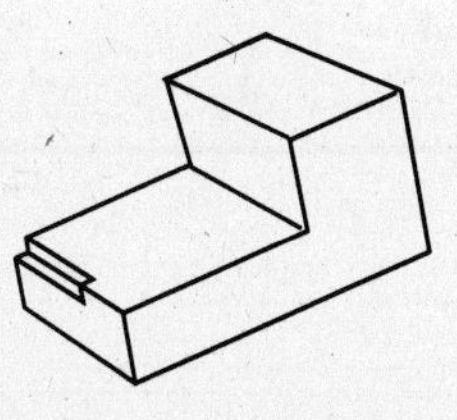 b.  c. 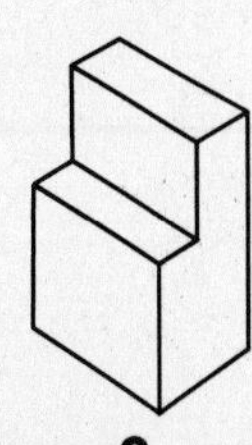 d. 

Teacher Notes

Use with
Objective 69
pages 238–241

Focus
Visual Thinking
Spatial Perception

Materials
Visual Thinking transparency (optional)

Overview
Students compare figures to determine which one of four choices is a different view of a given figure.

Teaching Suggestions
Questions: *Does the given figure in Problem 1 have any sides that are angled?* [No] *What choices does that eliminate?* [**a** and **d**] *Of choices* **b** *and* **c**, *which one most closely resembles the given figure and why?* [**c**; Possible answer: Because the top and bottom appear to be squares]

Suggest to students that they use an approach similar to that used in Problem 1 for analyzing each choice to eliminate possibilities.

Alternate Approach: Complete the activity as a class using the optional Visual Thinking transparency.

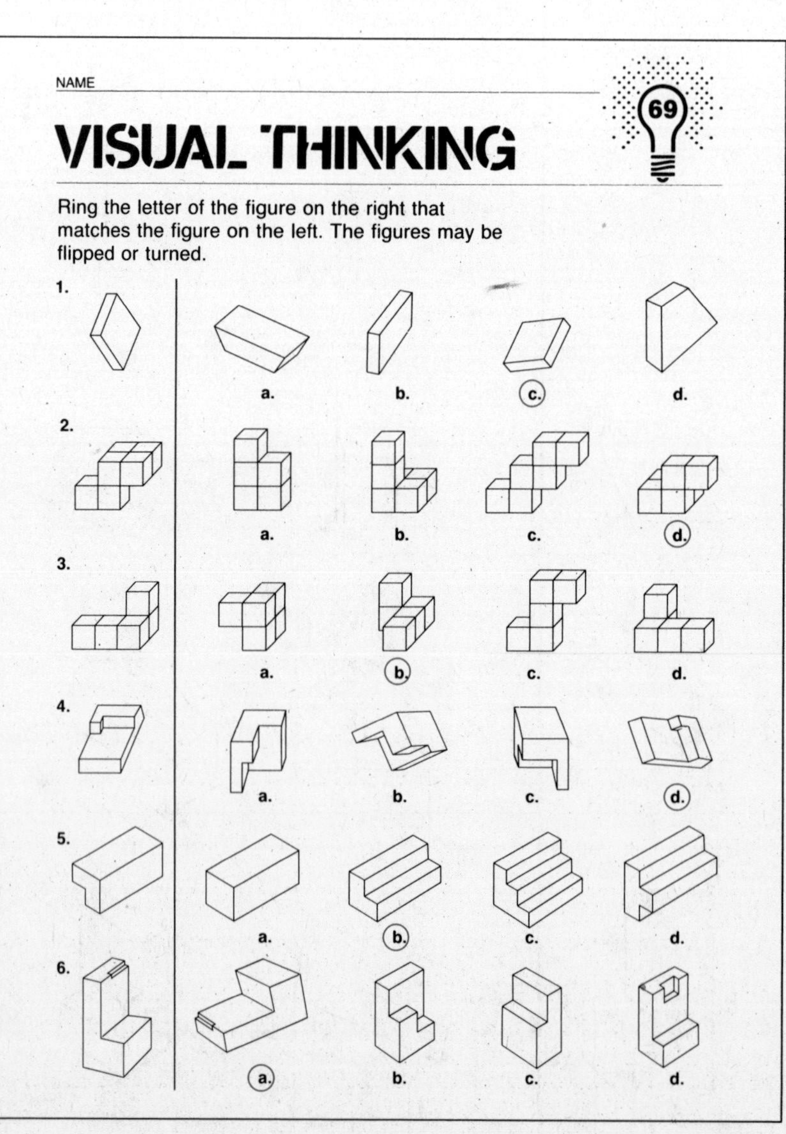

NAME ______________________________

PROBLEM SOLVING

As an assignment, Mr. Matson asked his students, "What fraction of your favorite television program is devoted to commercials?"

Mari and Kevin gathered the following information.

Mari Gomez Grade 6

"Kid Kapers"
Monday: 3:30 - 4:30

Commercial Segment	Time
1st	1 min 30 sec
2nd	2 min 30 sec
3rd	3 min
4th	1 min
5th	2 min

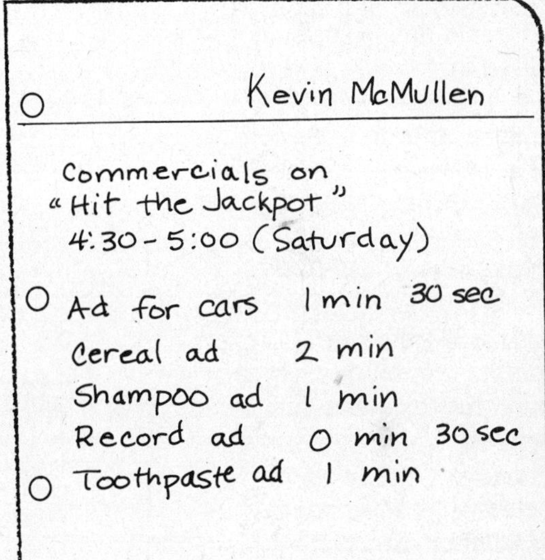

Kevin McMullen

Commercials on "Hit the Jackpot"
4:30 - 5:00 (Saturday)

Ad for cars	1 min 30 sec
Cereal ad	2 min
Shampoo ad	1 min
Record ad	0 min 30 sec
Toothpaste ad	1 min

1. How many minutes are in Mari's program that runs from 3:30 to 4:30? How many minutes are devoted to commercials? What fraction of the hour is devoted to commercials?

____

2. What fraction of Kevin's favorite program is devoted to commercials?

____

3. What part of the total programming is devoted to commercials?

____

Teacher Notes

Use with
Objective 70
pages 242–243

Focus
Problem Solving
Make a Table

Overview
Students add time that is expressed in minutes and seconds and work with fractions in order to find what part of a television program is devoted to commercials.

Teaching Suggestions
Begin this activity by reminding students that there are 60 seconds in a minute. Have them find the following sum.

1 minute	30 seconds
0 minutes	30 seconds
1 minute	30 seconds
2 minutes	
[4 minutes	90 seconds =
5 minutes	30 seconds]

In Problem 1, point out that Mari and Kevin each decided to *make a table* to record the number of commercial minutes. Have students answer the first two questions in Problem 1. ***Questions:*** *To find the fraction of the hour that is devoted to commercials, what number will go in the numerator of the fraction?* [10] *In the denominator?* [60]

Have students solve Problem 2. ***Question:*** *In which program is the fraction of the program devoted to commercials greater, Mari's or Kevin's?* [Kevin's]

In Problem 3, be sure students realize that they must divide the total number of commercial minutes in both segments (16) by the total number of programming minutes in both segments (90). They cannot simply add the fractions 1/6 and 1/5.

Extension
Explain that there are restrictions on the number of minutes of advertising permitted during a program. Have students check with local television stations to find out the restrictions in their area. Then have each student watch a different program, record the number of commercial minutes, and compare their results to the local restrictions.

NAME ______________________

PROBLEM SOLVING

As an assignment, Mr. Matson asked his students, "What fraction of your favorite television program is devoted to commercials?"

Mari and Kevin gathered the following information.

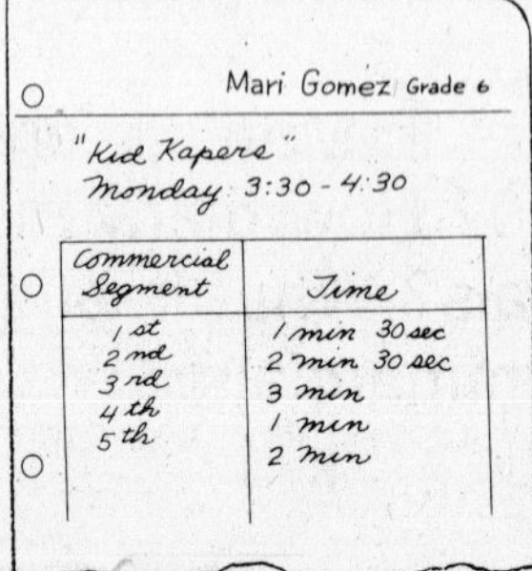

Mari Gomez Grade 6

"Kid Kapers"
Monday 3:30 - 4:30

Commercial Segment	Time
1st	1 min 30 sec
2nd	2 min 30 sec
3rd	3 min
4th	1 min
5th	2 min

Kevin McMullen

Commercials on
"Hit the Jackpot"
4:30 - 5:00 (Saturday)

Ad for cars	1 min 30 sec
Cereal ad	2 min
Shampoo ad	1 min
Record ad	0 min 30 sec
Toothpaste ad	1 min

1. How many minutes are in Mari's program that runs from 3:30 to 4:30? How many minutes are devoted to commercials? What fraction of the hour is devoted to commercials?
60 min; 10 min; $\frac{10}{60}$ or $\frac{1}{6}$

2. What fraction of Kevin's favorite program is devoted to commercials?
$\frac{6}{30}$ or $\frac{1}{5}$

3. What part of the total programming is devoted to commercials?
$\frac{16}{90}$ or $\frac{8}{45}$

NAME ______________________________

VISUAL THINKING

Ring the letters of the two figures on the right that will form the figure on the left when joined. The figures may be flipped or turned, but they cannot overlap, and there cannot be gaps.

1.  a. b. c. d. e.

2. 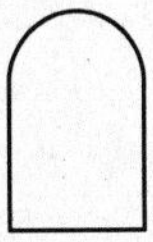 a. b. c. d. e.

3. 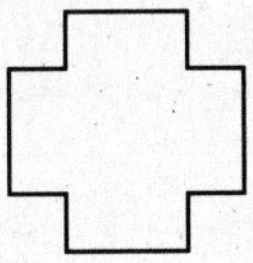 a. b. c. d. e.

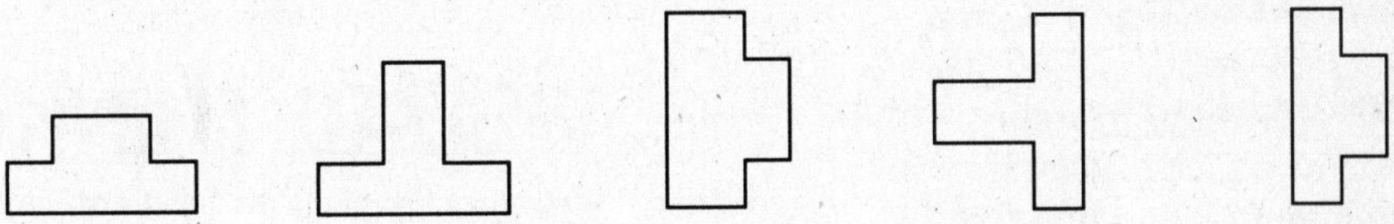

4. 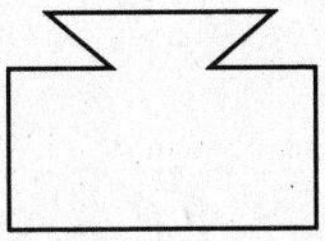 a. b. c. d. e.

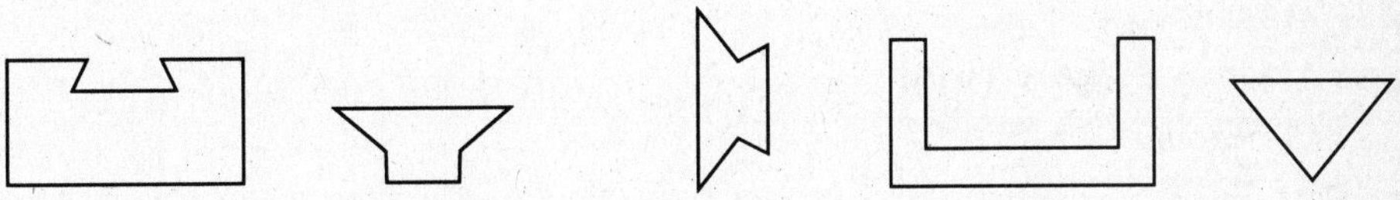

5. 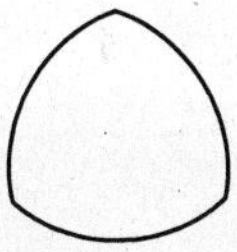 a. b. c. d. e.

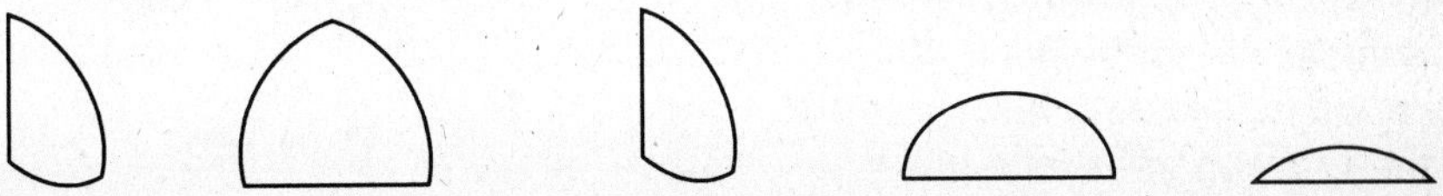

6. 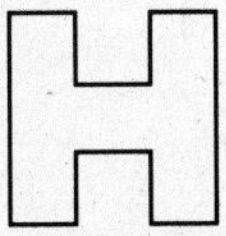 a. b. c. d. e.

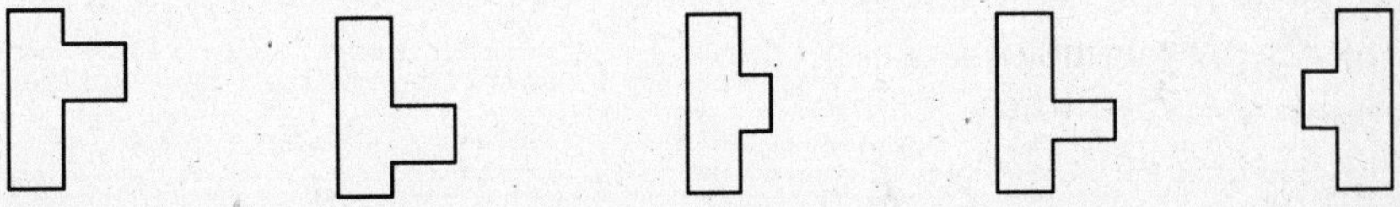

7.  a. b. c. d. e.

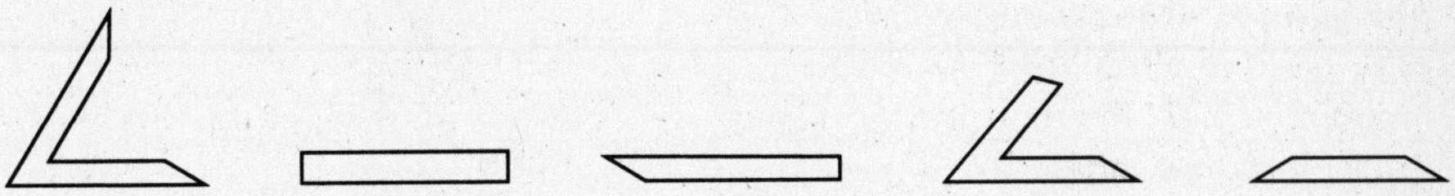

Use after pages 244–245.

Teacher Notes

Use with
Objective 71
pages 244–245

Focus
Visual Thinking
Spatial Perception

Materials
Visual Thinking transparency (optional)

Overview
Students study shapes to determine which pair, when put together, forms the given shape.

Teaching Suggestions
Have students look at the figure given in Problem 1, then look at figure **a**. ***Questions:*** *What would you need to combine with figure* ***a*** *to make the given figure?* [A quarter-circle] *Is there a quarter-circle shown?* [No] Point out that this means that figure **a** cannot be one of the ones used to make the given figure. ***Question:*** *Since figure* ***a*** *is eliminated, what figure must be part of your answer and why?* [Figure **c**, because **b, d,** and **e** together would make less than half a circle.] Have students then decide which of figures **b, d,** and **e** should be combined with **c.** [**d**] If students have trouble deciding, suggest that they trace figure **c** and put the tracing over the given figure.

Suggest to students that they use a strategy similar to that used in Problem 1 to solve Problems 2–7. Remind them that the figures may be flipped or turned.

Extension
Divide the class into seven groups. Assign each group one of the problems in the activity. Have them trace and cut out the five choices (**a**–**e**) given in their problem and find all possible figures that can be made with different pairs of the figures.

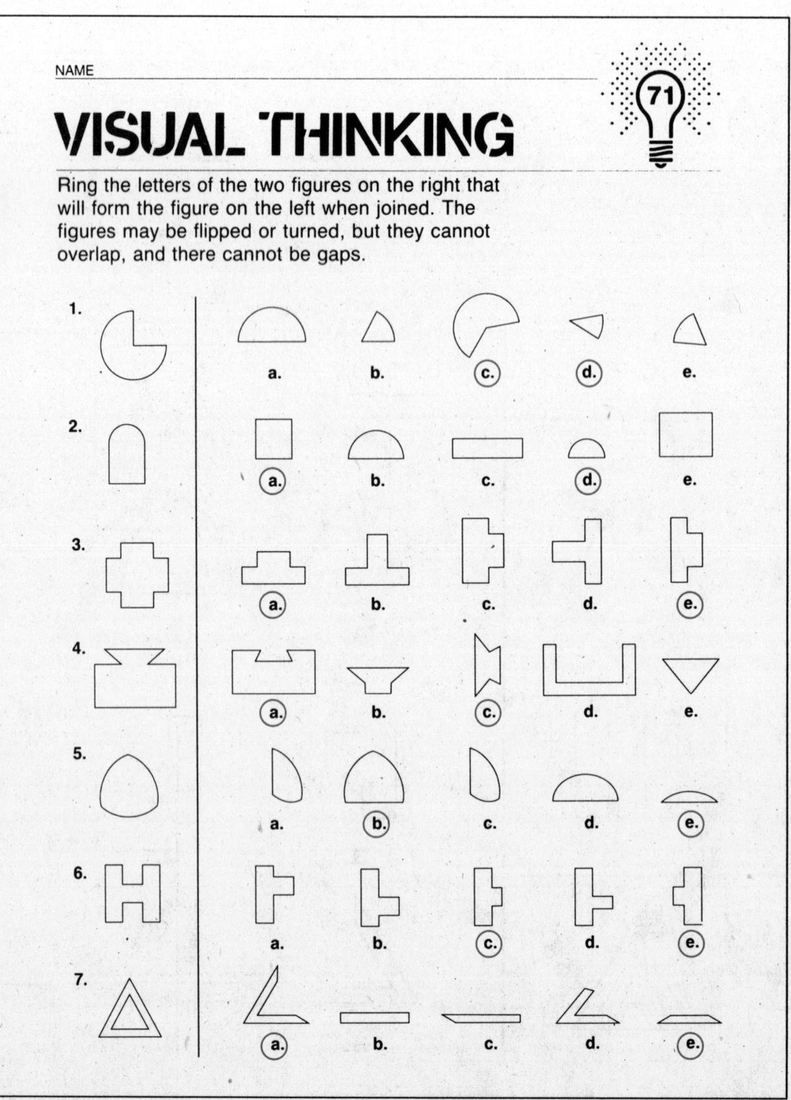
NAME

71

VISUAL THINKING

Ring the letters of the two figures on the right that will form the figure on the left when joined. The figures may be flipped or turned, but they cannot overlap, and there cannot be gaps.

1. a. b. (c.) (d.) e.
2. (a.) b. c. (d.) e.
3. (a.) b. c. d. (e.)
4. (a.) b. (c.) d. e.
5. a. (b.) c. d. (e.)
6. a. b. (c.) d. (e.)
7. (a.) b. c. d. (e.)

NAME

PROBLEM SOLVING

Write the whole numbers 1 through 8 in the squares below. No line may connect consecutive numbers. For example, the square with a 4 cannot connect to a square with a 3 or a square with a 5. Each number may only be used once.

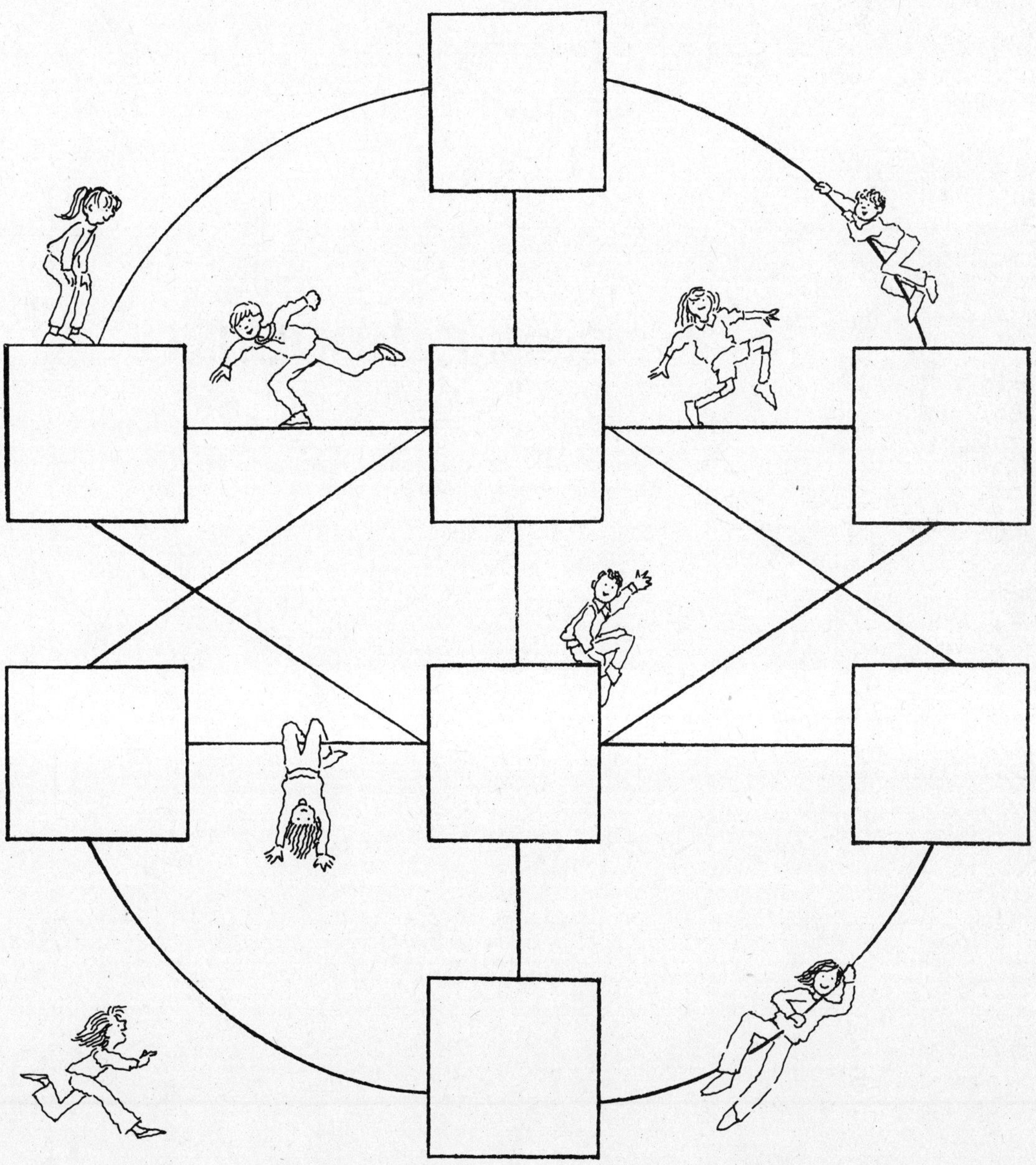

Teacher Notes

Use with
Objective 72
pages 248–249

Focus
Problem Solving
Try and Check

Overview
Students *try and check* various arrangements of the digits 1–8 so that no two consecutive digits are connected.

Teaching Suggestions
Tell students that they will probably have to *try and check* many arrangements before they find one that works. Point out that there is more than one solution.

Help students get started thinking about how to place the numbers. ***Question:*** *If you put 1 in the top square, what restrictions are placed on the position of the 2?* [It cannot go in any of the 3 squares in the second row.] Suggest that the students put the 2 in any one of the four remaining squares. ***Question:*** *Where can the 3 go?* [Answers will depend on where they put the 2; the 3 cannot connect with the 2.] Have the students experiment with various combinations until they find one that works.

Extension
Have students find a second arrangement that will work. An example is shown below.

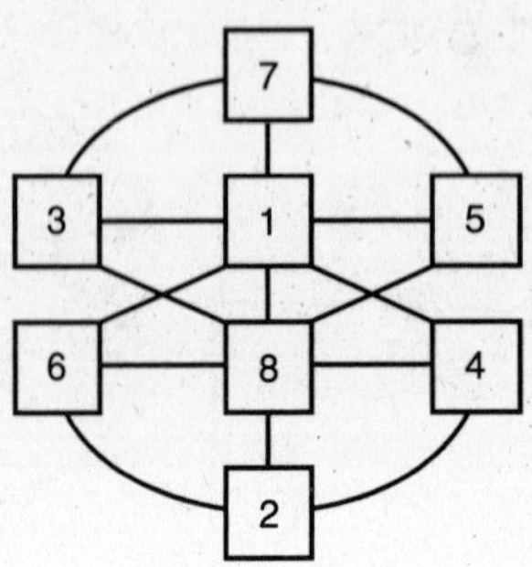

NAME

PROBLEM SOLVING

Write the whole numbers 1 through 8 in the squares below. No line may connect consecutive numbers. For example, the square with a 4 cannot connect to a square with a 3 or a square with a 5. Each number may only be used once.

Possible answer:

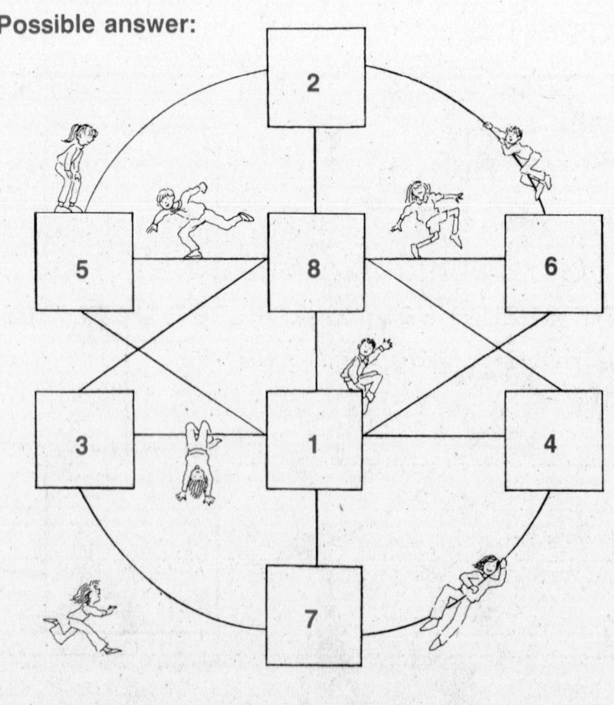

NAME ___

CRITICAL THINKING

Janet and Benjamin are making oatmeal bars for a party at school. They only have $\frac{1}{8}$-, $\frac{1}{4}$-, and $\frac{1}{2}$- cup measuring containers. Below is the recipe for the oatmeal bars. They want to measure the ingredients using only these 3 measuring cups.

1. Fill in the table below.

Oatmeal Bars	Measuring Cups
$\frac{3}{8}$ cup margarine	
$2\frac{1}{4}$ cups flour	
$1\frac{3}{4}$ cups oatmeal	
$\frac{5}{8}$ cup honey	
$1\frac{3}{8}$ cups nuts	

2. Benjamin thought that they should make a double batch of the oatmeal bars. How should they measure each of the ingredients using only those 3 measuring cups?

___

___

___

Use after pages 250–251.

Teacher Notes

Use with
Objective 73
pages 250–251

Focus
Critical Thinking
Using Number Sense

Materials
1/8-, 1/4-, and 1/2-cup measures (optional)
Something to measure, such as rice, sand, or beans (optional)

Overview
Students determine how to use specific measuring units to measure various amounts.

Teaching Suggestions
Help students think about the ways to combine the measures they have been given. ***Questions:*** *Using the given measures, how many ways could you measure out 1 cup?* [Two 1/2 cups; four 1/4 cups; eight 1/8 cups; one 1/2 cup and two 1/4 cups; one 1/2 cup, one 1/4 cup, and two 1/8 cups; three 1/4 cups and two 1/8 cups; two 1/4 cups and four 1/8 cups; one 1/4 cup and six 1/8 cups] *Which of these ways would you most likely choose?* [Possible answer: Two 1/2 cups]

Suggest to students that for each measurement they use the greatest number of 1/2-cup measures as possible, then as many 1/4-cup measures as possible, then use 1/8-cup measures.

Alternate Approach: Have students use the 1/8-, 1/4-, and 1/2-cup measures to measure out rice, sand, or beans of each required amount.

Extension
Suppose Janet wanted to make a half-batch of oatmeal bars. For which ingredients would she have to approximate her measuring if she could only use the three measures given? [Margarine, honey, and nuts] Explain. [She does not have a 1/16-cup measure. To measure half of 3/8 cup margarine (which would be 3/16 cup), she would need one 1/8-cup measure and one 1/16-cup measure.]

NAME ____________________

CRITICAL THINKING

Janet and Benjamin are making oatmeal bars for a party at school. They only have $\frac{1}{8}$-, $\frac{1}{4}$-, and $\frac{1}{2}$-cup measuring containers. Below is the recipe for the oatmeal bars. They want to measure the ingredients using only these 3 measuring cups.

Answers may vary.

1. Fill in the table below.

Oatmeal Bars	Measuring Cups
$\frac{3}{8}$ cup margarine	**three $\frac{1}{8}$ cups**
$2\frac{1}{4}$ cups flour	**four $\frac{1}{2}$ cups + one $\frac{1}{4}$ cup**
$1\frac{3}{4}$ cups oatmeal	**three $\frac{1}{2}$ cups + one $\frac{1}{4}$ cup**
$\frac{5}{8}$ cup honey	**one $\frac{1}{2}$ cup + one $\frac{1}{8}$ cup**
$1\frac{3}{8}$ cups nuts	**two $\frac{1}{2}$ cups + three $\frac{1}{8}$ cups**

2. Benjamin thought that they should make a double batch of the oatmeal bars. How should they measure each of the ingredients using only those 3 measuring cups?

Possible answer: margarine, three $\frac{1}{4}$ cups; flour, nine $\frac{1}{2}$ cups; oatmeal, seven $\frac{1}{2}$ cups; honey, two $\frac{1}{2}$ cups + $\frac{1}{4}$ cup; nuts, five $\frac{1}{2}$ cups + one $\frac{1}{4}$ cup

NAME ______________________________

DECISION MAKING

Moira scheduled her time for Thursday as follows:

Task	Time
School	$6\frac{3}{4}$ h
Sleep	9 h
Meals	$1\frac{3}{4}$ h
Volleyball practice	$1\frac{1}{4}$ h
Homework	$1\frac{1}{4}$ h
Babysitting	$2\frac{1}{2}$ h
Other activities	$1\frac{1}{2}$ h

Total ____________ h

1. Has she budgeted the entire 24 hours?

____

2. Moira has to do $\frac{3}{4}$ hour more homework. Also, she has to spend $\frac{3}{4}$ hour cleaning her room. The time she budgeted under Other activities includes 1 hour for tasks that she must do like washing and getting dressed. How should Moira change her time budget?

____

____

____

____

____

Teacher Notes

Use with
Objective 74
pages 252–255

Focus
Decision Making

Overview
Students make decisions about scheduling various activities.

Teaching Suggestions
Have students read Problems 1 and 2. ***Questions:*** *Which areas of Moira's schedule would probably be the least flexible to allow for changes?* [Possible answer: School, volleyball practice, and baby-sitting] *How much time does she have left over under "Other activities" after she accounts for things like washing and getting dressed?* [1/2 hour] *How much additional time does she need to find?* [1 hour] *If she decides to do some of her homework while baby-sitting, what might she have to consider?* [Possible answer: Whether the children will be in bed most of the time or whether she will have to entertain them]

Several answers are possible. Accept any answer the students can justify.

Extension
Have students make up their own 24-hour schedule for a typical weekday. Have them cite which areas could be adjusted for changes.

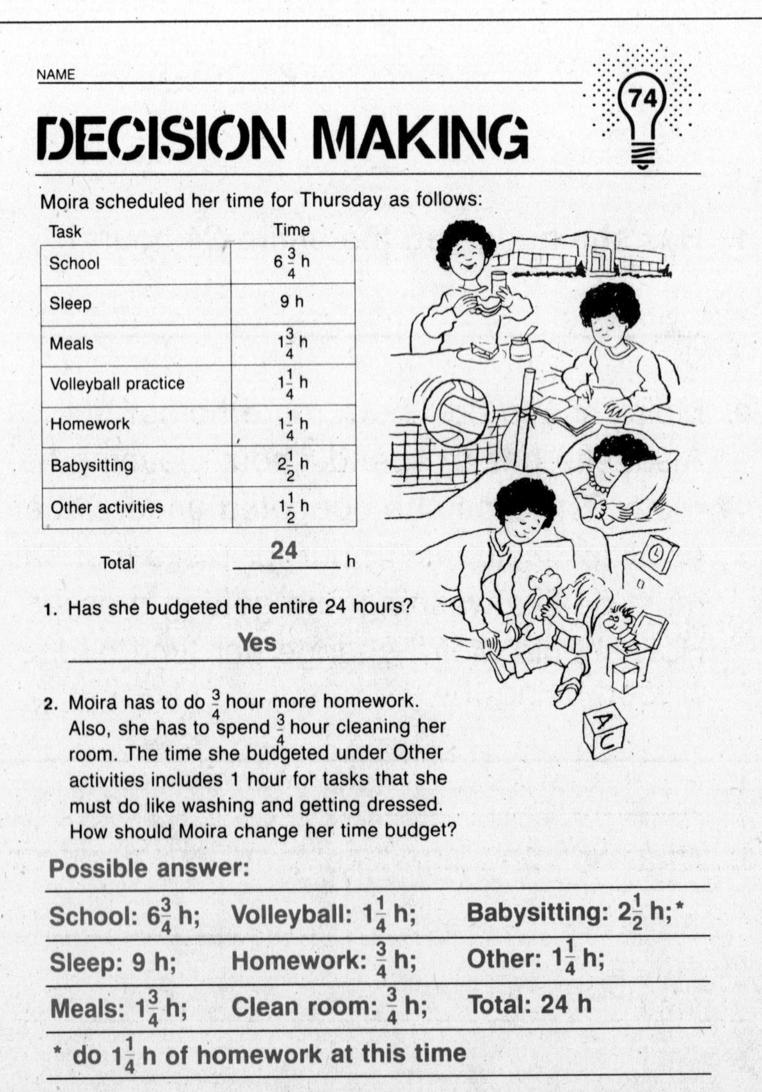

NAME ____________________

DECISION MAKING

74

Moira scheduled her time for Thursday as follows:

Task	Time
School	$6\frac{3}{4}$ h
Sleep	9 h
Meals	$1\frac{3}{4}$ h
Volleyball practice	$1\frac{1}{4}$ h
Homework	$1\frac{1}{4}$ h
Babysitting	$2\frac{1}{2}$ h
Other activities	$1\frac{1}{2}$ h

Total **24** h

1. Has she budgeted the entire 24 hours?
Yes

2. Moira has to do $\frac{3}{4}$ hour more homework. Also, she has to spend $\frac{3}{4}$ hour cleaning her room. The time she budgeted under Other activities includes 1 hour for tasks that she must do like washing and getting dressed. How should Moira change her time budget?

Possible answer:

School: $6\frac{3}{4}$ h; Volleyball: $1\frac{1}{4}$ h; Babysitting: $2\frac{1}{2}$ h;*

Sleep: 9 h; Homework: $\frac{3}{4}$ h; Other: $1\frac{1}{4}$ h;

Meals: $1\frac{3}{4}$ h; Clean room: $\frac{3}{4}$ h; Total: 24 h

*** do $1\frac{1}{4}$ h of homework at this time**

NAME ______________________________

PROBLEM SOLVING

At Ned's Natural Food Store, bulk food and spices are sold by the pound. Ned weighs the food on a balance scale and uses only these 5 weights.

1. How many different weights of food can be determined by the weights $\frac{1}{2}$ lb, $\frac{1}{4}$ lb, and $\frac{1}{8}$ lb? List them.

____

2. How can the grocer weigh $\frac{11}{16}$ pound of food using the weights $\frac{1}{2}$ lb, $\frac{1}{4}$ lb, and $\frac{1}{16}$ lb?

____

3. What one additional weight would allow the grocer to weigh $2\frac{15}{16}$ pounds and $4\frac{15}{16}$ pounds of food?

____

Teacher Notes

Use with
Objective 75
pages 256–257

Focus
Problem Solving
Make a Table

Overview
Students use specific weights to make various combinations.

Teaching Suggestions
For Problem 1, point out that students may use one, two, or three of the weights in combination.

For Problem 2, students may find it helpful to first change the three given weights to sixteenths. ***Questions:*** *Can any combination of the three weights make a total of 11/16?* [No] *Can you combine two of the weights on one side of the balance and the other weight and the 11/16 pound of food on the other side so that they will balance? How?* [Yes; 1/2 lb + 1/4 lb = 12/16 lb. 11/16 pound of food + 1/16 lb = 12/16 lb]

Have students read Problem 3. Suggest that they begin with the 4-15/16 pounds of food. ***Questions:*** *What is the total of the grocer's five weights?* [1-15/16 lb] *What additional weight would be needed to weigh 4-15/16 lb?* [A 3-lb weight] *How could this also be used to weigh 2-15/16 lb?* [By placing the 3-lb weight on one side and the 2-15/16 lb of food and the 1/16-lb weight on the other side]

Alternate Approach: To solve Problem 1, some students may find it easier to *make a table* as shown below.

1/2 lb	1/4 lb	1/8 lb	Total
x			1/2 lb
x	x		3/4 lb
x		x	5/8 lb
x	x	x	7/8 lb
	x		1/4 lb
	x	x	3/8 lb
		x	1/8 lb

Extension
Have the students imagine putting one or more of the five weights on a scale. Ask them to give the least weight they can make [1/16 lb] and the greatest weight they can make [1-15/16 lb]. Ask them what other combinations are possible. [In sixteenths of a pound, it is possible to find combinations from 1/16 lb to 1-15/16 lb.]

NAME

75

PROBLEM SOLVING

At Ned's Natural Food Store, bulk food and spices are sold by the pound. Ned weighs the food on a balance scale and uses only these 5 weights.

1. How many different weights of food can be determined by the weights $\frac{1}{2}$ lb, $\frac{1}{4}$ lb, and $\frac{1}{8}$ lb? List them.

   7; $\frac{1}{8}$ lb, $\frac{1}{4}$ lb, $\frac{3}{8}$ lb, $\frac{1}{2}$ lb, $\frac{5}{8}$ lb, $\frac{3}{4}$ lb, $\frac{7}{8}$ lb

2. How can the grocer weigh $\frac{11}{16}$ pound of food using the weights $\frac{1}{2}$ lb, $\frac{1}{4}$ lb, and $\frac{1}{16}$ lb?

   $\frac{1}{2}$ lb + $\frac{1}{4}$ lb on one side, $\frac{1}{16}$ lb on side with food

3. What one additional weight would allow the grocer to weigh $2\frac{15}{16}$ pounds and $4\frac{15}{16}$ pounds of food?

   A 3-lb weight

NAME ______________________________

VISUAL THINKING

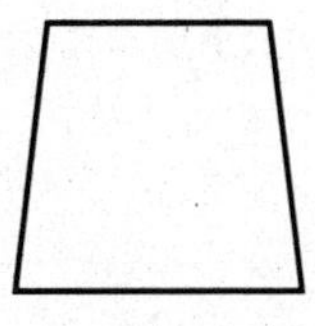
a.

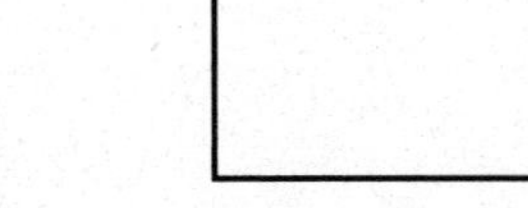
b.

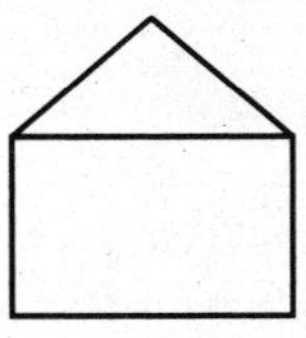
c.

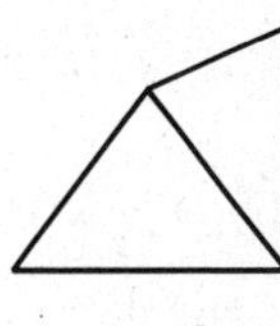
d.

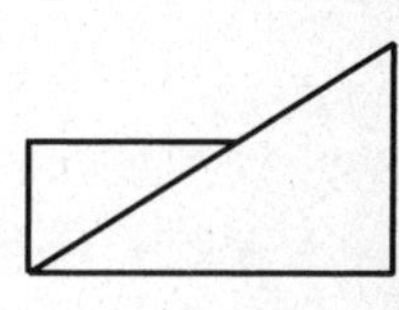
e.

One of the figures above is hidden in each of the figures below. Color the hidden shape in the figure. Then write the letter of the hidden figure in the blank.

1.

_____

2.
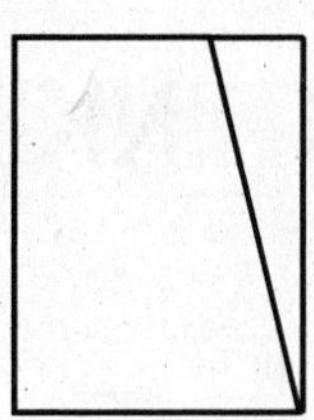
_____

3.
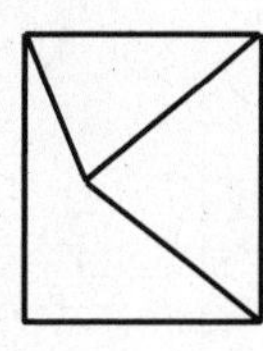
_____

4.
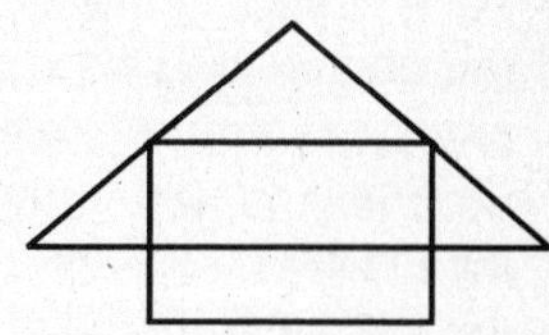
_____

5.
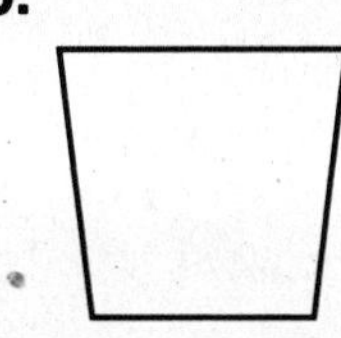
_____

6.
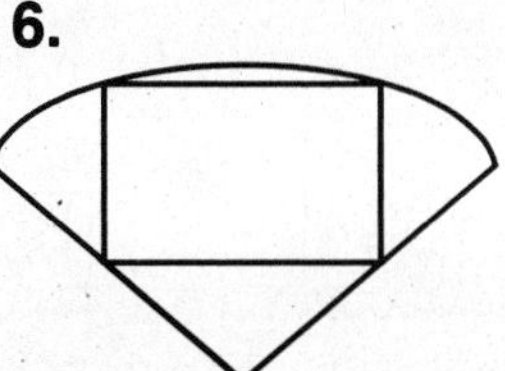
_____

7.
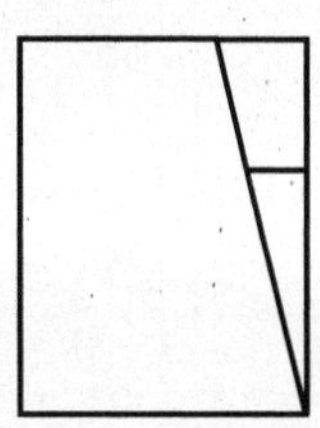
_____

8.
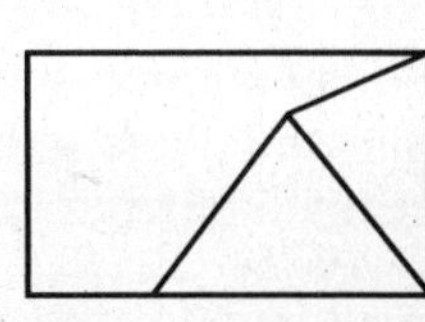
_____

9.
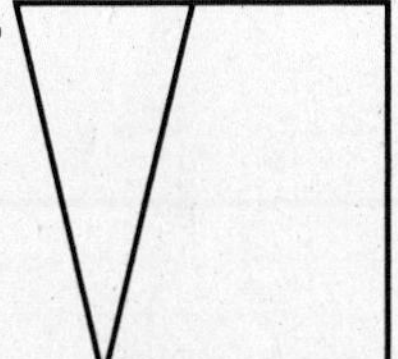
_____

10.
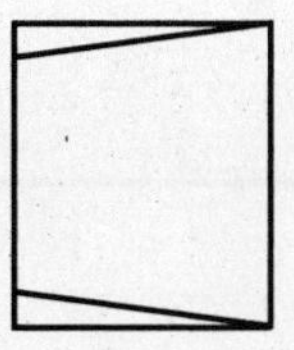
_____

11.
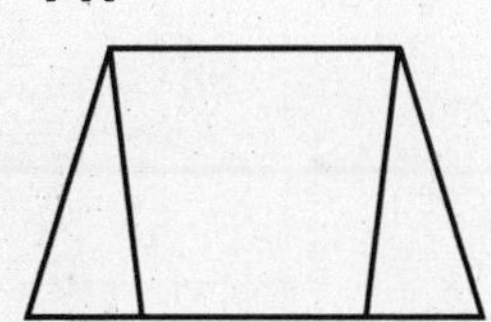
_____

12.
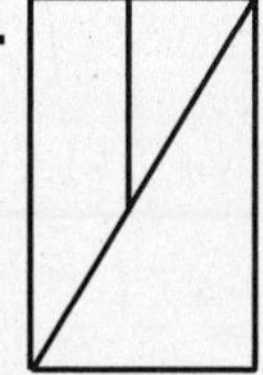
_____

Use after pages 272–275.

Teacher Notes

Use with
Objective 76
pages 272–275

Focus
Visual Thinking
Spatial Perception

Materials
Visual Thinking transparency (optional)

Overview
Students find simple figures contained in complex figures.

Teaching Suggestions
Make sure that students understand that the outline of each simple figure is visible in the complex figures. They can study each complex figure and eliminate simple figures which cannot be contained in them. For example, simple figure **a** cannot be contained in complex figure 1, because there is no quadrilateral outlined. This method can be used for the remaining complex figures.

Alternate Approach: Have students trace and cut out the simple figures **a** through **e** and use the cutouts to place over problems 1–12 to find where each shape is hidden.

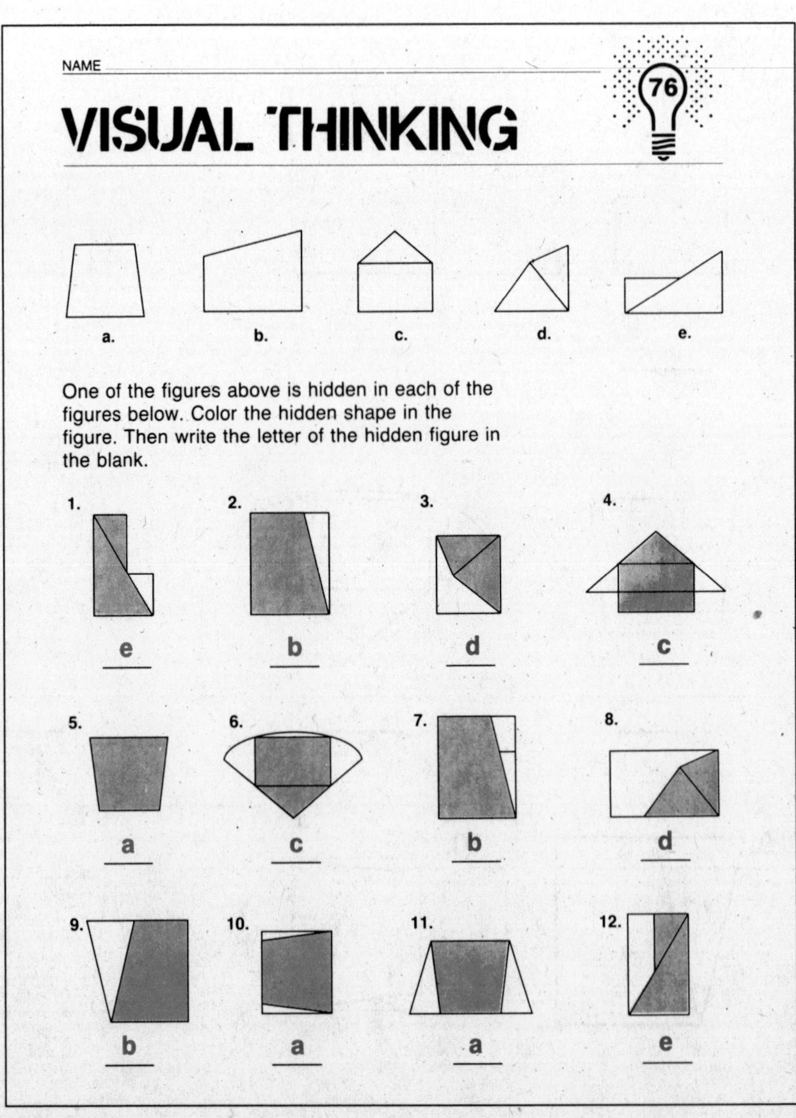

NAME
VISUAL THINKING
76
a.
b.
c.
d.
e.
One of the figures above is hidden in each of the figures below. Color the hidden shape in the figure. Then write the letter of the hidden figure in the blank.
1. e
2. b
3. d
4. c
5. a
6. c
7. b
8. d
9. b
10. a
11. a
12. e

NAME ____________________

CRITICAL THINKING

To crawl from the fallen branch to the mushroom, the turtle must first crawl half the distance. Then the turtle must crawl half the remaining distance, then half the remaining distance, and so on. No matter how much the turtle crawls, half the distance always is left. So the turtle will never get to the mushroom!

Is the above argument reasonable? Why or why not?

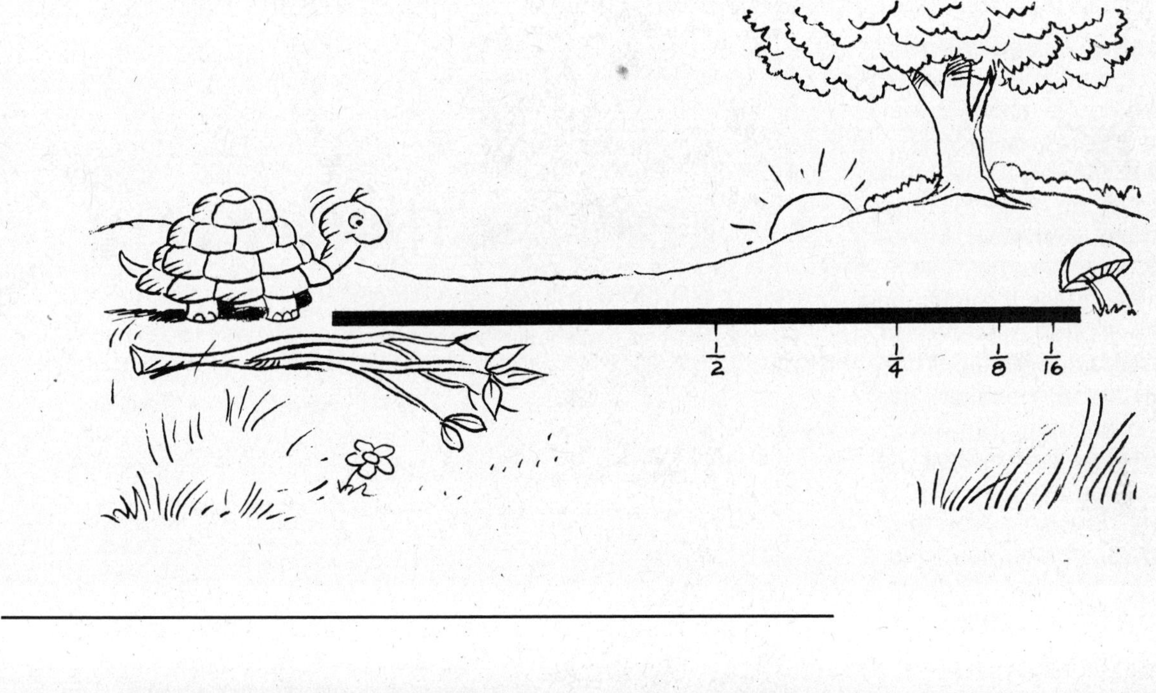

Teacher Notes

Use with
Objective 77
pages 276–279

Focus
Critical Thinking
Using Logic
Evaluating Evidence and Conclusions

Overview
Students evaluate an argument and decide if it is reasonable.

Teaching Suggestions
After students have read and completed the activity page, lead a class discussion of student answers. If students think that the turtle will never reach the mushroom, have a student measure half the distance across the classroom floor. Ask another student to walk half the distance. Then have a student measure half that distance and ask the student to walk this distance. Continue in this manner until the distance left is less than the step of the student who is walking. Then ask students if they think the turtle will reach the mushroom.

Extension
Ask students to look in reference books about logic or puzzles to find situations similar to the one described in this activity. Have them share the problems with the class so students can discuss the reasonableness of the conclusions.

NAME

CRITICAL THINKING

To crawl from the fallen branch to the mushroom, the turtle must first crawl half the distance. Then the turtle must crawl half the remaining distance, then half the remaining distance, and so on. No matter how much the turtle crawls, half the distance always is left. So the turtle will never get to the mushroom!

Is the above argument reasonable? Why or why not?

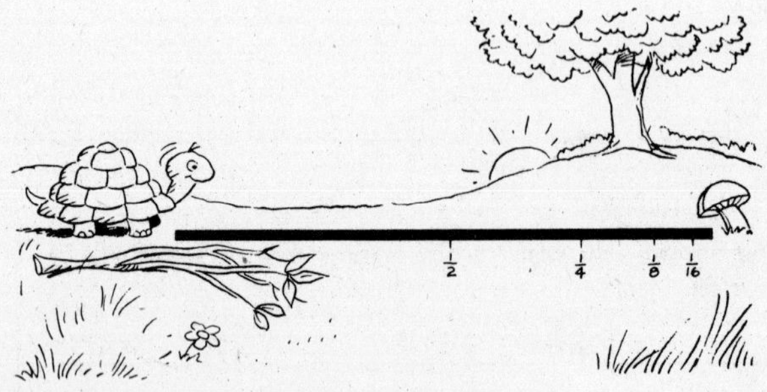

No. Possible answer: The half of the distance that remains gets smaller and smaller, but the steps the turtle takes stay the same size. So, at some point one of the turtle's steps will be more than half the remaining distance, and the turtle will reach the mushroom.

NAME ______________________________

VISUAL THINKING

Find the solution to each of the puzzles below.

1. Starting from circle 1, go through all other 8 circles using 4 straight paths. You may not go through any circle, except circle 1, twice, and you may not lift your pencil from the paper.

(1) (2) (3)

(4) (5) (6)

(7) (8) (9)

2. Starting at point *P*, follow a path to point *Q* going along all the lines. You may not trace any line twice and you may not lift your pencil from the paper.

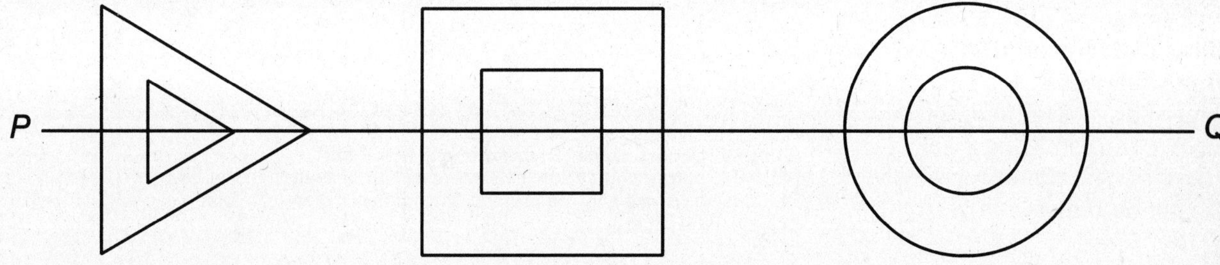

Use with
Objective 78
pages 280–281

Focus
Visual Thinking
Visual Patterns

Materials
Visual Thinking transparency (optional)

Overview
Students trace paths through certain points without retracing any lines or lifting their pencils from the paper.

Teaching Suggestions
To introduce the activity, draw the following figures on the chalkboard or overhead.

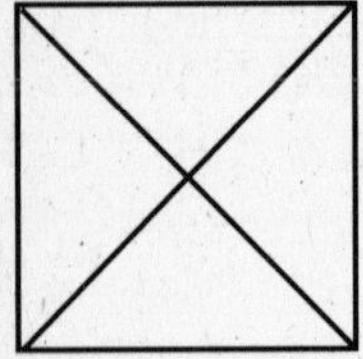
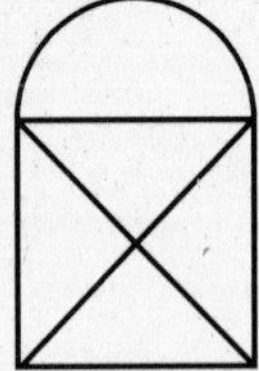

Ask students if they think the figures can be drawn without lifting their pencils. [The first figure cannot be, the second figure can.] Ask a student volunteer to show how each figure can be drawn, or why it cannot be drawn.

Extension
Ask several volunteers to draw some figures on the chalkboard or on an overhead without lifting their chalk or marker from the writing surface. Encourage students to draw a variety of figures and try to make them as complex as possible.

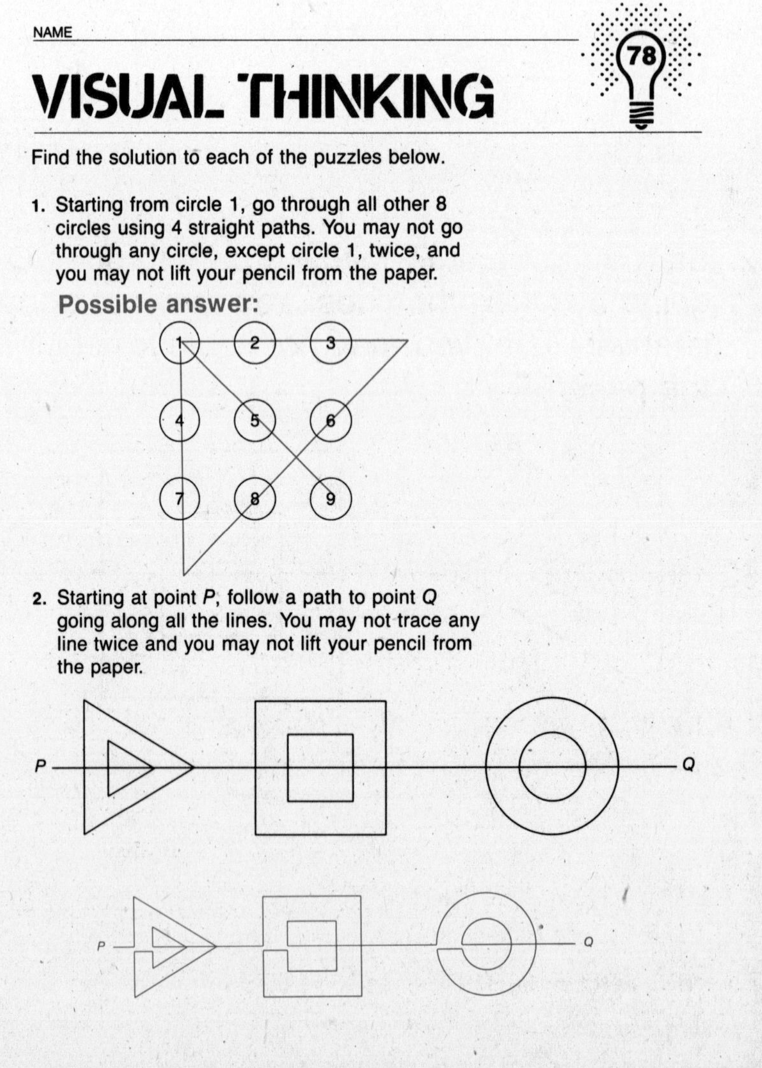

NAME ______________________

VISUAL THINKING

78

Find the solution to each of the puzzles below.

1. Starting from circle 1, go through all other 8 circles using 4 straight paths. You may not go through any circle, except circle 1, twice, and you may not lift your pencil from the paper.

Possible answer:

2. Starting at point *P*, follow a path to point *Q* going along all the lines. You may not trace any line twice and you may not lift your pencil from the paper.

NAME

PROBLEM SOLVING

The students in Mr. Whimsey's math class are playing a game. They are trying to see who can make the most $1.00 words.

Each letter of the alphabet is assigned a monetary value as follows:

a	$0.01	f	$0.06	k	$0.11	p	$0.16	u	$0.21
b	0.02	g	0.07	l	0.12	q	0.17	v	0.22
c	0.03	h	0.08	m	0.13	r	0.18	w	0.23
d	0.04	i	0.09	n	0.14	s	0.19	x	0.24
e	0.05	j	0.10	o	0.15	t	0.20	y	0.25
								z	0.26

In this game, a word is worth the sum of its letter values.

r	e	c	i	p	r	o	c	a	l
$0.18 +	0.05 +	0.03 +	0.09 +	0.16 +	0.18 +	0.15 +	0.03 +	0.01 +	0.12

1. Find the $1.00 word for each clue below.

$26 + 4$, $\frac{90}{3}$, 15×2, $33 - 3$ T __ __ __ __ T __

1, 4, 9, 16, 25, 36 __ Q __ __ __ __ __ S

16%, 18%, 31%, 67% __ __ R C __ __ __ __

2. Find three other $1.00 words.

____

Teacher Notes

Use with
Objective 79
pages 282–283

Focus
Problem Solving
Use Logical Reasoning
Try and Check

Overview
Students use a table of monetary values assigned to the 26 letters of the alphabet to make words with a value of $1.00.

Teaching Suggestions
Some other $1.00 words are *elephants, inflation, elsewhere, pumpkin, writing, Wednesday, prevent,* and *outrank.*

Extension
Have students work in small groups to construct the following: a ten-word sentence worth $10.00, a sentence made up of only $1.00 words, a $5.00 advertising slogan, and a $20.00 limerick.

You might also want to assign different values to the letters of the alphabet. One way is to assign values based on relative frequency of use. Letters that are used only rarely are worth more than letters which are used often.

A	$0.03	B	$0.20	C	$0.13
D	0.10	E	0.01	F	0.16
G	0.19	H	0.08	I	0.05
J	0.23	K	0.22	L	0.11
M	0.14	N	0.06	O	0.04
P	0.15	Q	0.26	R	0.09
S	0.07	T	0.02	U	0.12
V	0.21	W	0.18	X	0.24
Y	0.17	Z	0.25		

NAME ______________________

PROBLEM SOLVING

The students in Mr. Whimsey's math class are playing a game. They are trying to see who can make the most $1.00 words.

Each letter of the alphabet is assigned a monetary value as follows:

a	$0.01	f	$0.06	k	$0.11	p	$0.16	u	$0.21
b	0.02	g	0.07	l	0.12	q	0.17	v	0.22
c	0.03	h	0.08	m	0.13	r	0.18	w	0.23
d	0.04	i	0.09	n	0.14	s	0.19	x	0.24
e	0.05	j	0.10	o	0.15	t	0.20	y	0.25
								z	0.26

In this game, a word is worth the sum of its letter values.

r	e	c	i	p	r	o	c	a	l
$0.18 +	0.05 +	0.03 +	0.09 +	0.16 +	0.18 +	0.15 +	0.03 +	0.01 +	0.12

1. Find the $1.00 word for each clue below.

   $26 + 4, \frac{90}{3}, 15 \times 2, 33 - 3$ T H I R T Y

   1, 4, 9, 16, 25, 36   S Q U A R E S

   16%, 18%, 31%, 67%   P E R C E N T S

2. Find three other $1.00 words.

   Possible answers: surely, crusts, excellent

NAME ______________________________

CRITICAL THINKING

There are 9 cans arranged along each side of the box on the right.

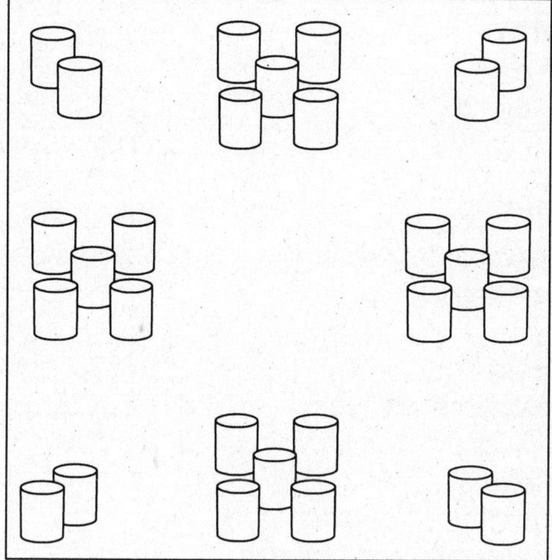

1. Take 4 cans away and rearrange the remaining cans so that there are still 9 cans along each side of the box. Draw your answer in the box on the right.

2. Take 4 *more* cans away and rearrange the remaining cans so that there are still 9 cans along each side of the box. Draw your answer in the box on the right.

Teaching Notes

Use with
Objective 80
pages 286–287

Focus
Critical Thinking
Using Logic
Using Number Sense

Materials
Small blocks or cubes

Overview
Students remove objects from an arrangement in a box and rearrange them so that the number of objects along each side of the box remains the same.

Teaching Suggestions
Guide the students in using logical thinking. ***Questions:*** *Which groups of cans affect the number of cans on more than one side of the box?* [The cans in the corners] *How many times is each group of corner cans counted?* [Twice; each corner is along two sides.] *Which groups of cans affect the total of only one side of the box?* [The groups in the middle of each side] *What happens if you remove 2 cans from the middle group of two opposite sides?* [The total of each side becomes 7.] *How many cans must you add to each side so that they total 9?* [2 cans]

Alternate Approach: Allow students to set up models of the drawings using small blocks or cubes. They can then move them around until they find an arrangement that works.

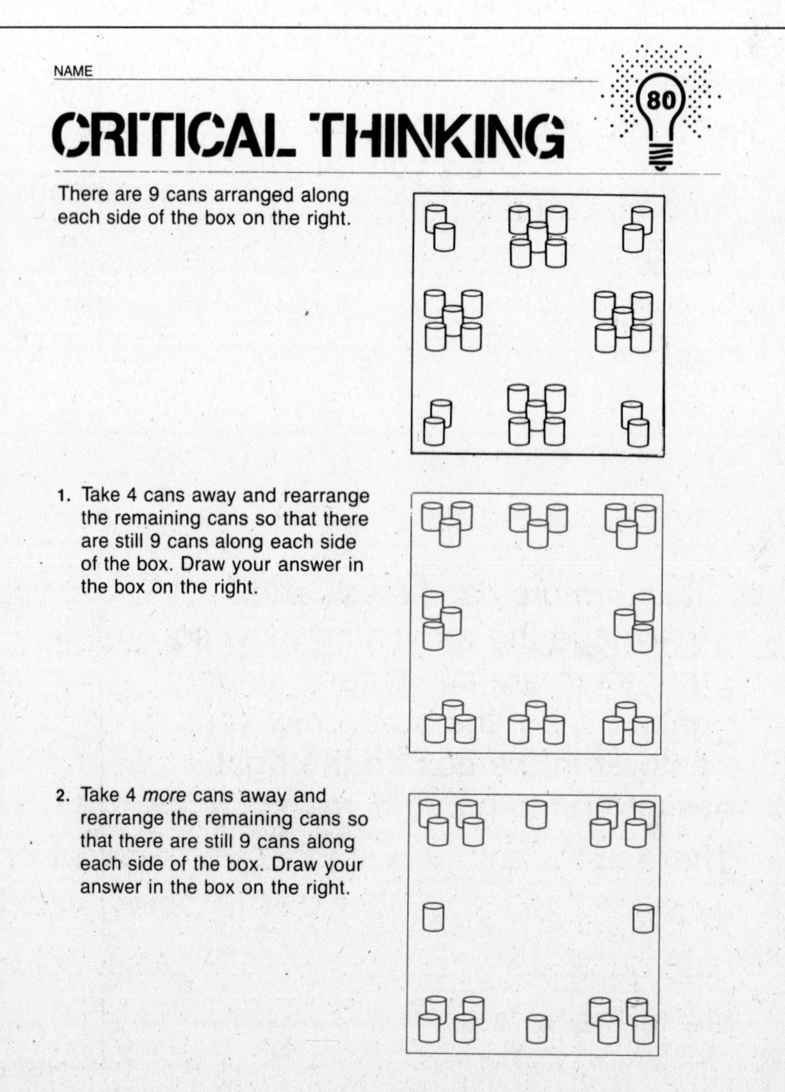

NAME

CRITICAL THINKING 80

There are 9 cans arranged along each side of the box on the right.

1. Take 4 cans away and rearrange the remaining cans so that there are still 9 cans along each side of the box. Draw your answer in the box on the right.

2. Take 4 *more* cans away and rearrange the remaining cans so that there are still 9 cans along each side of the box. Draw your answer in the box on the right.

NAME ___________________________

PROBLEM SOLVING

Solve each problem.

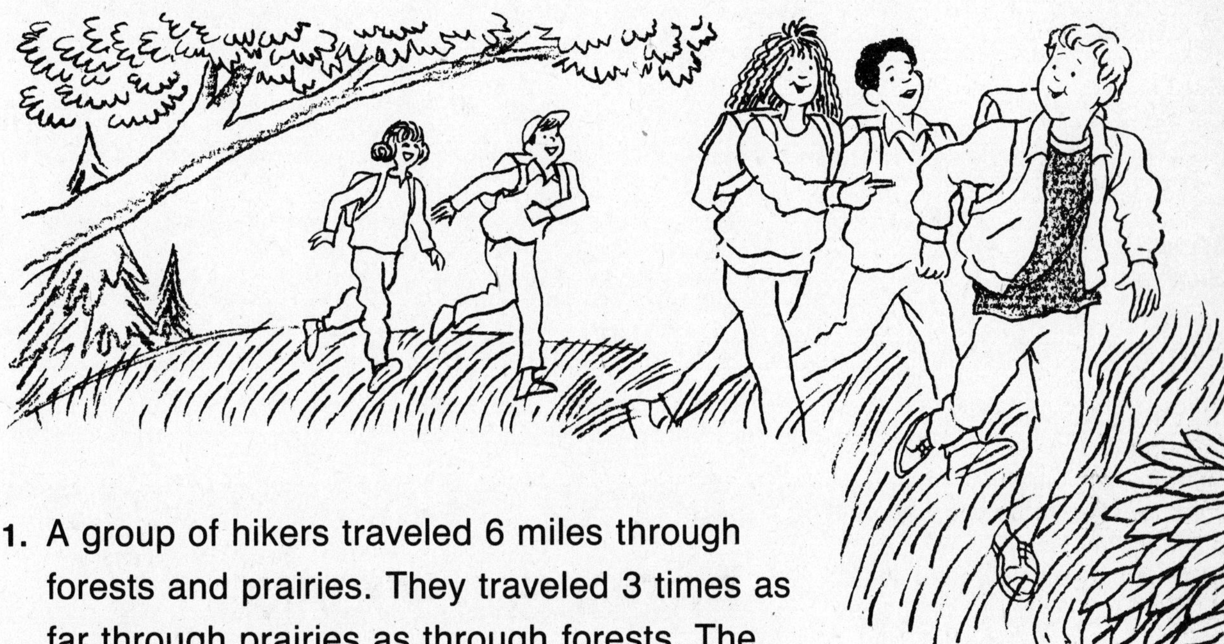

1. A group of hikers traveled 6 miles through forests and prairies. They traveled 3 times as far through prairies as through forests. The number of miles that they traveled through forests equaled $\frac{1}{2}$ the number of people in the group, which was 3 less than the number of miles they traveled through prairies. How far did they travel through prairies?

____

2. A coin purse is $4\frac{3}{4}$ inches long. It contains 5 coins and has been placed on a shelf that is 3 feet long and $5\frac{1}{2}$ feet above the floor. The design on the purse is made up of circles. There are 2 more circles than the number of coins. The value of the coins is 35 cents. The date on one of the coins is 1989. What coins are in the purse?

____

Teacher Notes

Use with
Objective 81
pages 288–289

Focus
Problem Solving
Use Logical Reasoning
Write an Equation

Overview
Students choose pertinent information and *write an equation* to solve problems.

Teaching Suggestions
Encourage students to read each problem carefully.
***Questions:** What do you have to find in Problem 1?* [The distance they traveled through the prairies.] *What information can you use to find this?* [They traveled 6 miles through forests and prairies. They traveled 3 times as far through prairies as through forests.] *How can you solve the problem?* [Write an equation.]

For Problem 2, students must realize that the only information they need is that the purse contains 5 coins which have a value of 35 cents. Then logical reasoning tells students that the coins must be nickels and dimes.

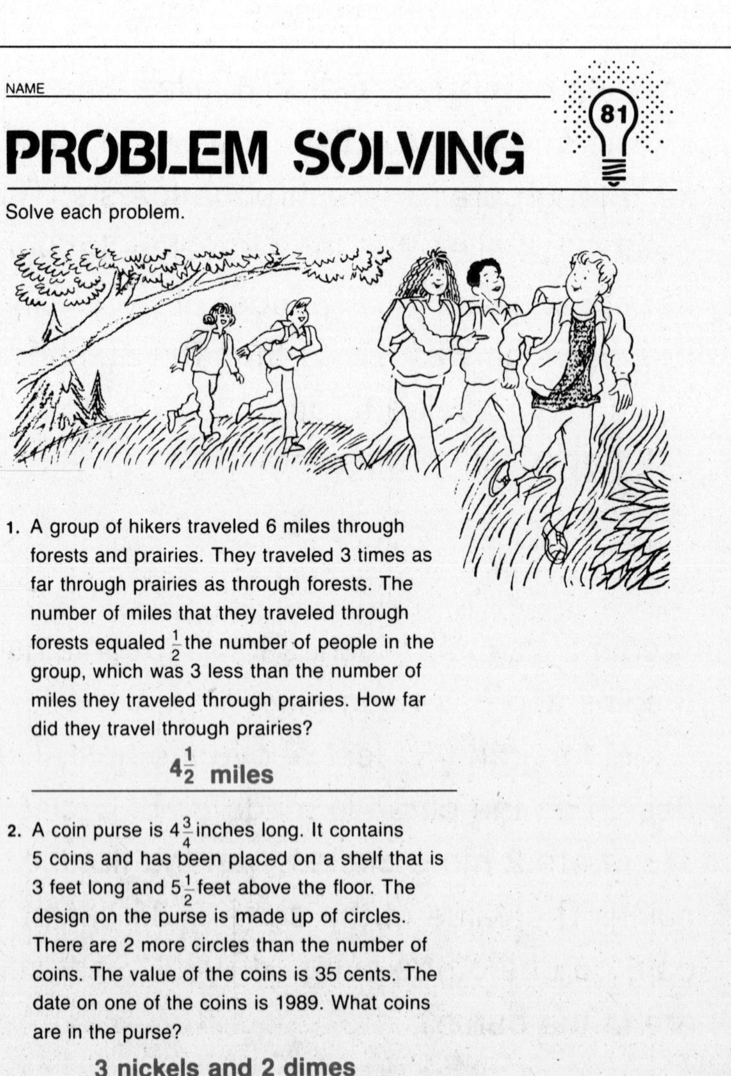

NAME

81

PROBLEM SOLVING

Solve each problem.

1. A group of hikers traveled 6 miles through forests and prairies. They traveled 3 times as far through prairies as through forests. The number of miles that they traveled through forests equaled $\frac{1}{2}$ the number of people in the group, which was 3 less than the number of miles they traveled through prairies. How far did they travel through prairies?

   $4\frac{1}{2}$ miles

2. A coin purse is $4\frac{3}{4}$ inches long. It contains 5 coins and has been placed on a shelf that is 3 feet long and $5\frac{1}{2}$ feet above the floor. The design on the purse is made up of circles. There are 2 more circles than the number of coins. The value of the coins is 35 cents. The date on one of the coins is 1989. What coins are in the purse?

   3 nickels and 2 dimes

NAME ____________________

VISUAL THINKING

Without drawing a path through the maze, write the letter of the exit. Then draw the path.

1.

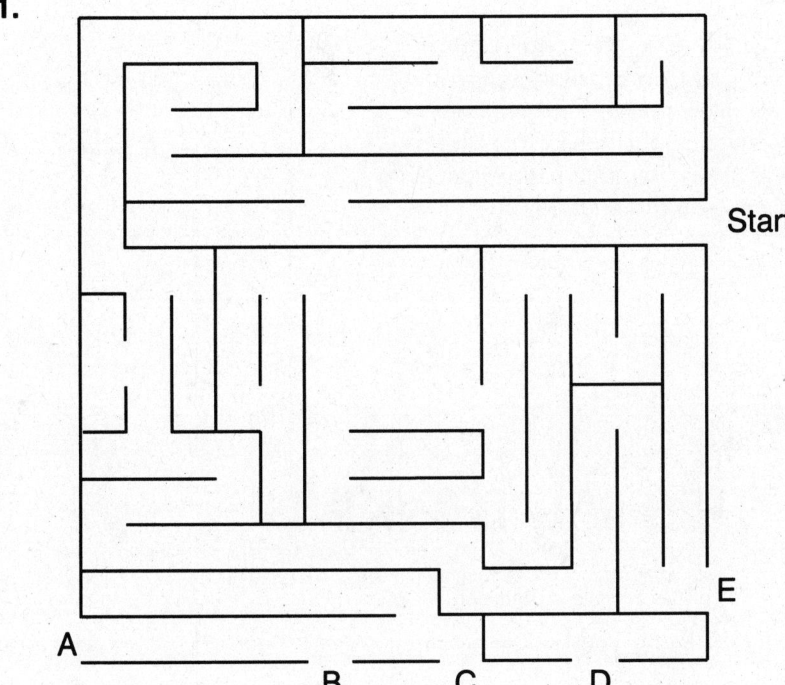

Exit: ______

2.

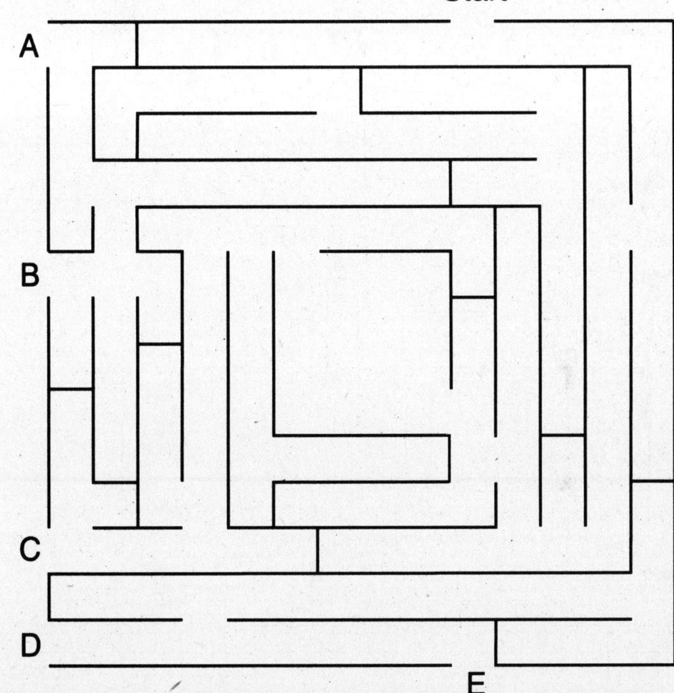

Exit: ______

Teacher Notes

Use with
Objective 82
pages 290–291

Focus
Visual Thinking
Spatial Perception

Overview
Students determine paths through mazes.

Teaching Suggestions
Help students see that they can eliminate exits that are wrong. ***Questions:*** *If you begin at Exit A and move into the maze, what happens?* [You reach a dead end.] *What happens if you begin at Exit B? At Exit C? At Exit D?* [Each exit leads to a dead end.] *What is the only exit from which you can leave the maze?* [Exit E] Then tell students to follow the same procedure for Problem 2. Tell them to try all the exits even after they find one that seems to work to find out if there is more than one possible exit.

Alternate Approach: You might want to tell students this foolproof way of finding a path through a maze: place one hand (when using diagrams, imagine doing this) against one wall and take only the paths that allow you to move without removing your hands from the wall. However, this path will not always be the shortest path.

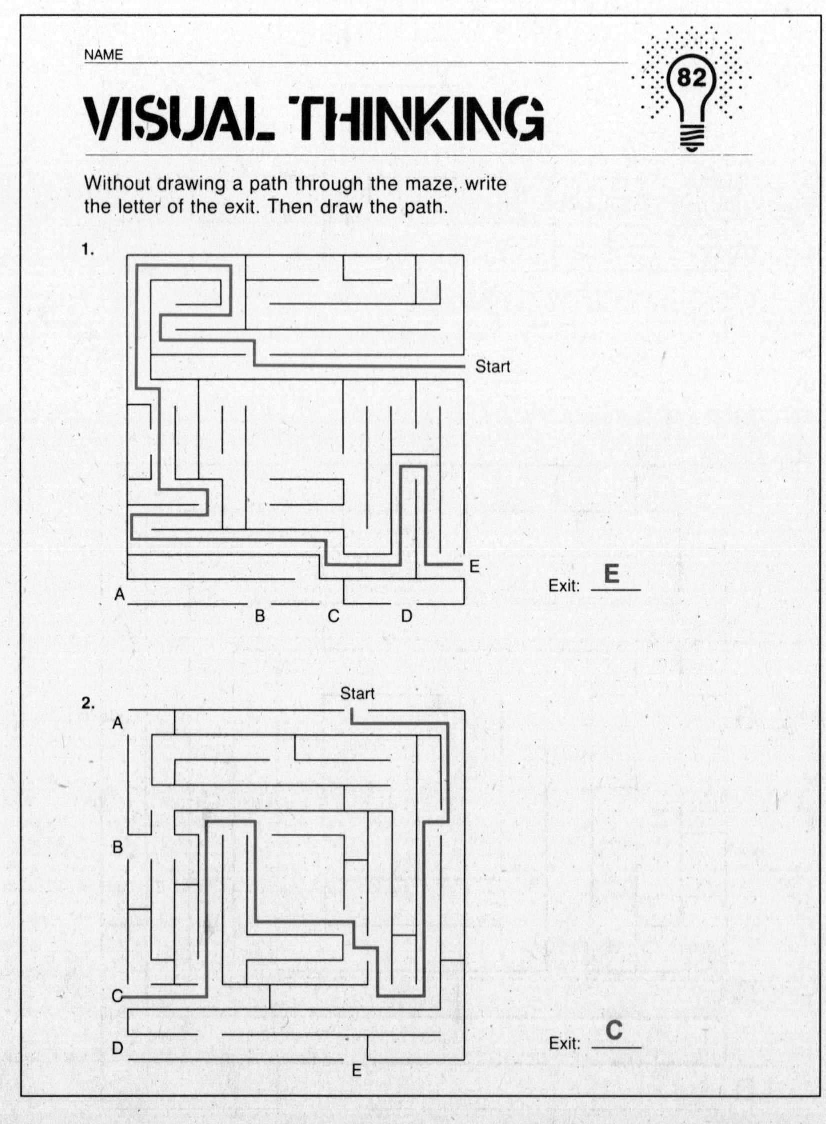
NAME
82
VISUAL THINKING
Without drawing a path through the maze, write the letter of the exit. Then draw the path.
1.
Start
A
B
C
D
E
Exit: E
2.
Start
A
B
C
D
E
Exit: C

NAME ______________________________

DECISION MAKING

Regal's Supermarket has the following three jobs open.

A. Clean-up after school for $2\frac{1}{2}$ hours per day, 3 days per week. Pays $5 per hour.

B. Help at checkout counters for $6\frac{1}{2}$ hours every Saturday. Pays $35.00 per day.

C. Unload delivery trucks every Saturday: 2 trucks must be unloaded; each truck requires $1\frac{1}{2}$ to 2 hours of work. Pays $12.00 per truck.

The manager is willing to hire you for only one of these jobs. Which would you decide to take? Give a reason for your decision.

____

____

____

____

____

____

____

Teacher Notes

Use with
Objective 83
pages 292–295

Focus
Decision Making

Overview
Students use information about working hours and pay rates to decide which of three jobs to take.

Teaching Suggestions
Discuss with students what might determine which of the jobs they would take. [Possible answers: The hourly rate, the number of hours they have to work, or the total amount of money they can make per week] Discuss which of these factors students consider more important and why. Discuss possible advantages and disadvantages of each job as a way of guiding students to specify what factors they consider important.

If students decide that they would want the job in which they earned the most money per week, ask how they can find the total weekly pay for job A. (The others are given.) [2-1/2 × $5 × 3 = $37.50]

If students decide that they want the job that pays the most per hour, then they need to find the hourly rate for jobs B and C. For job B, ask students how to find the hourly rate. [$35 divided by 6-1/2 = about $5.38 per hour] For job C, see "Possible answer" on the activity page.

NAME

DECISION MAKING

Regal's Supermarket has the following three jobs open.

A. Clean-up after school for $2\frac{1}{2}$ hours per day, 3 days per week. Pays $5 per hour.

B. Help at checkout counters for $6\frac{1}{2}$ hours every Saturday. Pays $35.00 per day.

C. Unload delivery trucks every Saturday: 2 trucks must be unloaded; each truck requires $1\frac{1}{2}$ to 2 hours of work. Pays $12.00 per truck.

The manager is willing to hire you for only one of these jobs. Which would you decide to take? Give a reason for your decision.

Possible answer: Job C; pays more per hour ($6-$8 per hour. For example, if each truck takes 2 hours, the pay is (12 × 2) ÷ 4, or $6 per hour, but if each truck takes $1\frac{1}{2}$ hours, the pay is (12 × 2) ÷ 3, or $8 per hour.)

NAME ____________________

DECISION MAKING

Heather and her parents are trying to decide which video game system to buy. The ProGame System costs $149 and comes with a $25 rebate. Each of the system's 48 game cartridges costs $20. The Helix Game System costs $99 and has over 100 games available. Each game costs $35. Many of Heather's friends have the Helix system, so she could trade games. The Big Star System costs $120 and has 60 games that cost $25 each. The video store charges $3 to rent Big Star games for 3 days.

1. How much would it cost to buy each system and one game cartridge?

   ProGame: ______ Helix: ______ Big Star: ______

2. How much would it cost to buy each system and five game cartridges?

   ProGame: ______ Helix: ______ Big Star: ______

3. Which system might Heather choose? Explain your answer.

   ____

   ____

Teacher Notes

Use with
Objective 84
pages 306–307

Focus
Decision Making

Overview
Students analyze data and apply generalizations to make decisions among alternate courses of action.

Teaching Suggestions
Ask students to describe various video game systems with which they are familiar. Discuss the cost of the systems and game cartridges named by students. Point out that manufacturers often offer special rates if you buy the video system and various accessories.

It may be helpful for students to organize the information given on the page in a table similar to the one shown below.

System	Price	Game price
ProGame	$124	$20
Helix	$99	$35
Big Star	$120	$25

Questions: Which video game system costs less? [Helix] *How does the cost of the Helix system and one game cartridge compare with that of the others?* [It is the best price.] *Should Heather consider the price with only one game cartridge?* [No; most people buy several games.] *What else might influence Heather's decision?* [The fact that she can trade Helix cartridges with her friends]

Extension
Have students look in newspapers for advertisements of video game systems. Encourage students to make a table that compares the price of each system they find in an ad. Using the information given in the ads, have students determine which system is the best buy, and explain their reasoning.

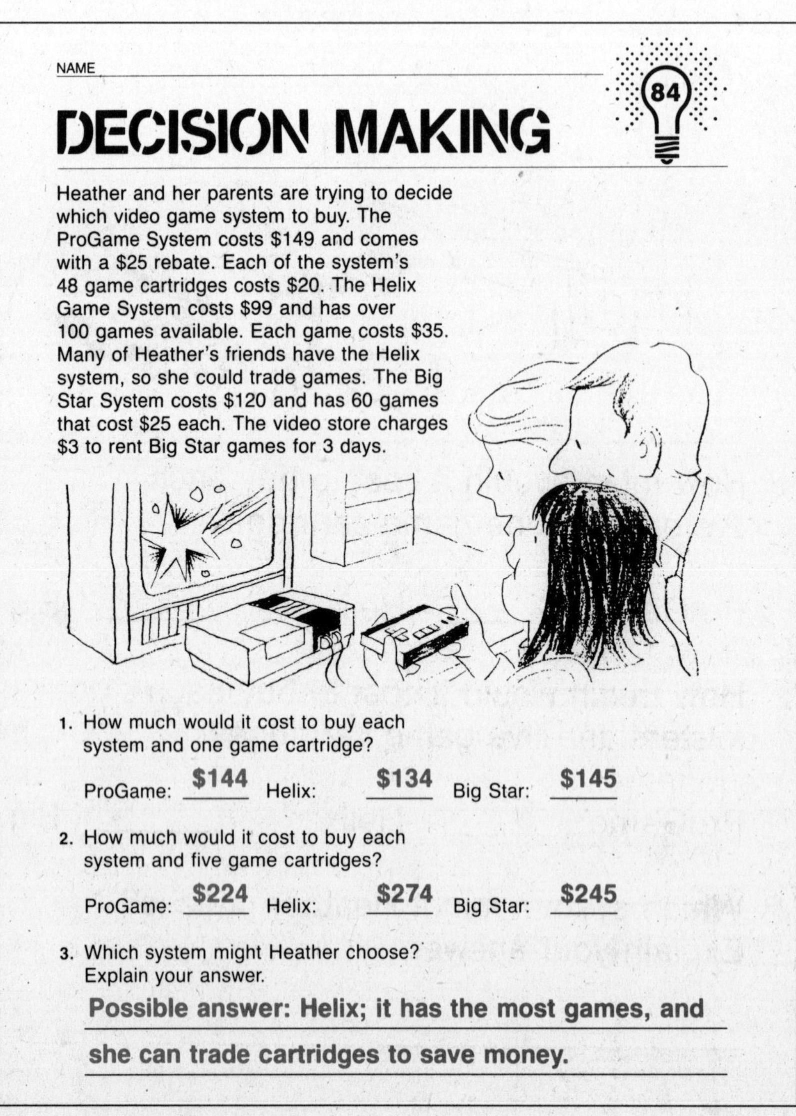

NAME ______________________________

DECISION MAKING

84

Heather and her parents are trying to decide which video game system to buy. The ProGame System costs $149 and comes with a $25 rebate. Each of the system's 48 game cartridges costs $20. The Helix Game System costs $99 and has over 100 games available. Each game costs $35. Many of Heather's friends have the Helix system, so she could trade games. The Big Star System costs $120 and has 60 games that cost $25 each. The video store charges $3 to rent Big Star games for 3 days.

1. How much would it cost to buy each system and one game cartridge?

   ProGame: **$144** Helix: **$134** Big Star: **$145**

2. How much would it cost to buy each system and five game cartridges?

   ProGame: **$224** Helix: **$274** Big Star: **$245**

3. Which system might Heather choose? Explain your answer.

   Possible answer: Helix; it has the most games, and she can trade cartridges to save money.

NAME ______________________________

CRITICAL THINKING

Use the pictures at right to help you find the areas of the figures.

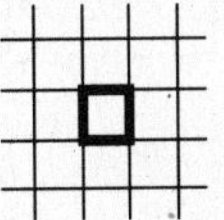

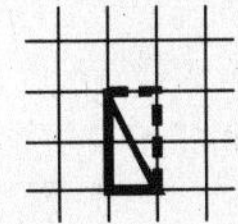

Find the area.

Area = 1 sq unit

1. 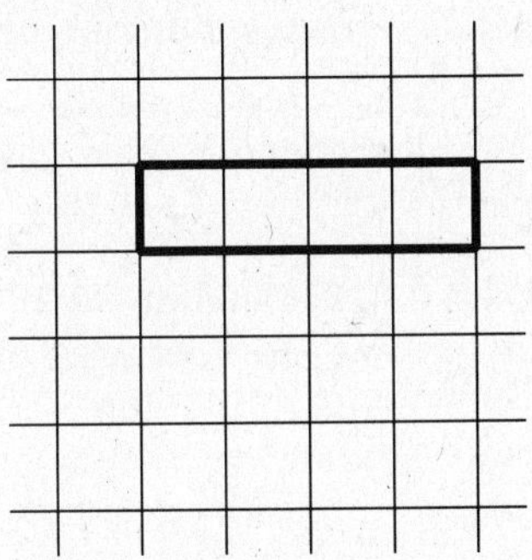

____

2. 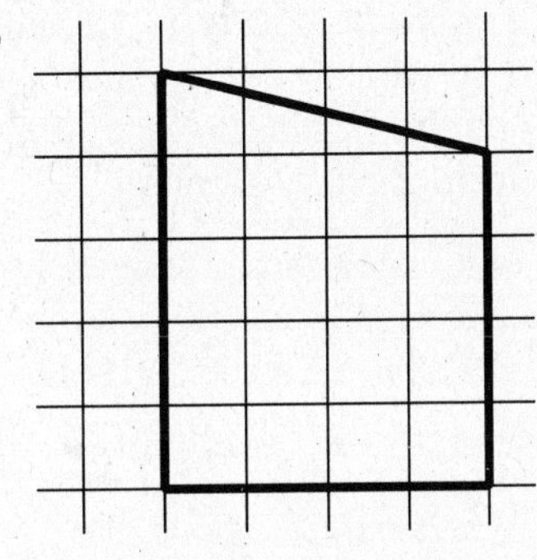

____

3. 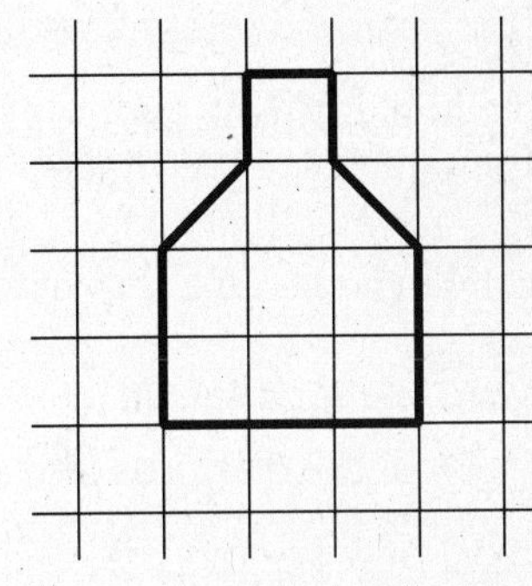

____

4. 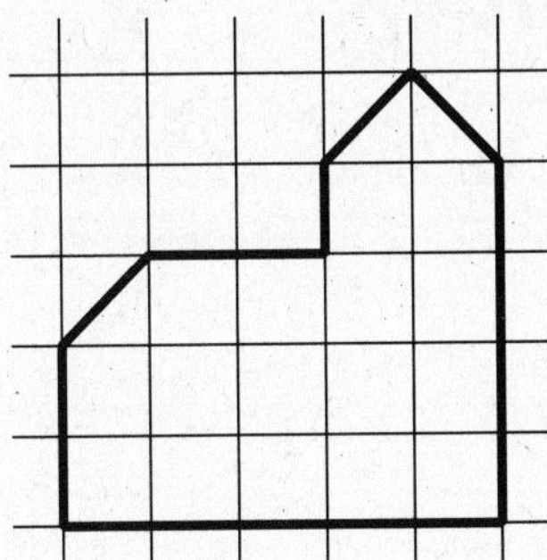

____

5. 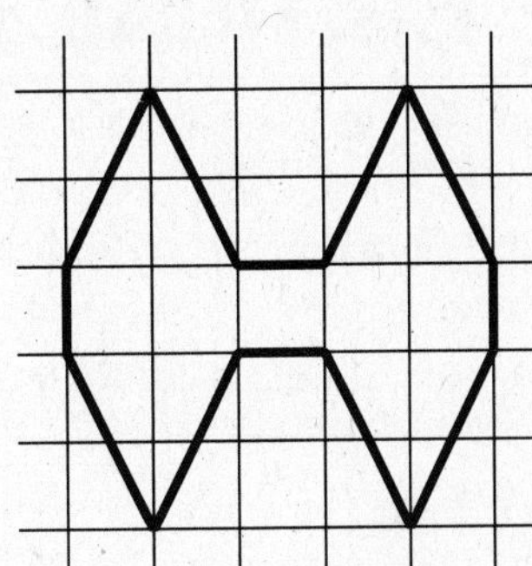

____

6. 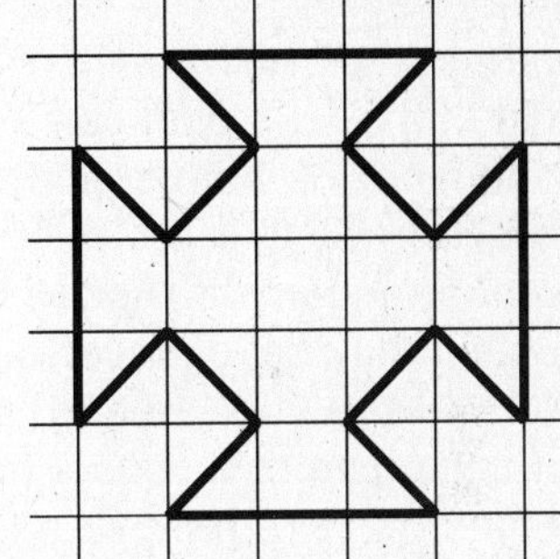

____

7. Draw a figure by connecting dots, leaving 3 unconnected dots inside. The area must be 6 square units.

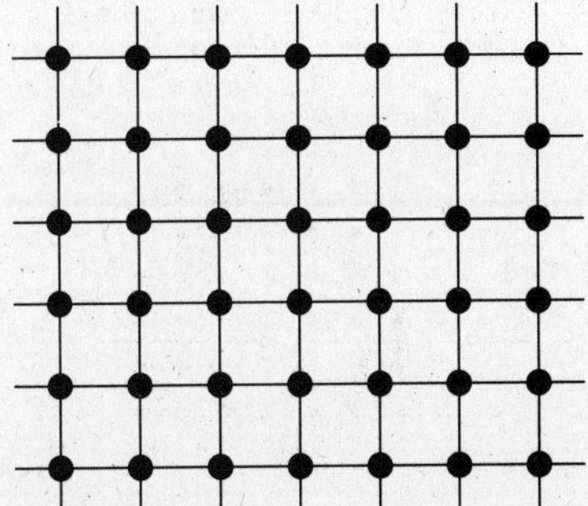

8. Draw a figure by connecting dots, leaving 3 unconnected dots inside. The area must be 7 square units.

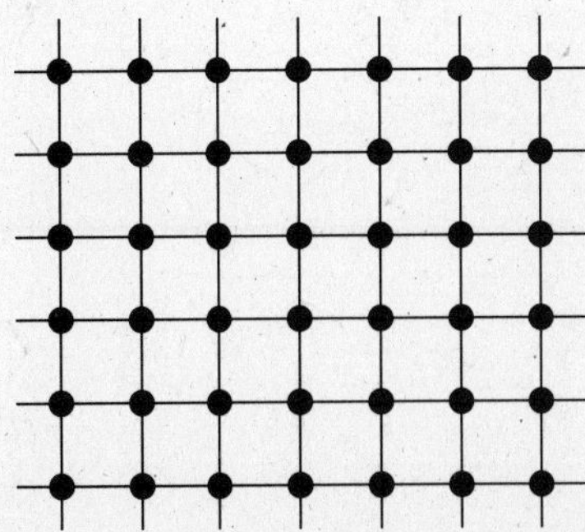

Teacher Notes

Use with
Objective 85
pages 308–309

Focus
Critical Thinking
Reasoning with Graphs and Charts

Materials
Grid paper

Overview
Students find the area of irregularly shaped figures and draw figures on a grid using the given specifications.

Teaching Suggestions
Ask students if they have ever wanted to rearrange the furniture in their bedroom. Explain that a floor plan can help them decide beforehand if the furniture will fit in a different arrangement. Ask students if they have pieces of furniture whose floor area is not in the shape of a square or rectangle. Explain that by using a grid, the floor area of these pieces can be determined. Point out the two small pictures on the top right side of the page. Explain that the shapes in both pictures have an area of 1 square unit.

Help students to see that in the second picture, the piece of the triangle in the upper square fits in the empty space in the lower square. ***Question:*** *How can you find the area of the figure in Problem 2?* [Count the 16 whole squares and piece the partial units together to form 2 square units.]

Have students explain which partial squares can be pieced together so that they have an area of 1 square unit.

In Problems 7 and 8, explain that in order for a dot to be unconnected it must be inside the figure.

Extension
Have students draw the floor plan of their kitchens and determine the floor area of each piece of furniture.

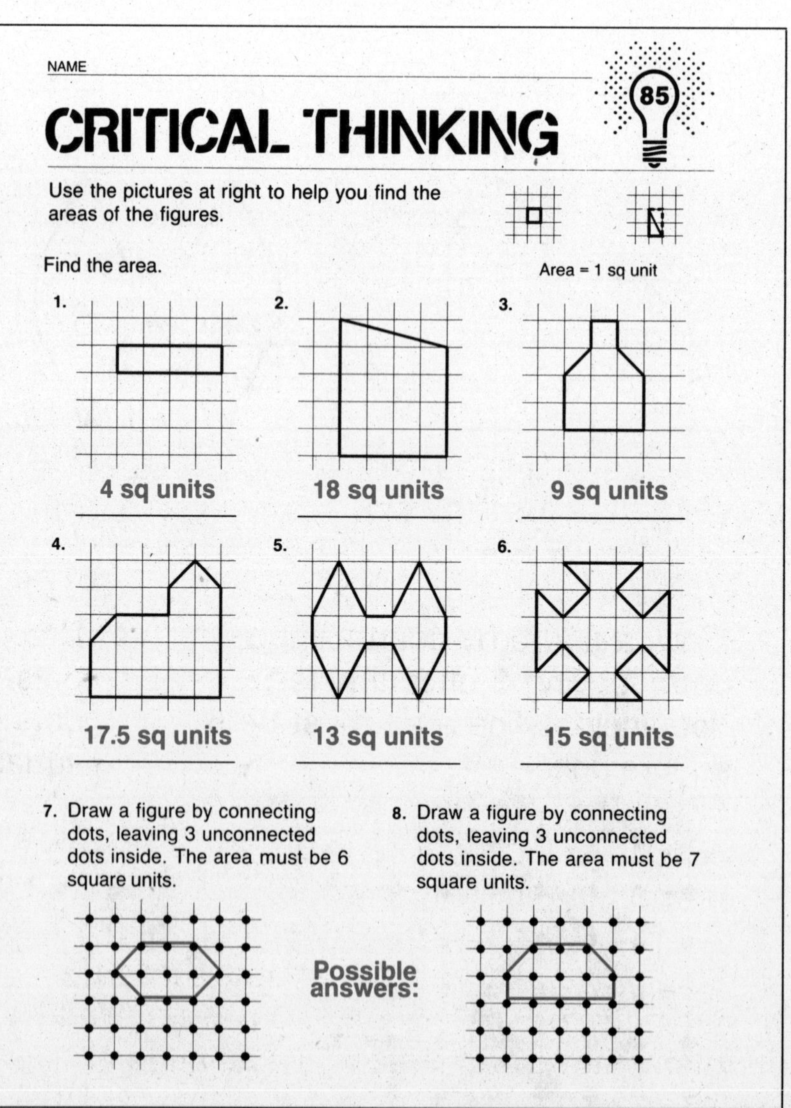

NAME
CRITICAL THINKING
85
Use the pictures at right to help you find the areas of the figures.
Area = 1 sq unit
Find the area.
1.
4 sq units
2.
18 sq units
3.
9 sq units
4.
17.5 sq units
5.
13 sq units
6.
15 sq units
7. Draw a figure by connecting dots, leaving 3 unconnected dots inside. The area must be 6 square units.
8. Draw a figure by connecting dots, leaving 3 unconnected dots inside. The area must be 7 square units.
Possible answers:

NAME ________________________________

PROBLEM SOLVING

To play *The Exchange Game,* you will need 6 pennies and 6 nickels. Place the coins on a game board as shown. Move the coins according to the following rules so that the pennies and the nickels exchange places, with the pennies on the right and the nickels on the left.

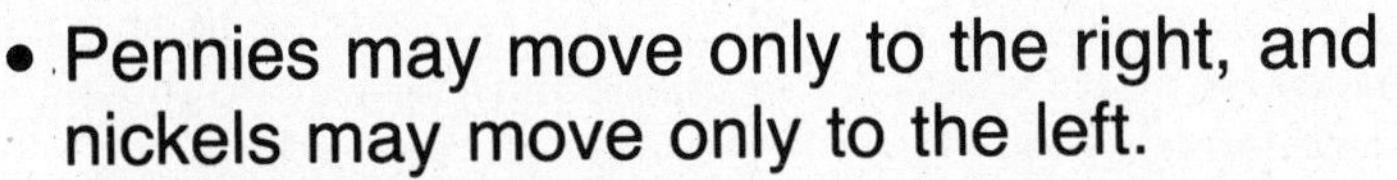

- Pennies may move only to the right, and nickels may move only to the left.
- A coin may move into an empty space next to it.
- A coin can only "jump" one or more coins of a different kind. There must be an empty space for the coin to land in.

1. How many moves does it take to exchange 1 penny and 1 nickel using three squares in a row? ____________

2. How many moves does it take to exchange 2 pennies and 2 nickels using five squares in a row? ____________

3. How many moves does it take to exchange 3 pennies and 3 nickels using seven squares in a row? ____________

4. Look for a pattern and use it to make a table up to 6 pennies and 6 nickels. How many moves will it take to exchange all 12 coins? ____________

Teacher Notes

Use with
Objective 86
pages 310–311

Focus
Problem Solving
Make a Table
Solve a Simpler Problem
Find a Pattern

Materials
6 pennies
6 nickels

Overview
Students try to determine the number of moves it takes to exchange 6 pennies on one side of the game board with 6 nickels on the other side of the board.

Teaching Suggestions
Have students make a game board consisting of 13 squares in a row like the one shown on the activity sheet. Explain the 3 rules of the game and make sure students understand the rules. Suggest that students *solve a simpler problem* (Problem 1), using their coins and 3 squares of their board. ***Question:*** *How many moves are needed to exchange 1 penny and 1 nickel?* [3 moves] Demonstrate the moves.

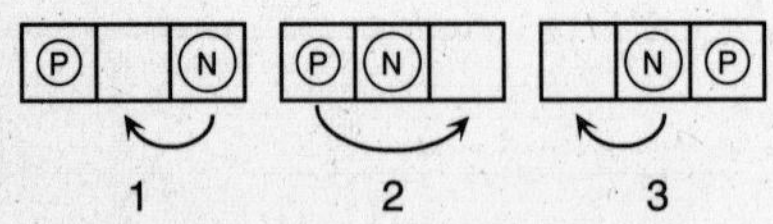

Have students *make a table* to record the number of moves needed to exchange pennies and nickels.

Number of coins		Number of moves
Pennies	Nickels	
1	1	3
2	2	8
3	3	15
4	4	24
5	5	35
6	6	48

Have students exchange 2 pennies and 2 nickels and record the number of moves. [8 moves]; 3 pennies and 3 nickels [15 moves].

Tell students to extend the table to 6 pennies and 6 nickels. ***Questions:*** *What pattern do you see in the "Number of moves" column?* [The differences between successive entries increase by 2.] *How many moves are needed for 5 pennies and 5 nickels?* [35]

Have students try to play the game making only 48 moves. To do this, they will need to move 2 or more of the same coins in succession.

NAME

PROBLEM SOLVING

86

To play *The Exchange Game,* you will need 6 pennies and 6 nickels. Place the coins on a game board as shown. Move the coins according to the following rules so that the pennies and the nickels exchange places, with the pennies on the right and the nickels on the left.

- Pennies may move only to the right, and nickels may move only to the left.
- A coin may move into an empty space next to it.
- A coin can "jump" only one coin of a different kind. There must be an empty space for the coin to land in.

1. How many moves does it take to exchange 1 penny and 1 nickel using three squares in a row? **3 moves**
2. How many moves does it take to exchange 2 pennies and 2 nickels using five squares in a row? **8 moves**
3. How many moves does it take to exchange 3 pennies and 3 nickels using seven squares in a row? **15 moves**
4. Look for a pattern and use it to make a table up to 6 pennies and 6 nickels. How many moves will it take to exchange all 12 coins? **48 moves**

NAME ______________________________

PROBLEM SOLVING

You want to make fruit mix for your math club meeting this week. Your grandmother's recipe for fruit mix, listed below, serves 8 people. Your math club has 96 members.

	Servings				
Fruit	8	16	24	48	96
pineapple	1 lb				
peaches	$1\frac{1}{2}$ lb				
pears	1 lb				
cherries	$\frac{1}{2}$ lb				
grapes	$\frac{1}{2}$ lb				
sugar	1 c				
orange juice	2 c				

1. Complete the table to find out how much of each ingredient you will need to serve more people.

2. Your grandmother makes her fruit mix for 8 in a 5-quart pot. What size pot will you need for each of these amounts?

16 servings: ______________ 24 servings: ______________

48 servings: ______________ 96 servings: ______________

3. You have a 20-gallon pot, and you need to make 96 servings. Will the pot be too large or too small? Explain your answer.

____

Teacher Notes

Use with
Objective 87
pages 312–313

Focus
Problem Solving
Use Logical Reasoning
Choose an Operation

Overview
Students *use logical reasoning* to complete a table showing the ingredients needed for larger amounts of a recipe.

Teaching Suggestions
Ask students for examples of recipes they or their parents use to make certain dishes. Discuss the number of servings that most recipes provide. Discuss which recipes might and might not be used to make larger numbers of servings. ***Questions:*** *If a recipe serves 8 people, could you still use the recipe if you wanted enough food to serve 16 people? How?* [Yes, by doubling the recipe] Explain that if a recipe is doubled, twice as much of each ingredient is needed.

Questions: *Which operation would you use to double a recipe?* [Possible responses: addition; multiplication] *By what number would you multiply the quantity of each ingredient to double the recipe?* [2] In Problem 1, have students complete the column for 16 servings. Have students complete the table.

For Problems 2–3, explain that one recipe of the fruit mix fills a 5-quart pot. ***Questions:*** *If you double the recipe, how large must the pot be?* [2 times as large or 10 quarts]

Extension
Have students look in a local newspaper for a recipe. Ask students to determine the number of servings the recipe provides and the number provided when the recipe is doubled and tripled. Then have students make a table listing the ingredients and quantities needed when the recipe is doubled and tripled.

NAME ____________________

PROBLEM SOLVING

You want to make fruit mix for your math club meeting this week. Your grandmother's recipe for fruit mix, listed below, serves 8 people. Your math club has 96 members.

	Servings				
Fruit	8	16	24	48	96
pineapple	1 lb	2 lb	3 lb	6 lb	12 lb
peaches	$1\frac{1}{2}$ lb	3 lb	$4\frac{1}{2}$ lb	9 lb	18 lb
pears	1 lb	2 lb	3 lb	6 lb	12 lb
cherries	$\frac{1}{2}$ lb	1 lb	$1\frac{1}{2}$ lb	3 lb	6 lb
grapes	$\frac{1}{2}$ lb	1 lb	$1\frac{1}{2}$ lb	3 lb	6 lb
sugar	1 c	2 c	3 c	6 c	12 c
orange juice	2 c	4 c	6 c	12 c	24 c

1. Complete the table to find out how much of each ingredient you will need to serve more people.

2. Your grandmother makes her fruit mix for 8 in a 5-quart pot. What size pot will you need for each of these amounts?

16 servings: **10-quart** 24 servings: **15-quart**

48 servings: **30-quart** 96 servings: **60-quart**

3. You have a 20-gallon pot, and you need to make 96 servings. Will the pot be too large or too small? Explain your answer.

Too large. You only need a 15-gallon pot.

NAME ______________________________

CRITICAL THINKING

Dr. Kenobi designed an experiment to test whether dogs are color blind, as has been thought. There were three lighted screens, two the same color, and the third a different one. He trained several dogs to choose the different-colored screen by pushing it with their noses. If they made the right choice, they received a snack pellet. The table shows the number of correct choices made by the dogs.

Color	Position of Screen	
	Middle	Shifting
Blue	91 out of 100 trials	82 out of 100 trials
Red	26 out of 100 trials	19 out of 100 trials
Yellow	31 out of 100 trials	16 out of 100 trials

1. Would the result of the trials with the blue screen always in the middle position show that the dogs can see color? Explain.

____

____

____

2. What conclusions might Dr. Kenobi draw from these results?

____

____

Teacher Notes

Use with
Objective 88
pages 314–317

Focus
Critical Thinking
Evaluating Evidence and Conclusions
Drawing Conclusions
Explaining Reasoning

Overview
Students evaluate experimental results shown in a table, draw a conclusion based on their evaluation, and explain their reasoning.

Teaching Suggestions
Explain that color blindness is more common in boys than girls. Explain that instead of seeing shades of blue and green, most color-blind people see shades of gray, which allows them to distinguish most colors. ***Questions:*** *According to the table, which color did the dogs correctly identify most of the time when it was in the middle position?* [Blue] *Which color were the dogs able to identify more frequently than the other colors when they were not in the middle position?* [Blue] As students answer Problem 1, ask them to think of factors Dr. Kenobi did not consider when setting up the experiment. Guide students to understand that factors such as color blindness and being rewarded for pushing the middle screen may have affected the results of the experiment.

Extension
Have students discuss how Dr. Kenobi might improve his experiment to test for color blindness in dogs. One possible experiment is to run the same experiment as before but substitute a shade of gray for each of the colors. Then compare the results from both experiments to determine if they are similar.

NAME ______________________

CRITICAL THINKING

Dr. Kenobi designed an experiment to test whether dogs are color blind, as has been thought. There were three lighted screens, two the same color, and the third a different one. He trained several dogs to choose the different-colored screen by pushing it with their noses. If they made the right choice, they received a snack pellet. The table shows the number of correct choices made by the dogs.

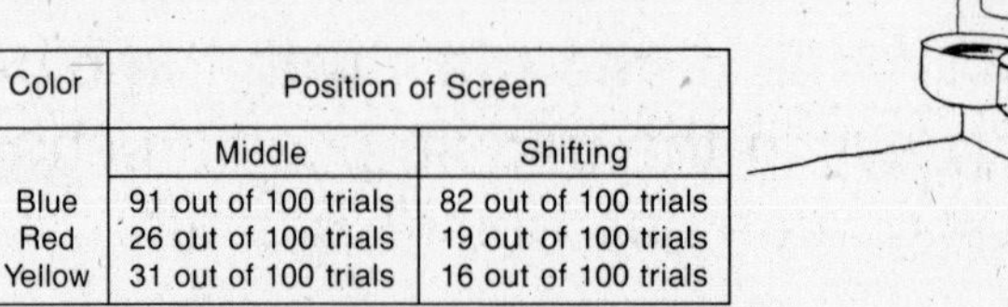

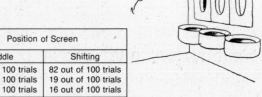

Color	Position of Screen	
	Middle	Shifting
Blue	91 out of 100 trials	82 out of 100 trials
Red	26 out of 100 trials	19 out of 100 trials
Yellow	31 out of 100 trials	16 out of 100 trials

1. Would the result of the trials with the blue screen always in the middle position show that the dogs can see color? Explain.

   No; they might be seeing the difference in value (light or dark), or learning to push the middle screen to get a reward.

2. What conclusions might Dr. Kenobi draw from these results?

   Possible answer: Dogs can see differences of value but not of color.

NAME ______________________________

VISUAL THINKING

Write the letter of each shape next to the number of an identical shape.

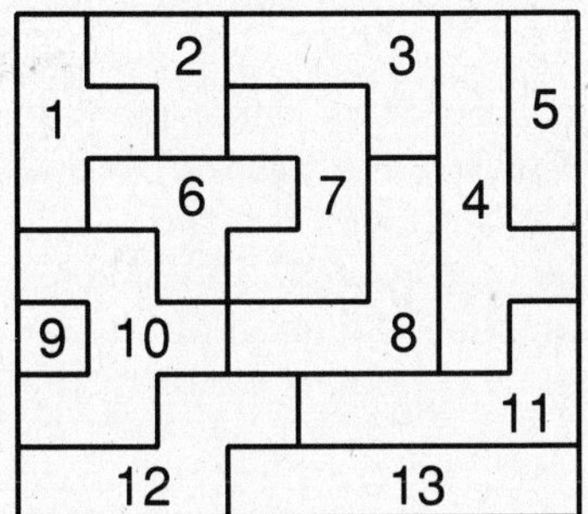

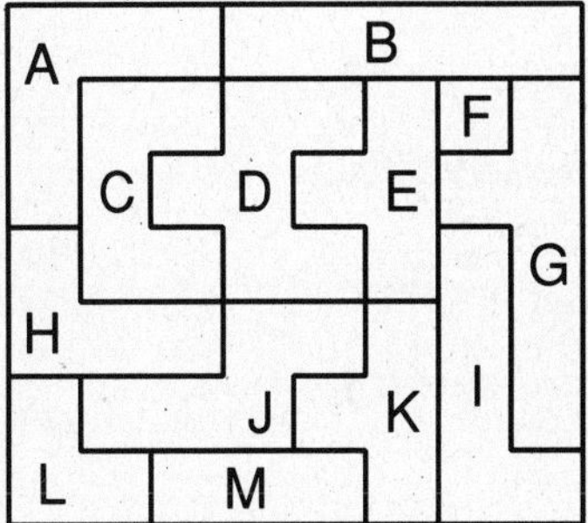

1. ________ 2. ________ 3. ________ 4. ________

5. ________ 6. ________ 7. ________ 8. ________

9. ________ 10. ________ 11. ________ 12. ________ 13. ________

14. Ring the letters of the two figures that are the same.

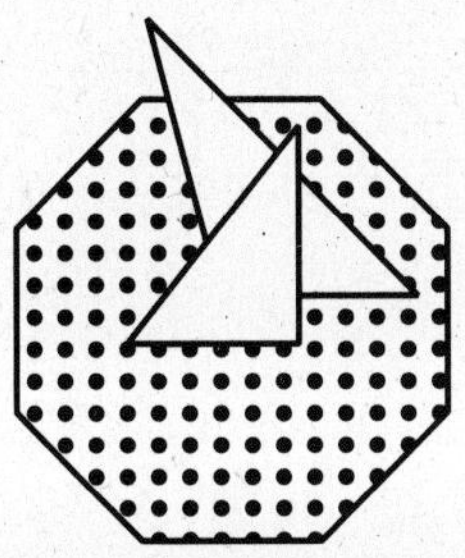

a.

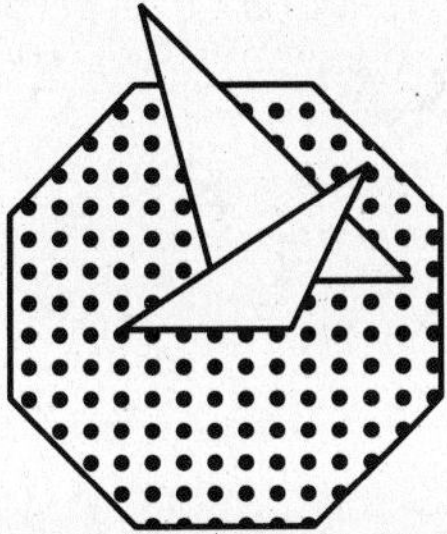

b.

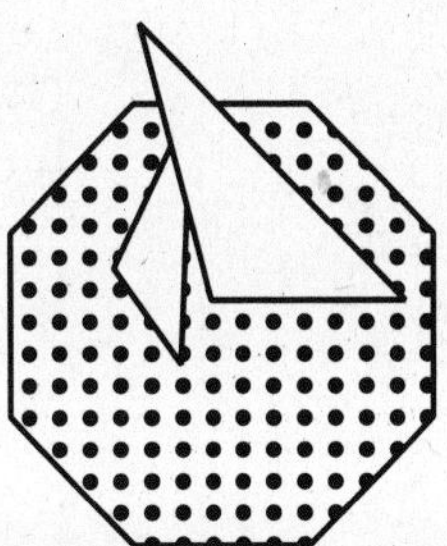

c.

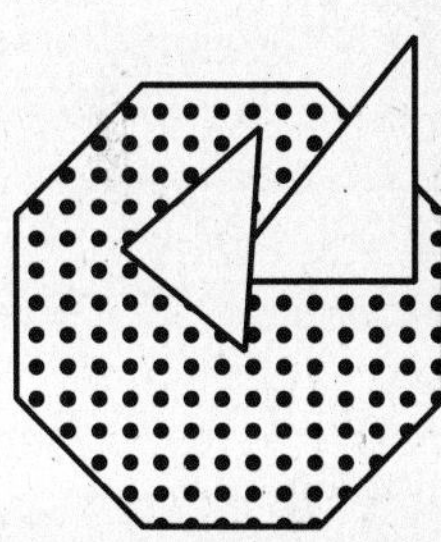

d.

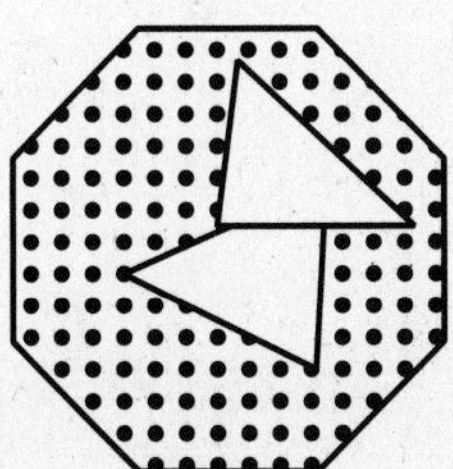

e.

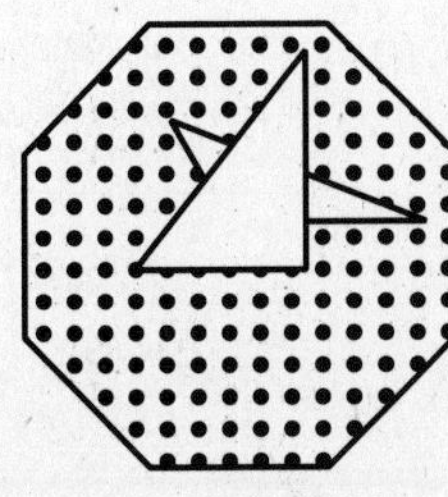

f.

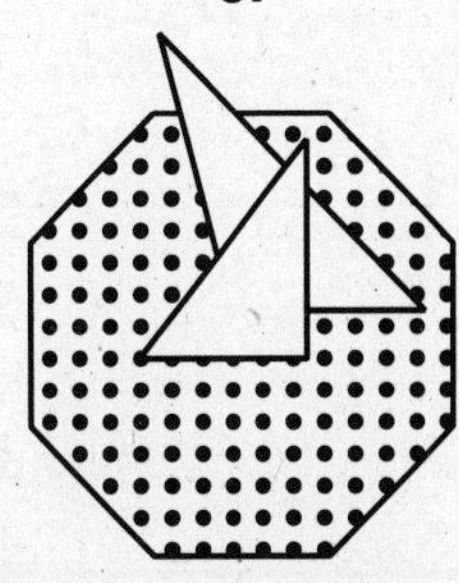

g.

h.

Teacher Notes

Use with
Objective 89
pages 320–321

Focus
Visual Thinking
Spatial Perception

Materials
Visual Thinking
transparency (optional)

Overview
Students *use spatial perception* to identify congruent shapes.

Teaching Suggestions
Draw the following optical illusion on the chalkboard.

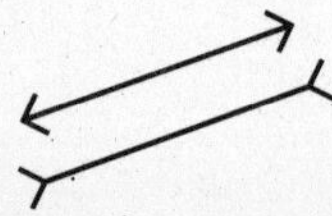

Question: *Are the two lines the same length?* [Possible answer: no] Explain that the lines are the same length. Guide students to understand that, even though one line looks longer than the other, this is an incorrect conclusion. In this case students should compare the lengths by tracing or measuring.

If students need help getting started, direct their attention to the first box of shapes. ***Questions:*** *Is shape 1 identical to any other shape in the box?* [Yes, shape 6.] *How could you prove that they are the same?* [By measuring or by tracing out one shape and placing it over the other.] *Is shape 5 identical to shape 11?* [No] *How do you know?* [They are not the same shape.]

Then have the students complete Problems 1–13 by matching each numbered shape in the first box with a lettered shape in the second box.

Alternate Approach: Complete the exercise as a class using the optional transparency.

Have students look at Problem 14. ***Questions:*** *How do the dots behind each figure affect how you see the figure?* [The dots cause your eyes to focus on them rather than the shapes of the figures.] Explain how you found the two identical figures. [Possible response: Counted the dots next to or below each figure]

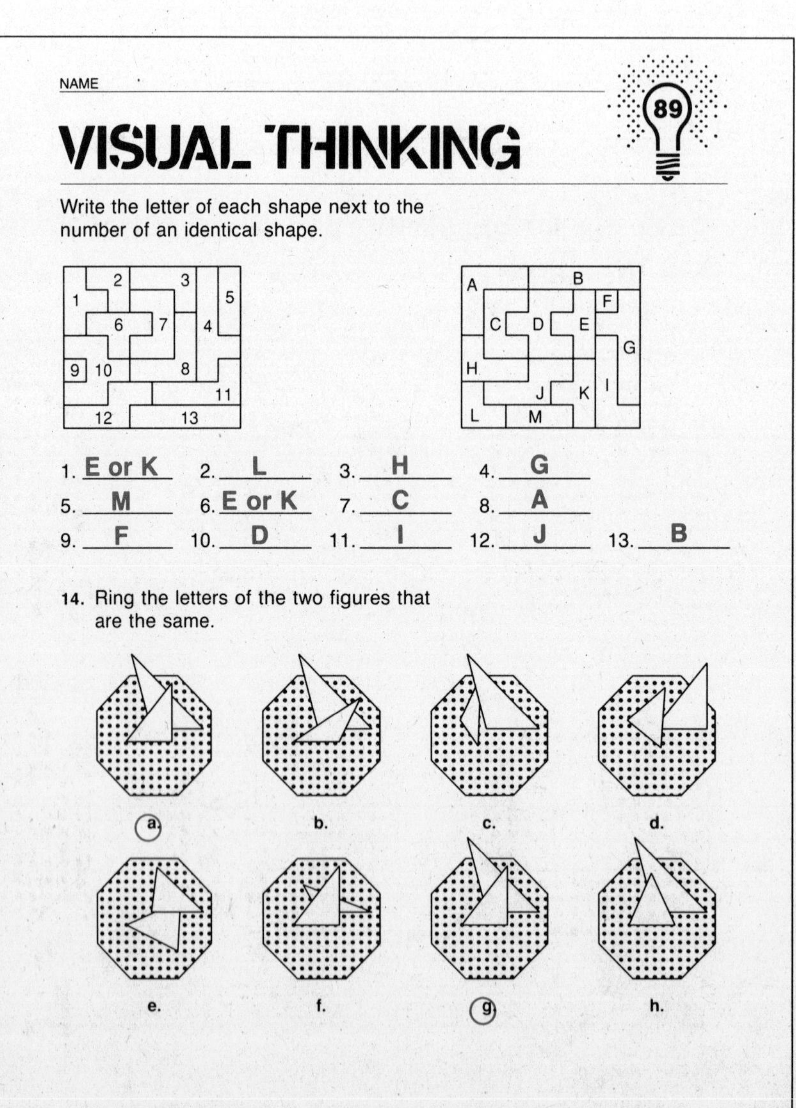

NAME ____

VISUAL THINKING

Draw and number all the lines of symmetry for each figure.

1.

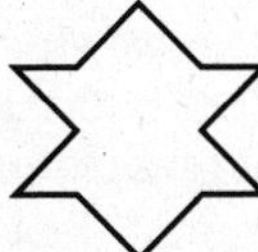

2.

3.

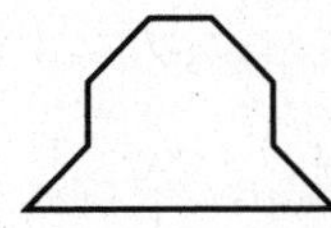

4.

5.

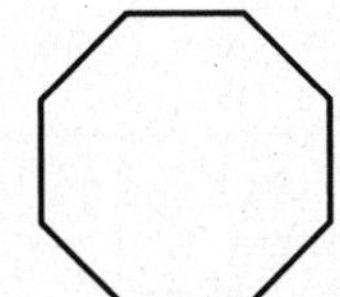

6.

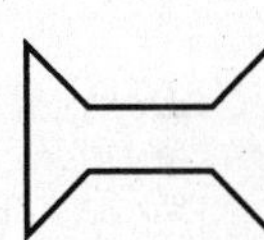

7.

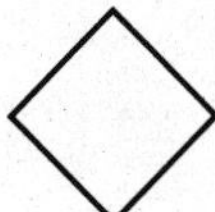

8.

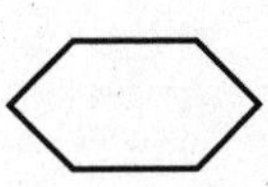

9.

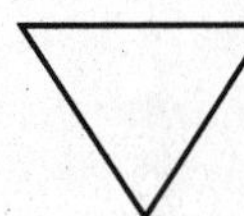

Write yes if the dotted line is a line of symmetry. Write no if it is not.

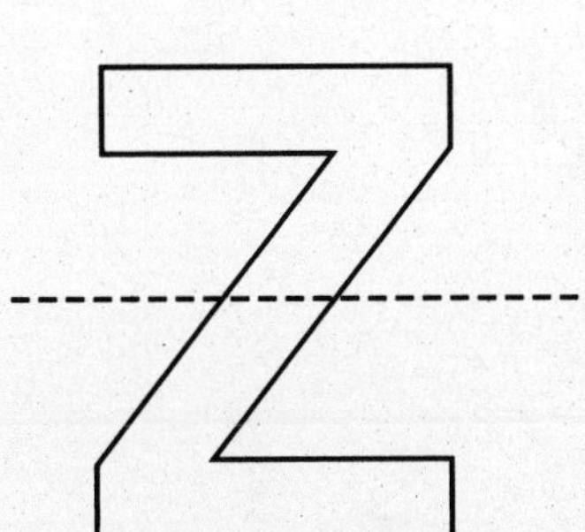

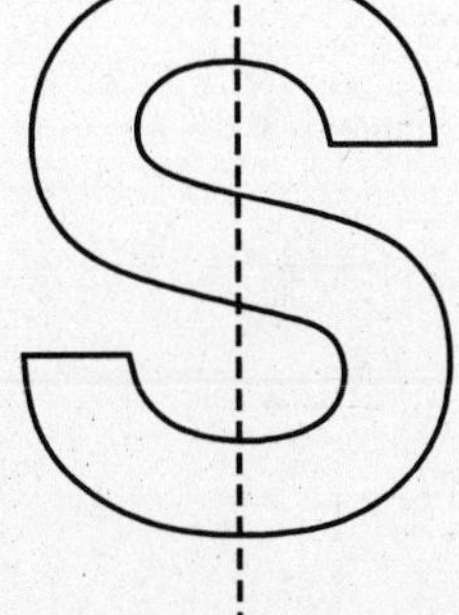

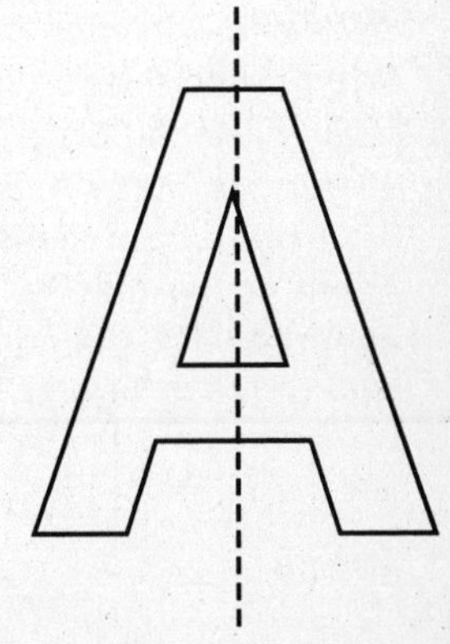

10. ____________ 11. ____________ 12. ____________

Teacher Notes

Use with
Objective 90
pages 322–323

Focus
Visual Thinking
Visual Patterns

Materials
Visual Thinking transparency (optional)

Overview
Students use *visual patterns* to identify lines of symmetry.

Teaching Suggestions
Remind students that a shape is symmetrical if the part on one side of the line of symmetry matches the part on the other side. Have students point to various symmetric objects, shapes, letters, or numbers in the classroom and identify a line of symmetry for each. ***Questions:*** *Can a figure have more than one line of symmetry?* [Yes] *Is there a limit to the number of lines of symmetry a shape may have?* [No, not as long as the parts on either side of the line match.]

Direct students' attention to Exercises 5 and 7. ***Questions:*** *How many lines of symmetry does each polygon have?* [8;4] *What do you notice about the sides of each polygon and its number of lines of symmetry?* [The number of sides is the same as the number of lines of symmetry.] Explain that this is true only for regular polygons.

Alternate Approach: If students have trouble visualizing a line or lines of symmetry, have them trace and cut out the shapes. They can fold the shapes to discover lines of symmetry.

Extension
Extend Problems 10–12 by asking students which other capital letters can be written so they are symmetric. [Besides A, which is shown, B, D, E, H, I, K, M, O, T, U, W, X, Y] Have students find and cut out pictures of objects in magazines that show symmetry. Have them draw the line or lines of symmetry. Display the pictures on the bulletin board.

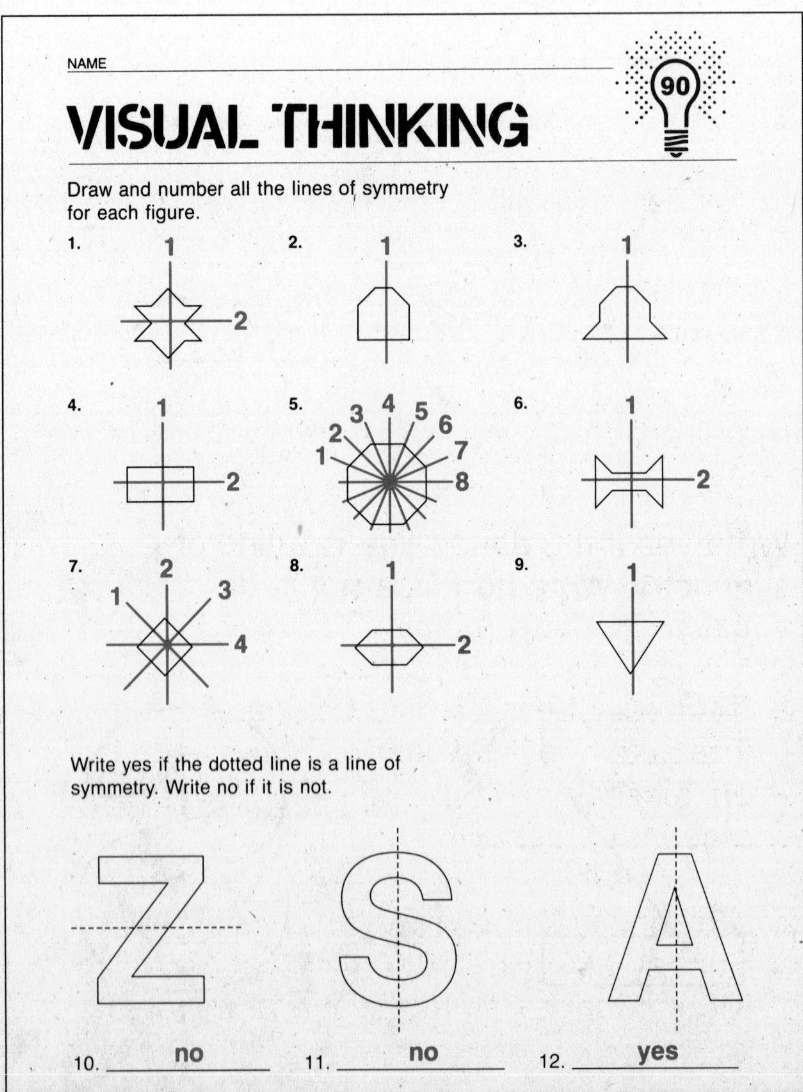
NAME
90
VISUAL THINKING
Draw and number all the lines of symmetry for each figure.
1.
2.
3.
4.
5.
6.
7.
8.
9.
Write yes if the dotted line is a line of symmetry. Write no if it is not.
10. no
11. no
12. yes

NAME ______________________________

PROBLEM SOLVING

Tina lives in New York City, Leon lives in Los Angeles, and Kit lives in Chicago. The chart below shows the calling rates for various times and days. The calling rate is determined from the city where the call is made. The day rate is \$0.015 per 50 miles each minute.

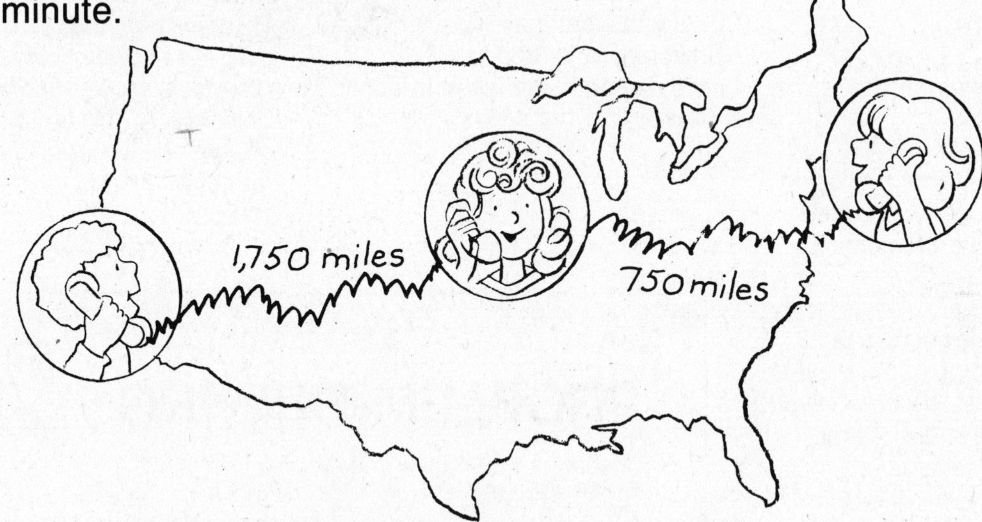

	M	T	W	T	F	S	S
8 A.M. to 5 P.M.	▩	▩	▩	▩	▩	☐	☐
5 P.M. to 11 P.M.	▨	▨	▨	▨	▨	☐	▨
11 P.M. to 8 A.M.	☐	☐	☐	☐	☐	☐	☐

Direct dialed out of state	▩ Day Rate	▨ Evening: $\frac{1}{3}$ discount	☐ Night: $\frac{1}{2}$ discount

1. How much will it cost if Leon calls Kit at 6 P.M. on Saturday for 13 minutes, then calls Tina for 5 minutes? ______________

2. If Kit calls Leon on Thursday at 4 P.M. for 7 minutes, for how long can she call Tina on Tuesday at 11 A.M. to spend the same amount of money? ______________

3. Which would cost Tina less: calling Kit on Sunday at 6 P.M. for 20 minutes, or calling Kit on Monday at 10 A.M. for 12 minutes?

____

Use after pages 324–325.

Teacher Notes

Use with
Objective 91
pages 324–325

Focus
Problem Solving
Use Logical Reasoning
Solve a Simpler Problem

Materials
State or national maps

Overview
Students *use logical reasoning* to analyze a telephone rate chart, and solve problems based on the rates.

Teaching Suggestions
Ask students if they have ever telephoned a friend or relative in a distant city. Explain that long-distance telephone companies charge different phone rates depending on the day and time you call. Ask students if they know on which day or days the telephone companies charge the lowest rate.

Direct students' attention to the chart and map on the activity sheet. Make sure they understand the labeling system used. If necessary, direct students by asking questions.

Questions: *Which rate will Leon be charged if he calls Kit at 8 A.M. on Monday?* [Day rate] *How much is the day rate?* [$0.015 per 50 miles per minute] *How many miles are there between Leon and Kit?* [1,750 miles] *How many groups of 50 miles?* [1,750 ÷ 50 = 35] *How much will Leon be charged per minute?* [35 × 0.015 = 0.525] *How much will Leon be charged per minute at the night rate?* [0.525 ÷ 2 = 0.2625] Then have them do Problems 1–3.

In Problem 3, remind students that there are different rates depending on the day and time when the call is made.

Extension
Have students think of one person in the United States whom they would like to telephone. Provide students with a table showing the distance between cities, or have them determine the appproximate distance from a map. Then have students use the chart on the pupil page to determine what the telephone charge would be for a call made on various days and times.

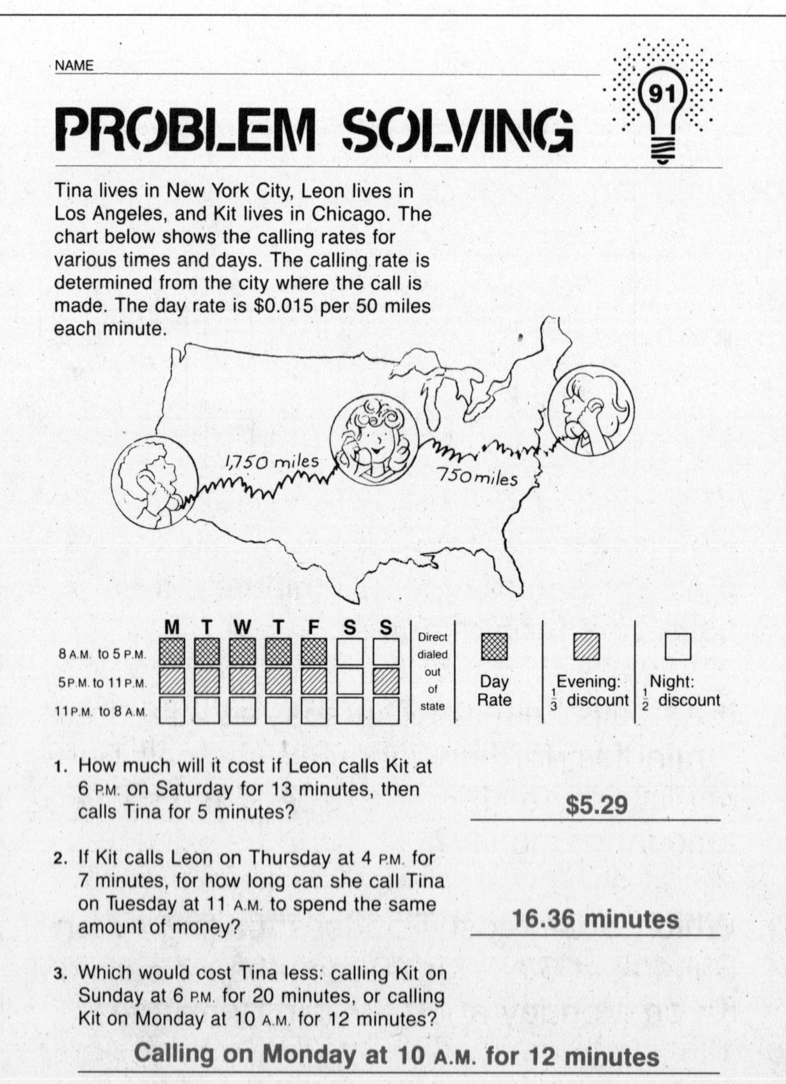

NAME ____________________

91

PROBLEM SOLVING

Tina lives in New York City, Leon lives in Los Angeles, and Kit lives in Chicago. The chart below shows the calling rates for various times and days. The calling rate is determined from the city where the call is made. The day rate is $0.015 per 50 miles each minute.

Direct dialed out of state	M	T	W	T	F	S	S
8 A.M. to 5 P.M.	Day	Day	Day	Day	Day	Night	Night
5 P.M. to 11 P.M.	Evening	Evening	Evening	Evening	Evening	Night	Evening
11 P.M. to 8 A.M.	Night	Night	Night	Night	Night	Night	Night

Day Rate | Evening: $\frac{1}{3}$ discount | Night: $\frac{1}{2}$ discount

1. How much will it cost if Leon calls Kit at 6 P.M. on Saturday for 13 minutes, then calls Tina for 5 minutes? **$5.29**

2. If Kit calls Leon on Thursday at 4 P.M. for 7 minutes, for how long can she call Tina on Tuesday at 11 A.M. to spend the same amount of money? **16.36 minutes**

3. Which would cost Tina less: calling Kit on Sunday at 6 P.M. for 20 minutes, or calling Kit on Monday at 10 A.M. for 12 minutes?
Calling on Monday at 10 A.M. for 12 minutes

NAME ______________________________

PROBLEM SOLVING

John works in a warehouse. He needs to stack boxes like those shown at the right. Boxes must be stacked with their lids on the top. A larger box cannot be stacked on top of a smaller box.

Top
1 ft
3 ft
2 ft

Top
3 ft
T
3 ft
2 ft

1. Show all the different stacks of 3 boxes John can make. Two stacks have been drawn for you.

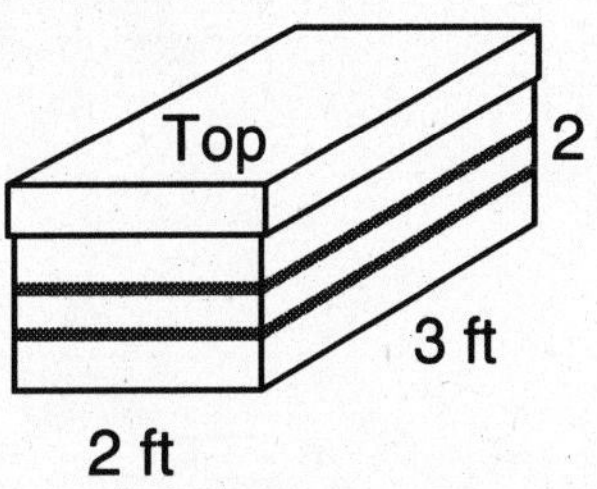

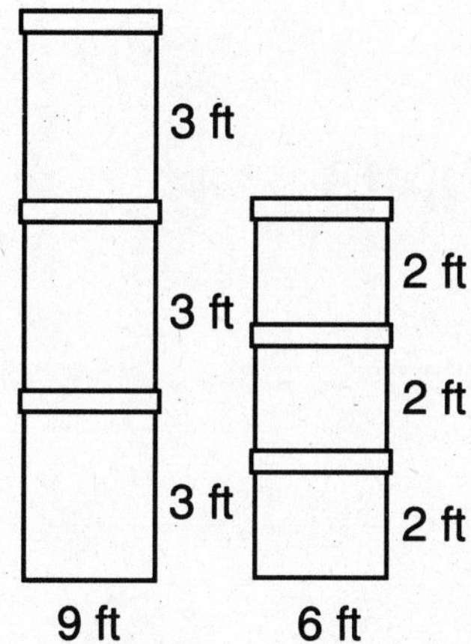

2. How many different heights can John make using any 3 boxes? ____________

3. John also has some boxes that are 6 inches wide and 8 inches long. They are 4 inches, 5 inches, or 7 inches high. How many different heights can he make using 3 of these boxes? ____________

4. Another type of box John has comes in three heights: 1 inch, 7 inches, and 8 inches. All the boxes have the same length and the same width. How many different heights can he make using any 3 of these boxes? ____________

Teacher Notes

Use with
Objective 92
pages 326–327

Focus
Problem Solving
Draw a Picture
Use Logical Reasoning

Overview
Students *draw a picture* of each different way that three boxes with the same bases and different heights can be stacked.

Teaching Suggestions
Be sure students understand that all boxes must be stacked with their lids on top, so that only the heights are a factor in determining the various possible combinations. Discuss the two possible stacks shown on the activity page.

For Problem 1, have students *draw a picture* of the various combinations. Encourage them to systematically organize their work to account for all possibilities.

Questions: *How many combinations are possible using boxes all the same height?* [3 combinations] *How many combinations are possible using only two boxes of the same height?* [6 combinations] *How many combinations are possible using boxes of all different heights?* [1 combination] There are 10 different ways to stack the three boxes.

For Problem 2, suggest that students first label each picture with the height of the stack of boxes. Then it is a simple matter to eliminate any duplications in heights.

For Problems 3 and 4, students should use a systematic procedure for listing all the possibilities.

Extension
Suppose there were 3 sizes of boxes, all of the same length and width, with heights of 3 in., 4 in., or 5 in. List the ways the boxes could be stacked so that they would fit between two shelves that are 12 in. apart. In each case, use the greatest number of boxes possible.
[5 in., 5 in.; 5 in., 4 in., 3 in.; 5 in., 3 in., 3 in.; 4 in., 4 in., 4 in.; 4 in., 4 in., 3 in.; 4 in., 3 in., 3 in.; 3 in., 3 in., 3 in., 3 in.]

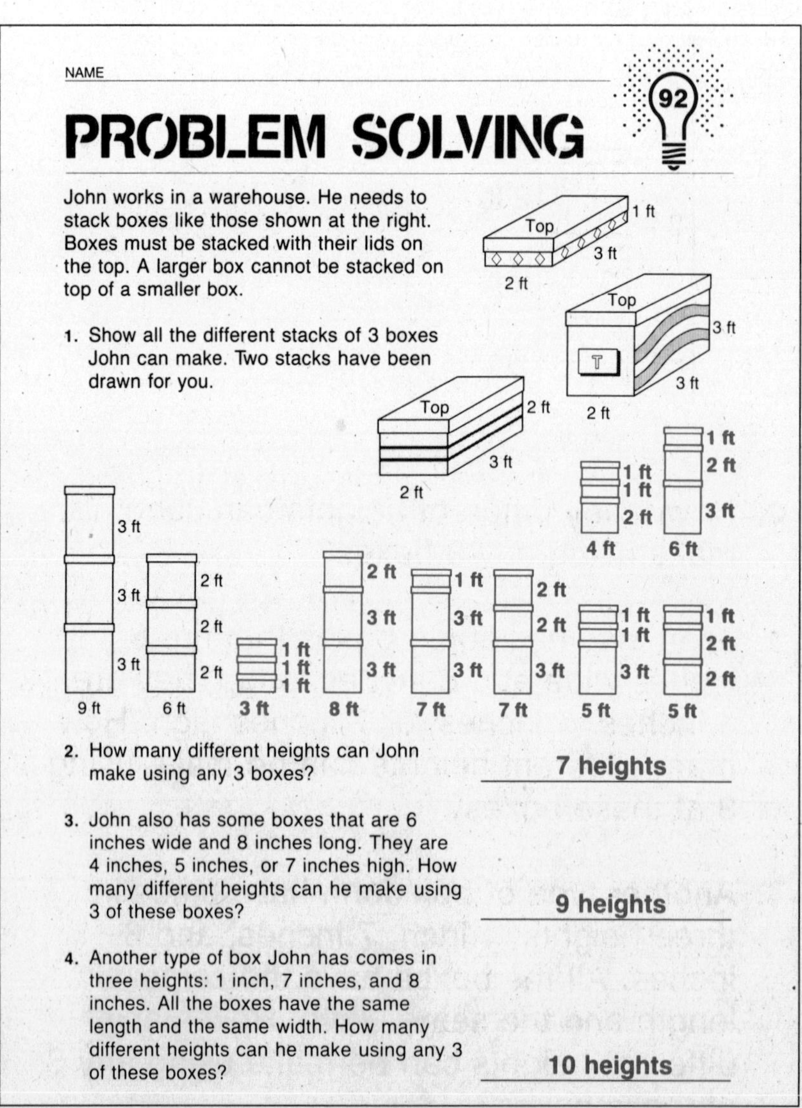

NAME ____________________

92

PROBLEM SOLVING

John works in a warehouse. He needs to stack boxes like those shown at the right. Boxes must be stacked with their lids on the top. A larger box cannot be stacked on top of a smaller box.

1. Show all the different stacks of 3 boxes John can make. Two stacks have been drawn for you.

2. How many different heights can John make using any 3 boxes? **7 heights**

3. John also has some boxes that are 6 inches wide and 8 inches long. They are 4 inches, 5 inches, or 7 inches high. How many different heights can he make using 3 of these boxes? **9 heights**

4. Another type of box John has comes in three heights: 1 inch, 7 inches, and 8 inches. All the boxes have the same length and the same width. How many different heights can he make using any 3 of these boxes? **10 heights**

NAME ______________________________

VISUAL THINKING

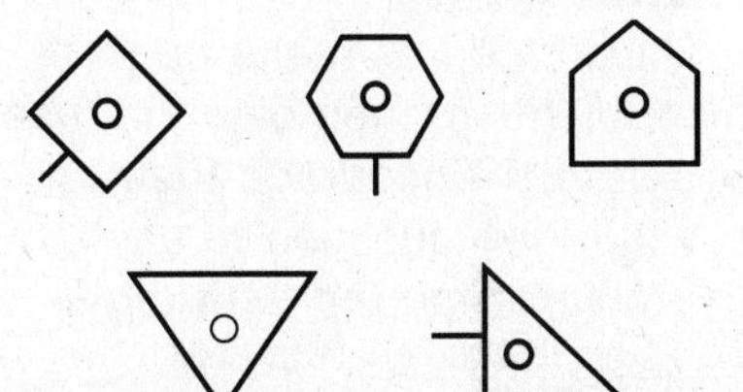

These products are made by Zeepo.

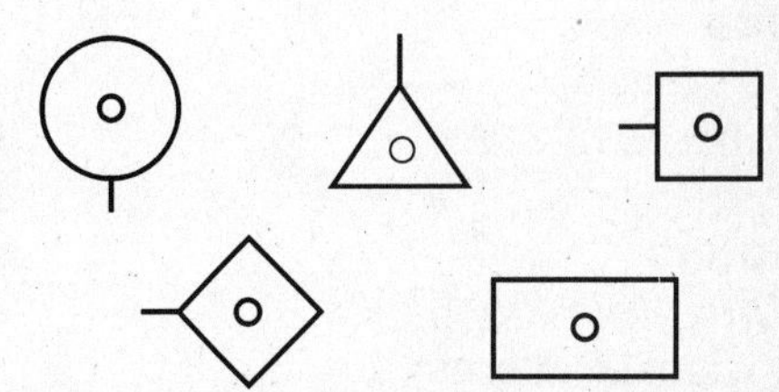

These products are made by Jeepo.

1. Which of the following are products made by Zeepo?

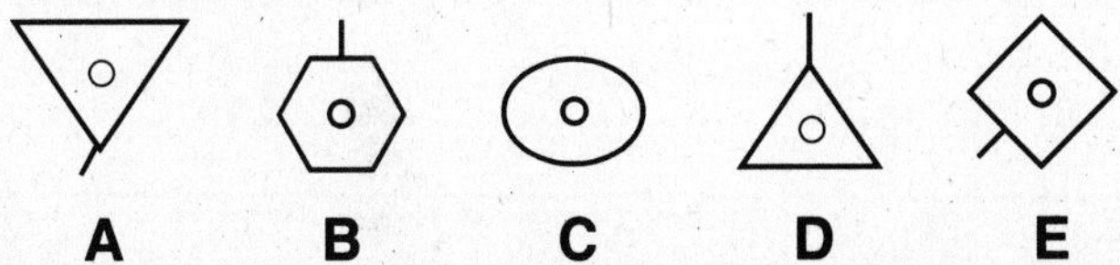

____

These products are Dino products.

These are Lino products.

2. Which of the following could be made by Dino?

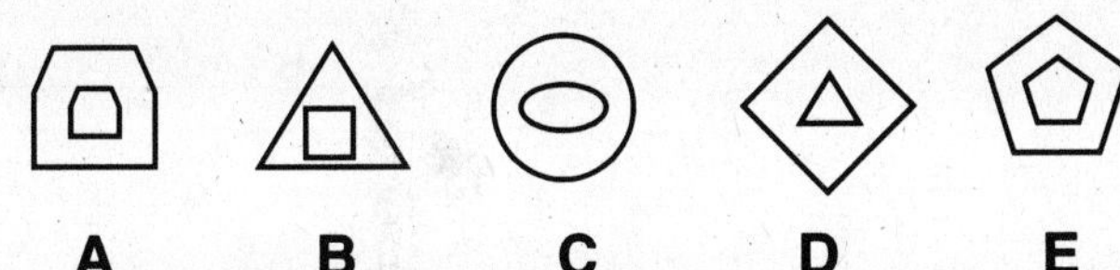

____

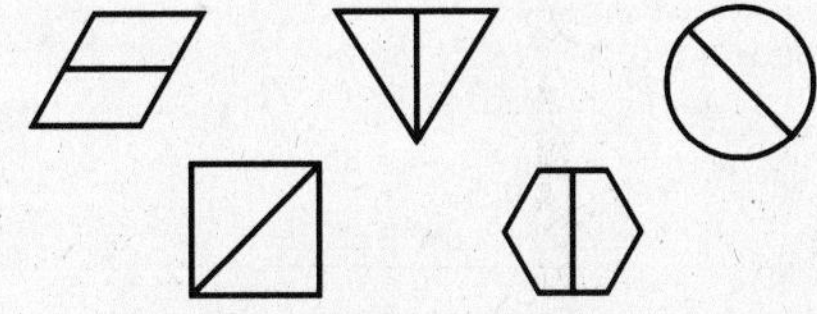

These are Kalina products.

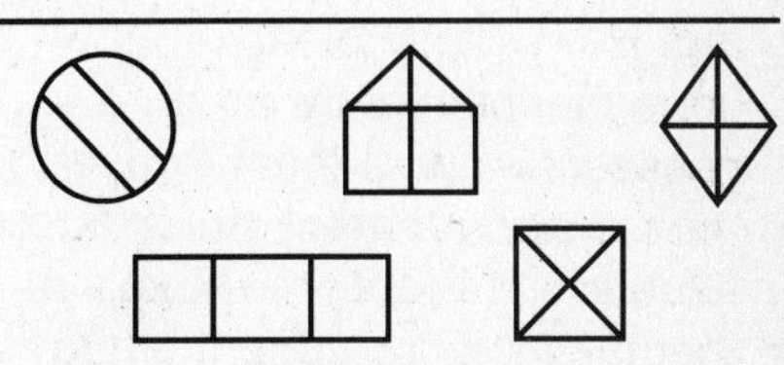

These are Jalina products.

3. Which of the following could be made by Jalina?

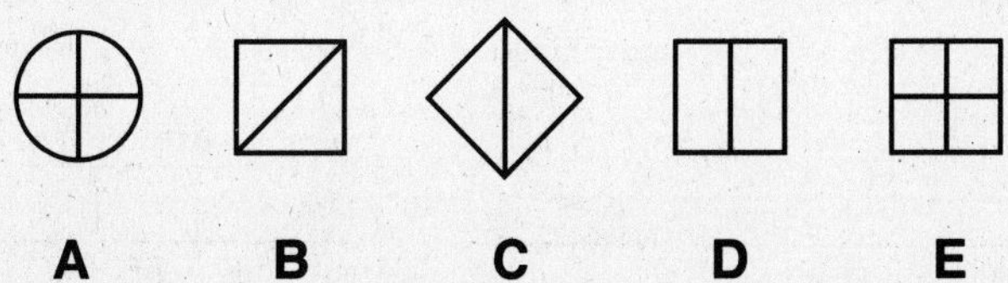

____

Teacher Notes

Use with
Objective 93
pages 328–329

Focus
Visual Thinking
Visual Patterns

Overview
Students analyze sets of shapes to recognize patterns and then use that pattern to classify other shapes.

For Problem 2, have students read the question. ***Question:*** *How is each of Dino's products similar?* [Each product contains a smaller version of its shape inside it.]

Have students read Problem 3. ***Question:*** *How are Jalina's products similar?* [Each product has two lines inside it.]

Extension
Have students make up three problems of their own that use patterns. Encourage them to write their question to each problem first and then draw their "products." When students have completed making their three problems, have them trade papers and answer each other's problems.

Teaching Suggestions
Draw a triangle, a square, a rectangle, and a pentagon on the chalkboard. ***Question:*** *What is similar about these figures?* [Each figure consists of straight lines and angles.] Draw a circle, a half circle, and a crescent shape next to the first set on the board. ***Question:*** *What is similar about these figures?* [Each figure contains an arc.] Draw an octagon below the two sets and discuss how the octagon belongs to the first set because it consists of straight lines and angles; it does not contain an arc. Have the students do the page independently, or, if necessary, direct them through the problems. Direct students' attention to Problem 1. Explain that the question asks them to find the products that are made by Zeepo by matching the shapes with those at the top of the page.

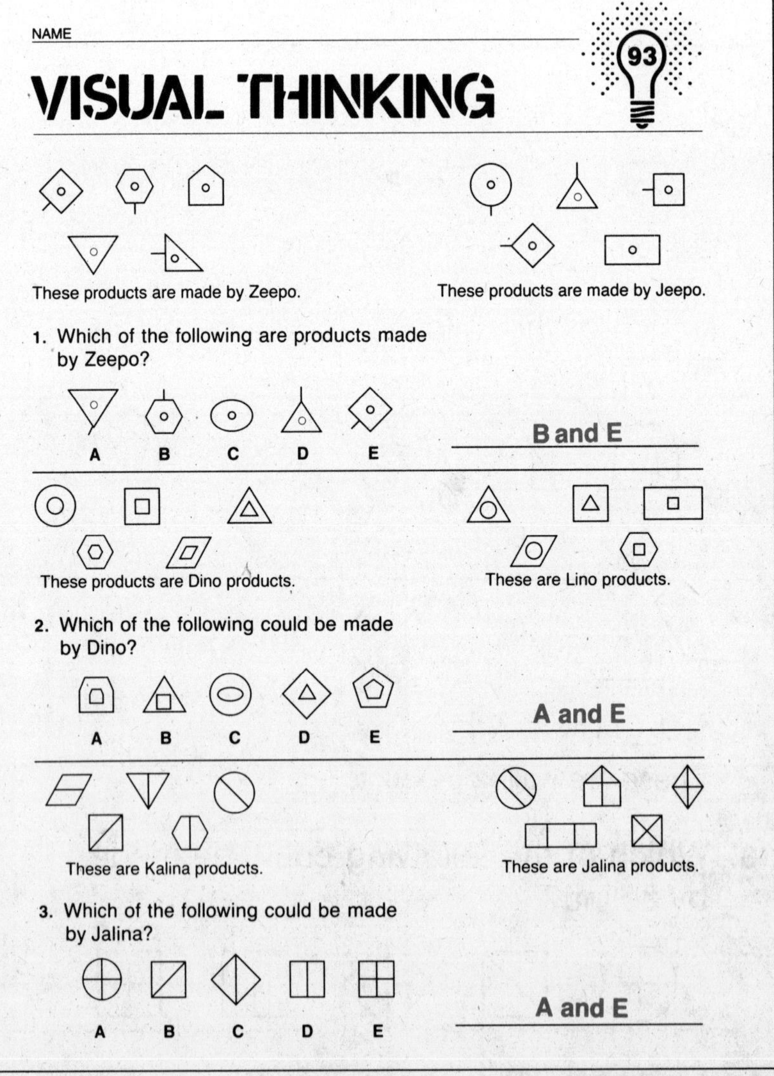
NAME
93
VISUAL THINKING
These products are made by Zeepo.
These products are made by Jeepo.
1. Which of the following are products made by Zeepo?
A B C D E
B and E
These products are Dino products.
These are Lino products.
2. Which of the following could be made by Dino?
A B C D E
A and E
These are Kalina products.
These are Jalina products.
3. Which of the following could be made by Jalina?
A B C D E
A and E

NAME ______________________________

PROBLEM SOLVING

Ms. Adams will be installing a laser beam security system in her jewelry store. The floor will be covered with square tiles and the walls will be mirrored to reflect the laser beam. The source of the beam and the receiver will be placed in different corners.

The beam travels in a straight line the same height off the floor. It must pass over every square floor tile as it travels from the source to the receiver to make the room secure. To maintain its path, the beam must approach the wall and reflect off the wall at a 45° angle.

It is important to determine the laser beam's path to ensure that the entire room is secure and that the display counters will not be placed in its path and set off the alarms.

Secure floor plan
(all tiles crossed)
Dimensions: 3 by 5

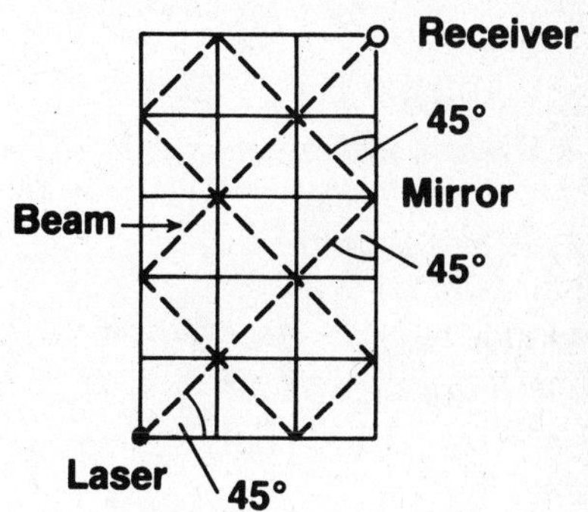

Insecure floor plan
Dimensions: 4 by 6

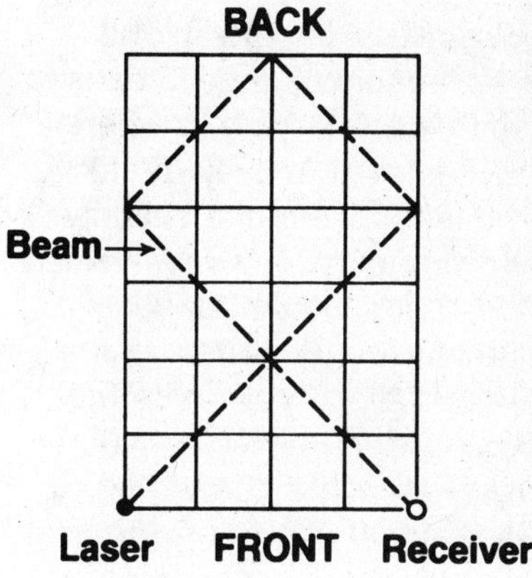

1. On graph or grid paper, draw rectangular floor plans with dimensions 3 by 8, 4 by 10, 2 by 3, and 6 by 9. Draw the laser paths to check which floor plans are secure. ______________________________

Draw several more rectangular floor plans with laser beams on your paper.

2. Now, without drawing more pictures, what are the dimensions of the rectangular floor plans that can be made secure?

____

____

Teacher Notes

Use with
Objective 94
pages 330–331

Focus
Problem Solving
Draw a Picture
Make a Table
Find a Pattern

Materials
Graph or grid paper

Overview
Students draw the path of a reflected laser beam on a grid, and look for patterns in the reflections.

Teaching Suggestions
Ask students if they have ever seen a mystery show where a person tried to avoid breaking the laser beam of a security system to get in a room. Read the description of the laser beam security system in the activity. Point out where the source and the receiver of the laser are located. Use the diagram to show how the beam passes over every square floor tile. For each floor plan in Problem 1, have students draw a picture on graph or grid paper and trace the path of the laser beam. Remind students that the source and the receiver of the laser beam must be located in the lower left and top right corners respectively and that a secure system has the beam passing over each square tile.

Have students draw laser paths for more floor plans and record their results in a table. Some secure floor plans are 3 by 4, 3 by 5, 3 by 7, 4 by 5, 4 by 7, 4 by 9, 8 by 15, and 7 by 12. Examples of insecure plans are 3 by 6, 4 by 10, 9 by 12, 8 by 12, and 10 by 15. When written as fractions, the dimensions of the *secure* floor plans are the fractions in lowest terms. *Insecure* floor plans are not in lowest terms.

Extension
Have students measure the length and width of the classroom to determine whether it could be made secure using laser beams. Have students draw diagrams to scale to illustrate why or why not the room could be made secure.

NAME ____________________

PROBLEM SOLVING

A laser-beam security system will be installed in a jewelry store. The rectangular floor will be covered with square tiles. The walls will be covered with mirrors so that the beam will bounce off the mirrored walls, remain parallel to the floor, and end up at a receiver in an appropriate corner of the room, and the beam will make an angle of measure 45° with a wall. The angle made by the beam as it reflects off a mirror is the same measure as the angle at which the beam strikes the mirror. For the room to be secure, the beam must pass over every square floor tile. The store's display counters will be placed so that they do not interfere with the laser beam's path.

Secure floor plan
(all tiles crossed)
Dimensions: 3 by 5

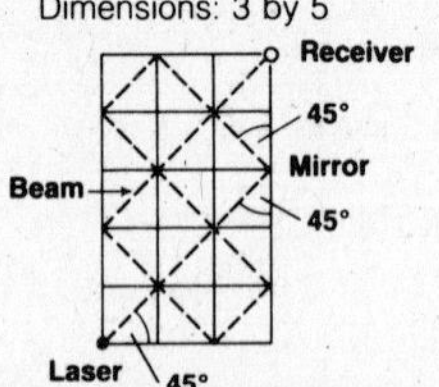

Insecure floor plan
Dimensions: 4 by 6

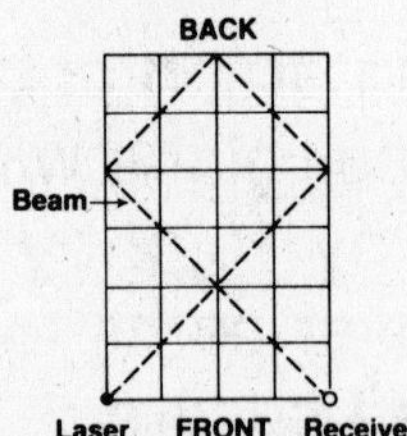

1. On graph or grid paper, draw rectangular floor plans with dimensions 3 by 8, 4 by 10, 2 by 3, and 6 by 9. Draw the laser paths to check which floor plans are secure.

3 by 8 and 2 by 3

Draw several more rectangular floor plans with laser beams on your paper.

2. Now, without drawing more pictures, what are the dimensions of the rectangular floor plans that can be made secure?

Possible answer: Any 2 numbers which can form a fraction in lowest terms. 4 by 5 → $\frac{4}{5}$

NAME ______________________________

VISUAL THINKING

Genevieve has one piece of fabric left over from a tablecloth she has made. She wants to use it to finish a quilt that is missing one square. To keep her sewing time to a minimum, she wants to make as few cuts in the fabric as she can. She has already made one cut as shown.

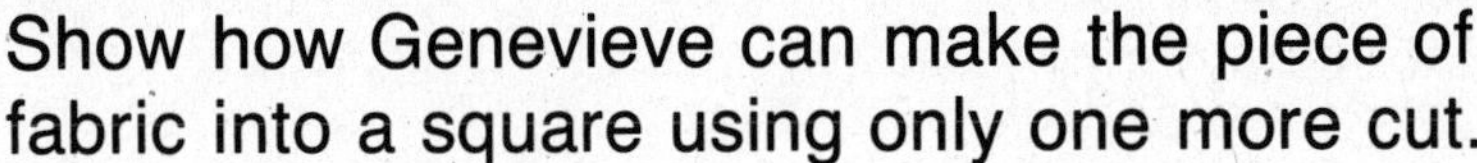

Show how Genevieve can make the piece of fabric into a square using only one more cut.

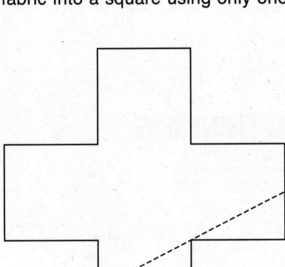

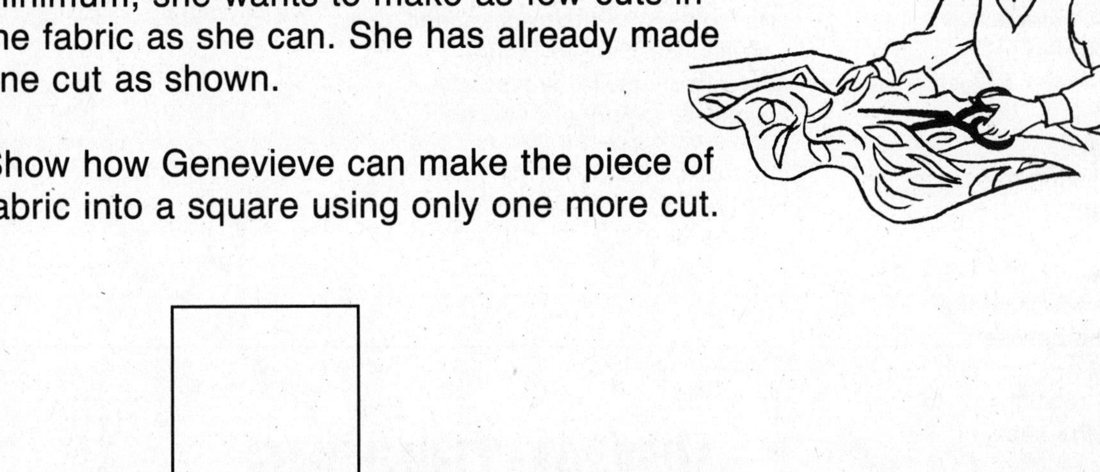

Teacher Notes

Use with
Objective 95
pages 342–343

Focus
Visual Thinking
Spatial Perception
Visual Patterns

Materials
Tracing paper
Visual Thinking transparency (optional)

Overview
Students recognize the relationship between two parts of a visual analogy and use this same relationship to complete the analogy.

Teaching Suggestions
Most students will be able to mentally rotate the two sections of the fabric to form the top and right side of the square. A cut perpendicular to Genevieve's cut will give two remaining pieces needed to complete the square.

Alternate Approach: Allow students having difficulty visualizing the pieces making up the square to use tracing paper to trace the two pieces produced by Genevieve's cut. Have them cut the tracings and manipulate them to form a partial square. Have students complete the square visually.

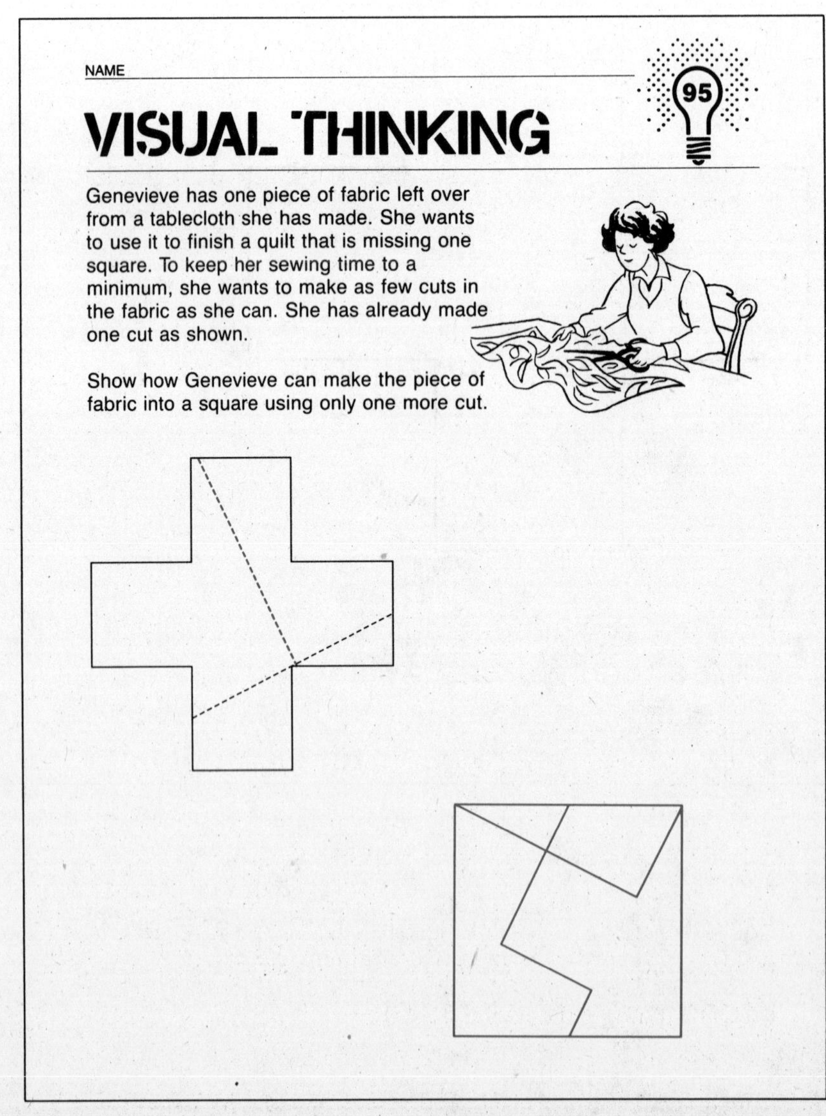

NAME

95

VISUAL THINKING

Genevieve has one piece of fabric left over from a tablecloth she has made. She wants to use it to finish a quilt that is missing one square. To keep her sewing time to a minimum, she wants to make as few cuts in the fabric as she can. She has already made one cut as shown.

Show how Genevieve can make the piece of fabric into a square using only one more cut.

NAME ____________________

CRITICAL THINKING

Dr. Nadia Pavlov, psychologist, teaches a mouse to run through the maze shown in the diagram. The mouse runs from the box toward the food. It never runs down a blind alley twice on each attempt to find the food. It goes back to the last intersection and tries a new path instead. The mouse always runs in the direction of the arrows.

1. How many possible paths to the food are there? You may wish to draw a tree diagram on a separate sheet of paper to help you. One has been started at the right.

____

2. How many possible paths to the food are there if the mouse is only allowed two wrong turns in the maze?

____

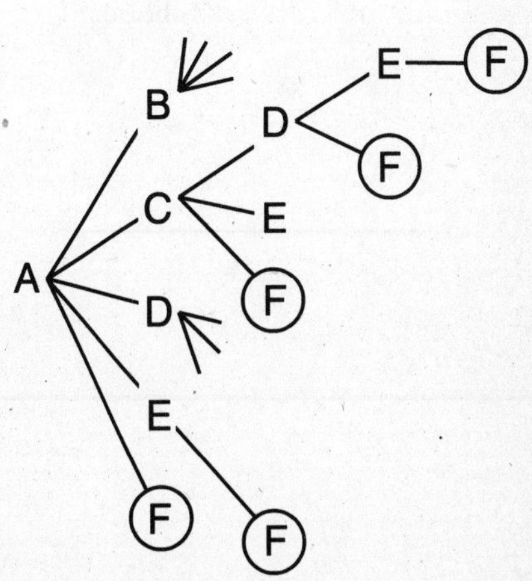

Teacher Notes

Use with
Objective 96
pages 344–345

Focus
Critical Thinking
Finding/Extending/Using Patterns
Developing Alternatves

Overview
Students draw a tree diagram to determine the number of possible paths for a mouse through a maze.

Teaching Suggestions
For Problem 1, students should systematically determine the 20 possible paths. From point A, the mouse can go to points B, C, D, E, or F. From B, it can go to C, D, E, or F. From C, the mouse can go to D, then to E and F, or it can go from D to F. Other possibilities from point C include going to point E or going directly to F. ***Question:*** *If the mouse goes from point A to point D, what are the possible paths it will take from D?* [The mouse can go from D to C, D to E, or D to F.]

Have students number the paths to facilitate counting the total number of possibilities.

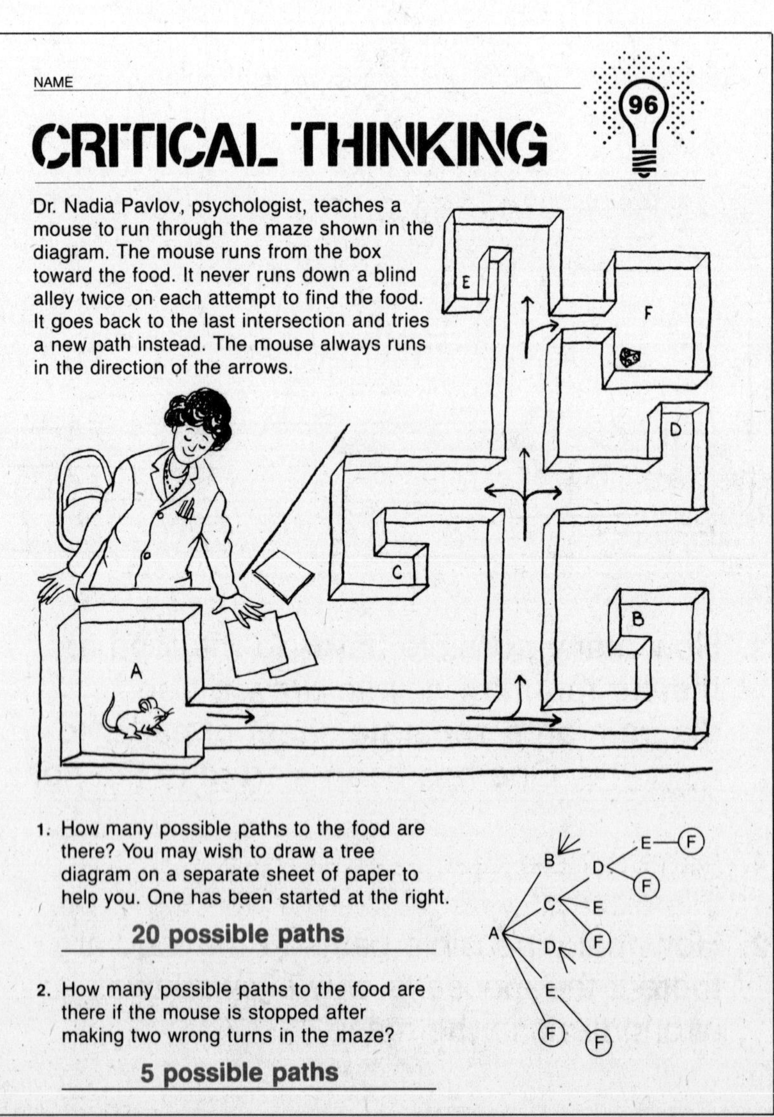

NAME

CRITICAL THINKING

96

Dr. Nadia Pavlov, psychologist, teaches a mouse to run through the maze shown in the diagram. The mouse runs from the box toward the food. It never runs down a blind alley twice on each attempt to find the food. It goes back to the last intersection and tries a new path instead. The mouse always runs in the direction of the arrows.

1. How many possible paths to the food are there? You may wish to draw a tree diagram on a separate sheet of paper to help you. One has been started at the right.

20 possible paths

2. How many possible paths to the food are there if the mouse is stopped after making two wrong turns in the maze?

5 possible paths

NAME ____

PROBLEM SOLVING

The famous Big Ben clock in London has faces that are 23 feet across.

1. How far does the tip of the minute hand travel each hour?

____

2. If there were a second hand on Big Ben, at what rate would the tip have to travel around the face to keep correct time?

____

Another large four-faced clock is on the Allen-Bradley Building in Milwaukee, Wisconsin. The minute hand is 20 feet long.

3. How far does the tip of the minute hand travel every hour?

____

4. If there were a second hand on this clock, how many times as fast would the tip have to travel to keep correct time than the tip of a similar hand on Big Ben?

____

Teacher Notes

Use with
Objective 97
pages 346–347

Focus
Problem Solving
Use a Formula

Materials
Classroom clock
Rulers

Overview
Students compute circumferences of clock faces and compare the rates at which second hands travel around them.

Teaching Suggestions
For Problem 1, students must compute the length of the radius of Big Ben's face given that the diameter is 23 feet. The equation used to find the radius of a circle is $r = d/2$, where d is the diameter, and r is the radius of the circle. ***Question:*** *What is the radius of Big Ben?* [11.5 feet] Students must then compute the circumference of the clock's face using the equation $C = 2\pi r$, where C is the circumference, π is the constant 3.14, and r is the radius.

Problem 4 can be solved by dividing the rate of movement of the hypothetical second hand on the clock in Milwaukee by the rate of movement of a hypothetical second hand on Big Ben. Thus, 125.6 ft/min divided by 72.2 ft/min equals about 1.7.

Extension
Have students compute minute and second hand rates using their own watches. Some students may be unsure how to proceed if the watch face is not circular. Point out that the hands always travel in circular paths, and that to compute the rate of the minute hand, they can draw a circle whose radius is equal to the length of the minute hand.

NAME ____________________

PROBLEM SOLVING

The famous Big Ben clock in London has faces that are 23 feet across.

1. How far does the tip of the minute hand travel each hour?
   About 72.2 ft

2. If there were a second hand on Big Ben, at what rate would the tip have to travel around the face to keep correct time?
   About 72.2 ft/min

Another large four-faced clock is on the Allen-Bradley Building in Milwaukee, Wisconsin. The minute hand is 20 feet long.

3. How far does the tip of the minute hand travel every hour?
   About 125.6 ft

4. If there were a second hand on this clock, how many times as fast would it have to travel to keep correct time than a similar hand on Big Ben?
   About 1.7 times as fast

NAME ______________________________

CRITICAL THINKING

At right is a picture of a 3-by-4 floor plan for a room with mirrored walls. A laser is installed in the back left corner and the laser beam makes an 45° angle with a wall. The beam passes over the square tiles diagonally. The beam will reflect off the mirrored walls at angles whose measures are 45° until it ends in a corner of the room. For a 3-by-4 floor plan, the beam touches the walls 7 times (including the starting and ending points).

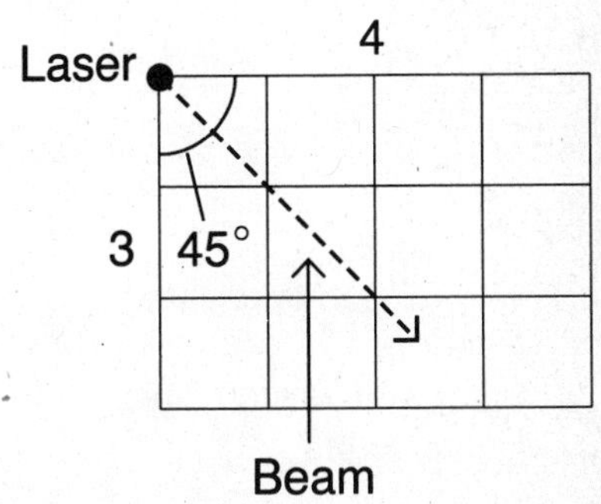

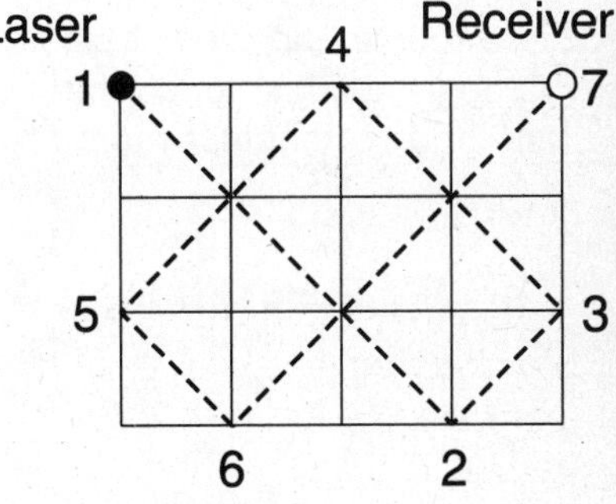

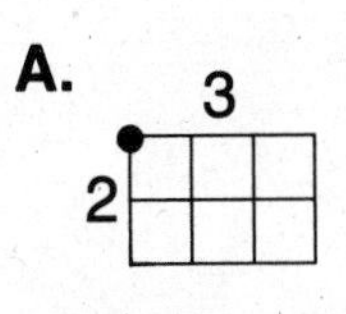

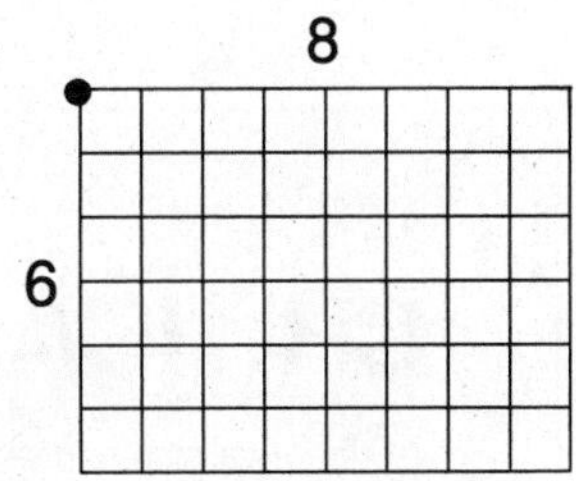

C. 8 × 6

1. How many times will the beam touch the walls in the rooms shown above?

   A: ______ B: ______ C: ______

2. Look at the fractions formed by the dimensions. Using these, how do you determine the number of times that the laser beam will touch the walls of any mirrored, rectangular room?

   ____

   ____

3. How can you predict the ending corner of the laser beam for any mirrored, rectangular room?

   ____

   ____

   ____

   ____

Teacher Notes

Use with
Objective 98
pages 348–349

Focus
Critical Thinking
Finding/Extending/Using Patterns
Making and Testing Predictions

Overview
Students trace the path of a laser beam around various sized rooms and predict where the beam will last touch the wall for a rectangular room of any size.

Teaching Suggestions
For Problem 1, have students trace the paths of the beams in Figures A–C. This will facilitate their counting the number of "touches." Remind students to include the starting point as well as the endpoint in each case.

Alternate Approach: Review how to reduce fractions to their lowest terms. To help students determine the relationship between the number of times the beam touches a wall and the room's dimensions, have them make a table with room dimensions in one column and number of "touches" in the other. Students should recognize that in the first two cases, A and B, the sum of the room dimensions equals the number of "touches." Some students may need more help to compute the answer for Figure C.

A table can be made to assist students in solving Problem 3.

Front Right	Back Right	Front Left
3 by 5 5 by 9	3 by 4 5 by 8	2 by 3 4 by 7

NAME ______________________

98

CRITICAL THINKING

At right is a picture of a 3-by-4 floor plan for a room with mirrored walls. A laser is installed in the back left corner and the laser beam makes an 45° angle with a wall. The beam passes over the square tiles diagonally. The beam will reflect off the mirrored walls at angles whose measures are 45° until it ends in a corner of the room. For a 3-by-4 floor plan, the beam touches the walls 7 times (including the starting and ending points).

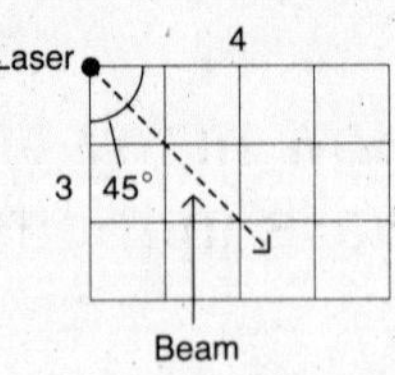

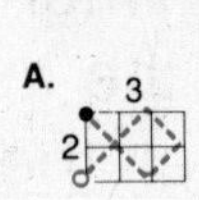

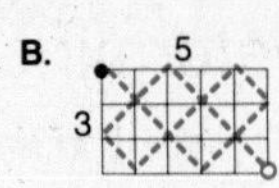

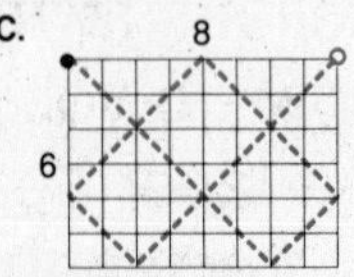

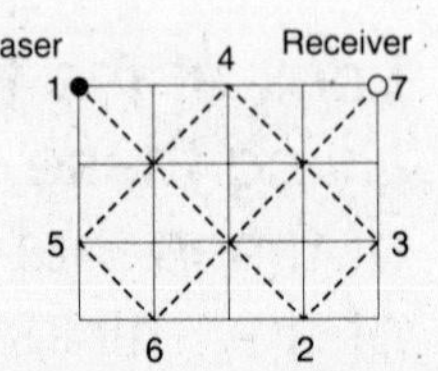

1. How many times will the beam touch the walls in the rooms shown above?
A: **5** B: **8** C: **7**

2. Look at the fractions formed by the dimensions. Using these, how do you determine the number of times that the laser beam will touch the walls of any mirrored, rectangular room?
Reduce fraction formed by dimensions to lowest terms, then add numerator and denominator.

3. How can you predict the ending corner of the
3. laser beam for any mirrored, rectangular room?
Find $\frac{\text{front to back dimension}}{\text{side to side dimension}}$. Put in lowest terms; state if the numerator and denominator are even or odd. $\frac{\text{odd}}{\text{odd}}$: front right corner. $\frac{\text{even}}{\text{odd}}$: front left corner. $\frac{\text{odd}}{\text{even}}$: back right corner.

NAME ______________________

PROBLEM SOLVING

Here is the outline of an ostrich's footprint, divided into square centimeters. Only the two toes of an ostrich's foot touch the ground when it walks or stands.

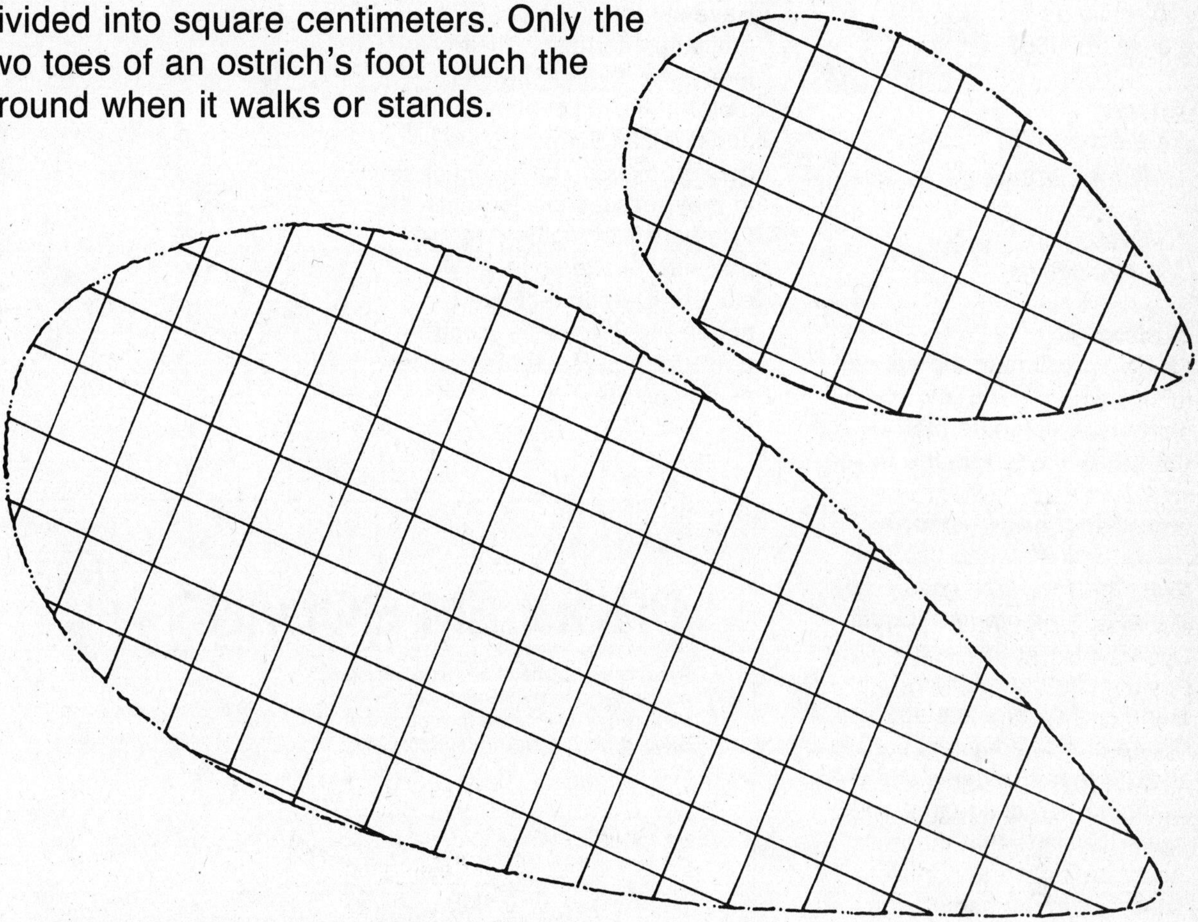

1. What is the approximate area of two footprints in square centimeters?

____

2. This ostrich has a mass of 120 kilograms. Assuming pressure is equal on all squares, what it the pressure to the nearest hundredth on the soles of the ostrich's two feet? Use the formula $P = \frac{M}{A}$, where *P* is pressure (in kilograms per square centimeter), *M* is mass (in kilograms), and *A* is area (in square centimeters).

____

Teacher Notes

Use with
Objective 99
pages 350–353

Focus
Problem Solving
Use a Formula

Materials
Transparencies

Overview
Students estimate the area of an irregular region and use a formula to compute the pressure exerted on the region.

Teaching Suggestions
Question: *How can you determine the area covered by an ostrich's footprint?* [Count the squares in the footprint.]

Suggest that students number the complete squares. There are 87 complete squares in both toes. Students can then combine partial squares and mark the parts that make up approximately one complete square with the same letter. The total of the two-toed footprint is about 114 cm^2. Two footprints cover about 228 cm^2.

Alternate Approach: Allow students having difficulties with estimating the number of partial squares to make a template of a whole square on a transparency. The template can be placed over each partial square allowing students to more closely estimate the area made of partial squares.

Extension
Have students compute the pressure exerted on their own feet. Have them trace their footprints using centimeter grid paper. Make sure students convert their weights in pounds to their masses in kilograms. Compare their results with the pressure exerted by the ostrich. [Ostrich feet exert about 4 to 5 times as much pressure per square centimeter as human feet.]

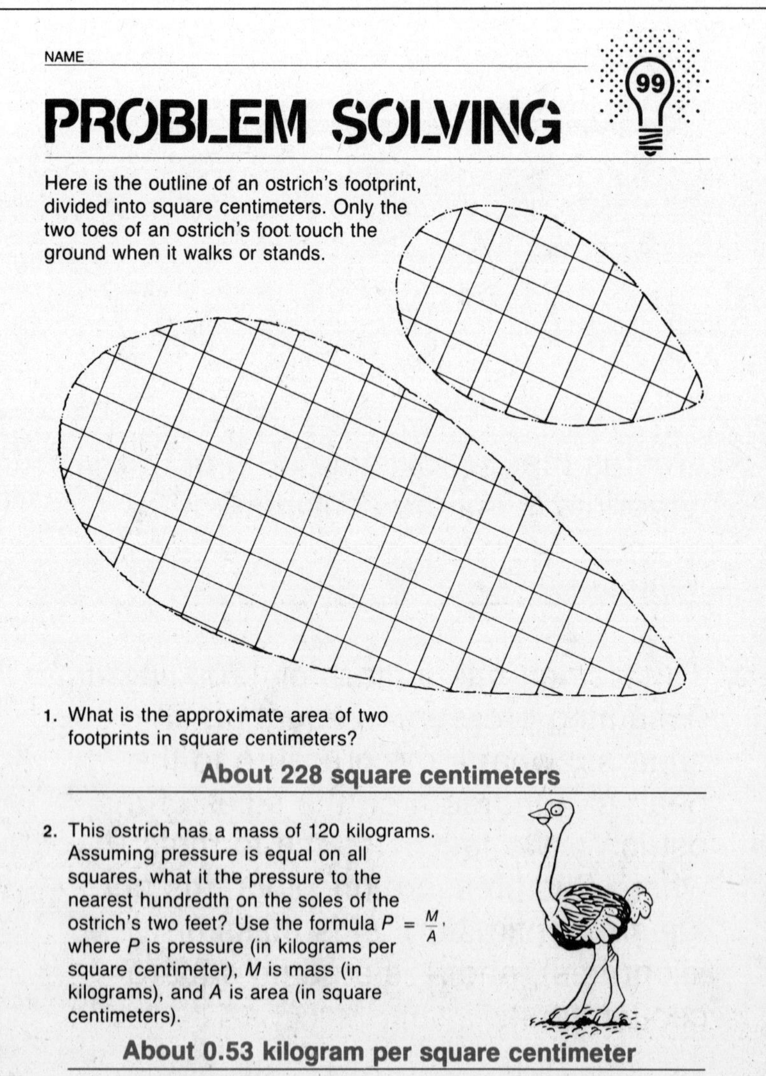

NAME ______________________

99

PROBLEM SOLVING

Here is the outline of an ostrich's footprint, divided into square centimeters. Only the two toes of an ostrich's foot touch the ground when it walks or stands.

1. What is the approximate area of two footprints in square centimeters?

   About 228 square centimeters

2. This ostrich has a mass of 120 kilograms. Assuming pressure is equal on all squares, what it the pressure to the nearest hundredth on the soles of the ostrich's two feet? Use the formula $P = \frac{M}{A}$, where P is pressure (in kilograms per square centimeter), M is mass (in kilograms), and A is area (in square centimeters).

   About 0.53 kilogram per square centimeter

NAME ______________________________

DECISION MAKING

You want to power a greenhouse ventilation system with a solar cell that converts sunlight into electricity. The system requires 25 watts of electricity. Solar cells can be made either circular or square, out of three different types of material.

Material	Power Output per sq ft	Cost per sq ft	Sq Ft Needed	Material Cost
Electrolot	.75 watt	$15.00		
Sun-Ray	.50 watt	$10.00		
Powerite	.60 watt	$12.50		

A circular solar cell costs 15% more per square foot to build than a square solar cell. Cells are available only with sides and radii that are whole numbers.

1. Complete the table to find the area needed and cost for each type of solar cell material.

2. What shape, size, and material would you choose for your solar cell? Explain your answer.

____

____

3. How much will your cell cost?

____

Teacher Notes

Use with
Objective 100
pages 356–357

Focus
Decision Making

Overview
Students make a table to decide among several options for constructing a solar cell.

Teaching Suggestions
To compute the amount of material needed, students need to divide the 25 watts of electricity needed by the system by the power output per square foot of material. To compute the amount of Powerite, divide 25 watts by 0.60 watt per square foot. The result is 41-2/3 square feet. The cost of Powerite equals 41-2/3 sq ft × $12.50 per sq ft or $520.83.

To find the radius of a circular cell, divide the total area needed by π, and try and check whole number squares. For Electrolot, 33-1/3 sq ft divided by π is about 10, so the radius must be between 3 and 4 feet.

If students choose circular cells, they must add 15% to the computed material cost.

After students have completed the activity, discuss their decisions and the relative value they assigned to various factors.

NAME ______________________

DECISION MAKING

You want to power a greenhouse ventilation system with a solar cell that converts sunlight into electricity. The system requires 25 watts of electricity. Solar cells can be made either circular or square, out of three different types of material.

Material	Power Output per sq ft	Cost per sq ft	Sq Ft Needed	Material Cost
Electrolot	.75 watt	$15.00	$33\frac{1}{3}$	$500.00
Sun-Ray	.50 watt	$10.00	50	$500.00
Powerite	.60 watt	$12.50	$41\frac{2}{3}$	$520.83

A circular solar cell costs 15% more per square foot to build than a square solar cell. Cells are available only with sides and radii that are whole numbers.

1. Complete the table to find the area needed and cost for each type of solar cell material.
2. What shape, size, and material would you choose for your solar cell? Explain your answer.

   Possible answer: Circular, 4-ft radius from Sun-Ray; will provide correct power output for smallest area
3. How much will your cell cost?

   Possible answer: $575.00

NAME ______________________________

PROBLEM SOLVING

Jason and Rocky wanted to meet to trade baseball cards. Jason said, "If we meet halfway between our houses, we will both walk the same number of blocks."

The grid lines represent streets. The boys always follow the street routes, do not take any shortcuts, and do not double back. For example, if they meet at the bakery, each boy will walk four blocks.

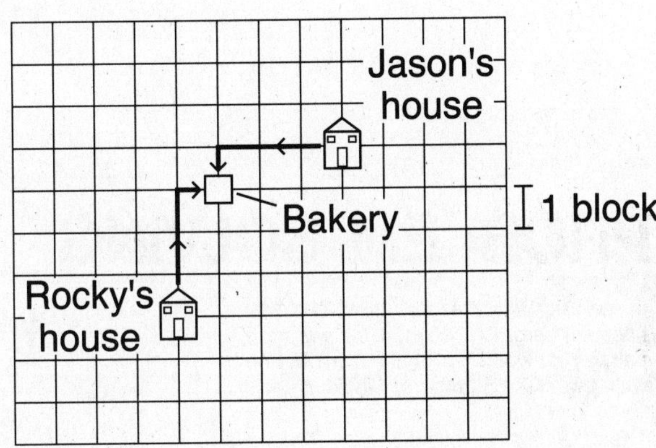

1. When Jason walks all the way to Rocky's house, how many blocks does he walk? ____________

2. Is there a meeting place that is less than 4 blocks from each boy's house? If so, where is it? ____________

3. Mark an *X* at each of the other points in the diagram that are 4 blocks from each boy's house.

4. Why might the boys not meet as they have planned? ____________

5. There are other points in the diagram that are the same number of blocks from each boy's house. Mark an *O* at each of these points you find.

Use after pages 358–359.

Teacher Notes

Use with
Objective 101
pages 358–359

Focus
Problem Solving
Draw a Picture
Try and Check

Materials
Graph paper

Overview
Students use a grid to find points that are equidistant from two given points.

Teaching Suggestions
In Problem 1, have students *try and check* several street routes between the two houses. They should find that given the restrictions on routes, Jason always walks eight blocks.

In Problem 3, students discover four points that are four blocks from each boy's house. These points, together with the bakery, are "halfway" points. This should suggest the answer to Problem 4. Jason's plan of meeting halfway was too vague. The boys might be waiting for each other at different halfway points. ***Question:*** *How should Jason have clarified "halfway?"* [Jason's "halfway" can be clarified by stating directions. For example, Jason could have said that the boys would meet "halfway—at the bakery," or "halfway—directly south of my house," and so on.]

Encourage students to find all 38 points that are equidistant from each house in Problem 5.

Extension
Have students use graph paper to solve the same problems for the houses shown below. "X" designates a halfway point, "O" represents equidistant points.

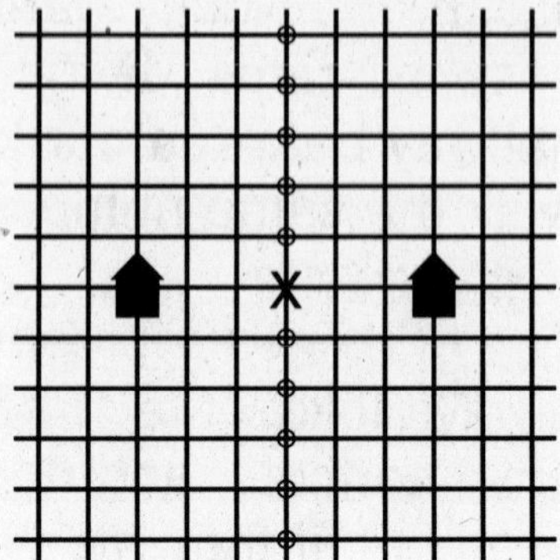

NAME ______________________________

PROBLEM SOLVING

101

Jason and Rocky wanted to meet to trade baseball cards. Jason said, "If we meet halfway between our houses, we will both walk the same number of blocks."

The grid lines represent streets. The boys always follow the street routes, do not take any shortcuts, and do not double back. For example, if they meet at the bakery, each boy will walk four blocks.

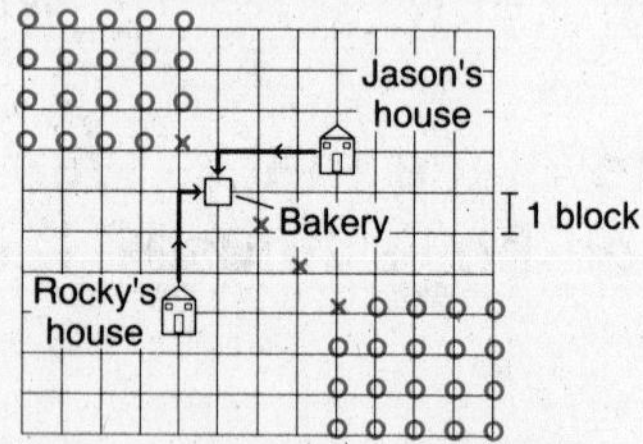

1. When Jason walks all the way to Rocky's house, how many blocks does he walk? **8 blocks**
2. Is there a meeting place that is less than 4 blocks from each boy's house? If so, where is it? **No**
3. Mark an *X* at each of the other points in the diagram that are 4 blocks from each boy's house.
4. Why might the boys not meet as they have planned? **Map has 5 midpoints**
5. There are other points in the diagram that are the same number of blocks from each boy's house. Mark an *O* at each of these points you find.

NAME ______________________________

VISUAL THINKING

Use the diagrams to solve the problems.

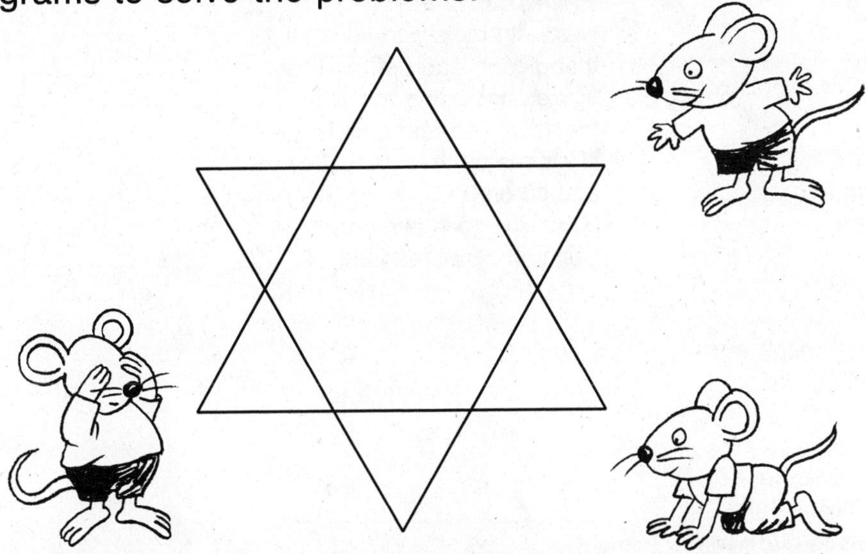

1. Each side of the triangle measures 3 units in length. Draw as many equilateral triangles as you can with sides that measure 1 unit in length. How many did you draw? ______________

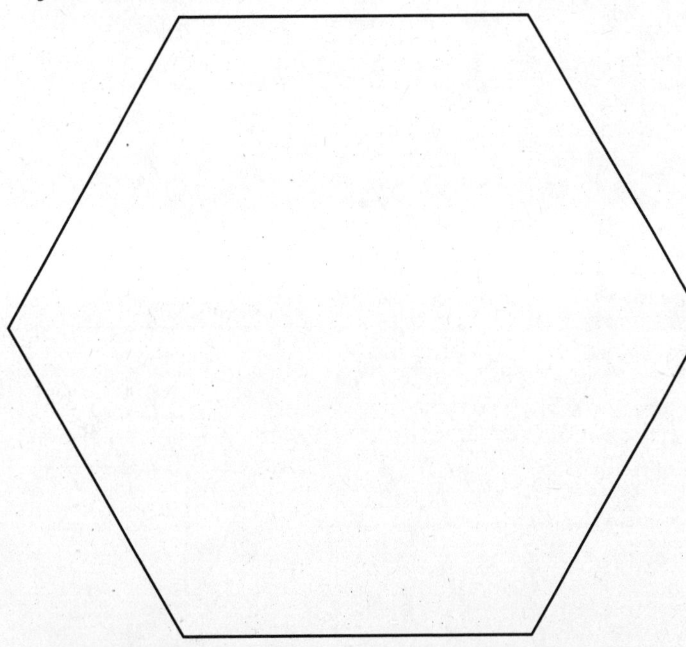

2. Each side of the hexagon measures 2 units in length. Draw as many equilateral triangles as you can with sides that measure 1 unit in length. How many did you draw? ______________

Teacher Notes

Use with
Objective 102
pages 360–361

Focus
Visual Thinking
Spatial Perception
Visual Patterns

Materials
Rulers
Visual Thinking transparency (optional)

Overview
Students determine the number of smaller figures contained in two larger figures.

Teaching Suggestions
For Problem 1, have students measure a side of the triangle and divide it into three parts, marking the divisions with dots. Have them repeat this procedure with the other two sides of the triangle. To make the unit triangles they can use their rulers to connect the dots with line segments parallel to a side of the original triangle. ***Question:*** *How many unit triangles did you draw?* [9 triangles]

For Problem 2, students should divide each side of the hexagon into two parts and use their rulers to connect dots and vertices with line segments parallel to two sides of the hexagon. ***Question:*** *How many unit triangles did you draw?* [24 triangles]

Extension
Have students find all the triangles in each of the two figures, including the unit triangles and triangles whose sides measure 2 units, 3 units, and so on.
[Triangle: 13 triangles;
Hexagon: 38 triangles]

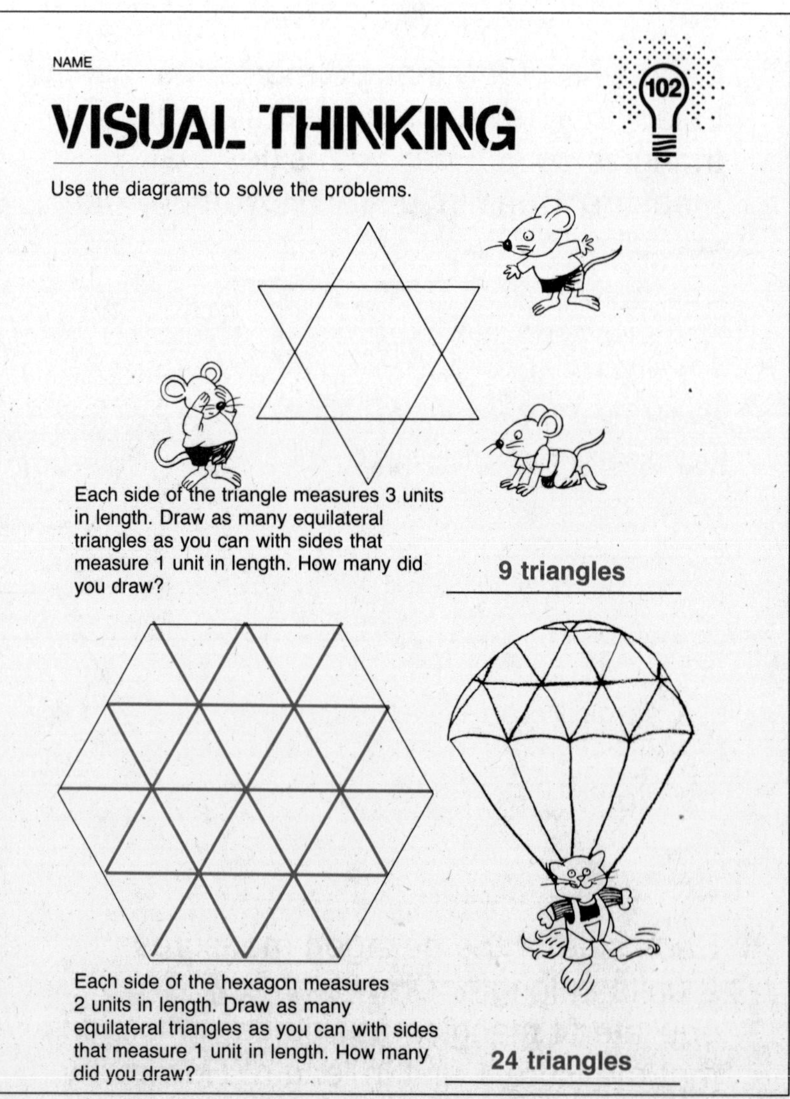
NAME
102
VISUAL THINKING
Use the diagrams to solve the problems.
Each side of the triangle measures 3 units in length. Draw as many equilateral triangles as you can with sides that measure 1 unit in length. How many did you draw?
9 triangles
Each side of the hexagon measures 2 units in length. Draw as many equilateral triangles as you can with sides that measure 1 unit in length. How many did you draw?
24 triangles

NAME ______________________________

PROBLEM SOLVING

In Juanita's office, there are a large number of clocks. Each clock consistently gains or loses a different whole number of seconds per hour. At noon today, all the clocks are set at exactly 12 o'clock.

1. How many hours ahead or behind must a clock be to show the correct time? ____________

2. If a clock gains 1 second per hour, when will it again show the correct time? Explain your answer.

____

____

3. If a clock gains 2 seconds per hour, will it show the correct time simultaneously with the clock in Problem 2? Explain.

____

____

4. If a clock loses 7 seconds per hour, will it show the correct time simultaneously with the clock in Problem 1? Explain.

____

____

5. When will all the clocks again show the correct time? ____________

Teacher Notes

Use with
Objective 103
pages 362–365

Focus
Problem Solving
Solve a Simpler Problem
Find a Pattern

Overview
Students determine when a number of clocks that gain or lose whole seconds per hour will all show the correct time.

Teaching Suggestions
The clocks show the correct time every 12 hours. So to solve Problem 2, the number of seconds gained in 12 hours is computed by multiplying 60 s/min by 60 min/h by 12 h to get 43,200 s. Since this clock gains 24 s/day, 43,200 s divided by 24 s/day equals 1,800 days.

Problem 3 is solved similarly: 43,200 s ÷ 48 s/day = 900 days. Thus, this clock will be correct in 900 days and in 1,800 days. ***Question:** What is the relationship between the number of seconds lost or gained by a clock and the days when it will show the correct time?* [If a clock gains or loses *n* number of seconds per hour, it will be correct every 1,800/*n* days, and in 1,800 days, the clock will be correct for the *n*th time.]

Extension
Provide students with a map showing the time zones of the world. Draw clocks showing the current time in eight to ten major cities in different time zones. Have students match each clock with the correct city. If necessary, provide a list of cities from which to choose.

NAME ______________________

PROBLEM SOLVING

In Juanita's office, there are a large number of clocks. Each clock consistently gains or loses a different whole number of seconds per hour. At noon today, all the clocks are set at exactly 12 o'clock.

1. How many hours ahead or behind must a clock be to show the correct time? **12 hours**
2. If a clock gains 1 second per hour, when will it again show the correct time? Explain your answer.
   In 1,800 days; it gains 24 seconds per day. It must gain 43,200 seconds. This will take 1,800 days.
3. If a clock gains 2 seconds per hour, will it show the correct time simultaneously with the clock in Problem 2? Explain.
   Yes; it will first show correct time in 900 days, but will also show it in 1,800 days.
4. If a clock loses 7 seconds per hour, will it show the correct time simultaneously with the clock in Problem 1? Explain.
   Yes; it will first be correct in $\frac{1800}{7}$ days, but will be correct for the 7th time in 1,800 days.
5. When will all the clocks again show the correct time? **In 1,800 days**

NAME ______

CRITICAL THINKING

In girls' softball, a pitcher's Earned Run Average (ERA) is determined by the formula shown below. The result is rounded to the nearest hundredth.

$$\text{ERA} = \frac{(\text{Earned Runs}) \times (7)}{\text{Total Number of Innings Pitched}}$$

A pitcher's ERA tells how many runs she has allowed per 7 innings. (A game lasts 7 innings.)

1. Use the ERA formula to calculate the ERAs of the pitchers in the table below.

Pitcher	Earned Runs	Innings Pitched	ERA
Jemez	10	30	
Rogers	15	30	
Weston	8	41	
Quincy	12	27	
Smith	12	29	

2. If a batter has a high batting average, she is considered to be a good batter. Does a pitcher want her ERA to be high or low? Explain your answer.

______

______

3. Which of the 5 pitchers above would an opposing team most like and least like to have pitching against them?

Most Like: ______ Least Like: ______

Teacher Notes

Use with
Objective 104
pages 376–377

Focus
Critical Thinking
Drawing Conclusions

Overview
Students analyze a data table and apply a formula to determine baseball earned run averages.

Teaching Suggestions
Introduce the activity with the following. ***Questions:*** *How many play baseball or softball?* [Answer will be a show of hands.] *How many innings in your games?* [Possible answers: 7, 8, 9] *What is the average number of runs scored by a team?* [Possible answers: 3 to 6] Point out that the formula for computing an ERA value in this activity is based on 7-inning games.

Alternate Approach: Have students compute simple ERAs, for complete 7-inning games, such as no runs given up [0], 1 run given up [1], and 1 run given up in each inning [7]. Then explain that many pitchers do not pitch a complete game, so the number of innings pitched is worked into the formula.

Have the class divide into groups to work on the activity sheet. When finished, have groups report their answers, with explanations.

Extension
Have students rewrite the formula for 9-inning games [Earned runs × 9 ÷ Total Number of Innings Pitched]. Then have them compute ERAs for fictional or real Major League baseball pitchers.

NAME ____________________

CRITICAL THINKING

In girls' softball, a pitcher's Earned Run Average (ERA) is determined by the formula shown below. The result is rounded to the nearest hundredth.

$$\text{ERA} = \frac{(\text{Earned Runs}) \times (7)}{\text{Total Number of Innings Pitched}}$$

A pitcher's ERA tells how many runs she has allowed per 7 innings. (A game lasts 7 innings.)

1. Use the ERA formula to calculate the ERAs of the pitchers in the table below.

Pitcher	Earned Runs	Innings Pitched	ERA
Jemez	10	30	**2.33**
Rogers	15	30	**3.50**
Weston	8	41	**1.37**
Quincy	12	27	**3.11**
Smith	12	29	**2.90**

2. If a batter has a high batting average, she is considered to be a good batter. Does a pitcher want her ERA to be high or low? Explain your answer.
Low. She wants to allow the fewest earned runs possible.

3. Which of the 5 pitchers above would an opposing team most like and least like to have pitching against them?
Most Like: **Rogers** Least Like: **Weston**

NAME ______________________

VISUAL THINKING

An analogy is a statement that compares properties of two pairs of objects as in the following example. Ring the letter of the figure on the right that will correctly complete the analogy on the left.

Example: ↑ is to → as ↓ is to ←.

1. 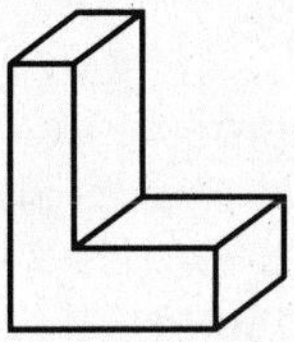 is to 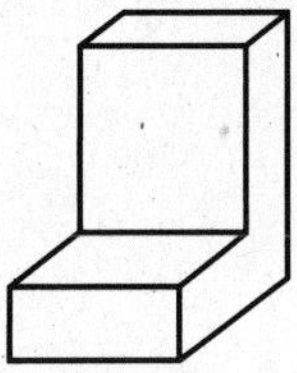 as 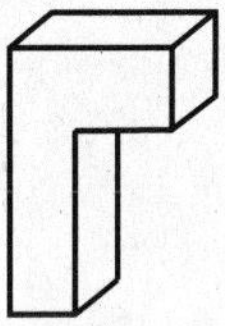 is to ______

2. 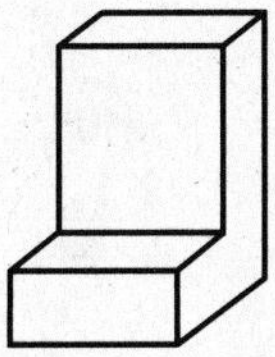 is to 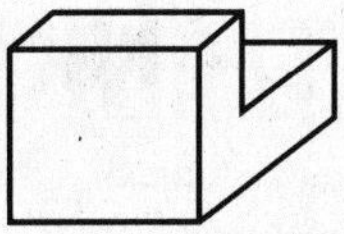 as 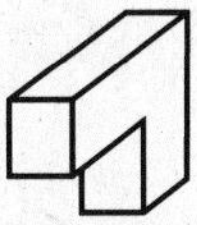 is to ______

3. 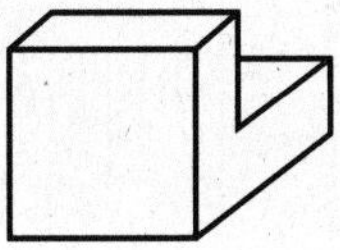 is to 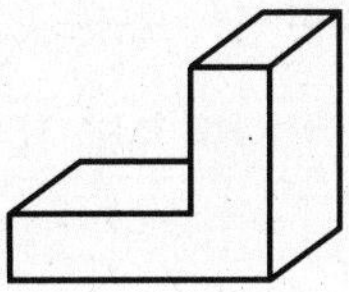 as 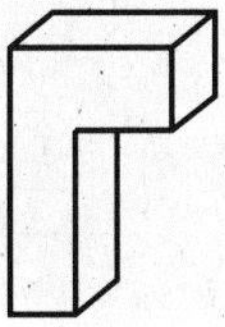 is to ______

4. 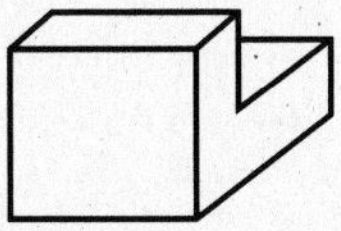 is to 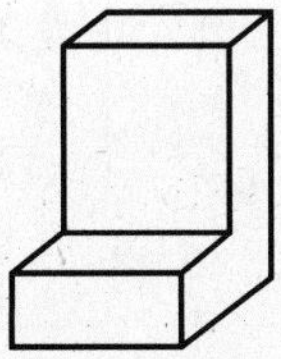 as 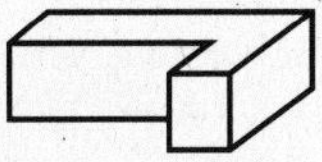 is to ______

5. 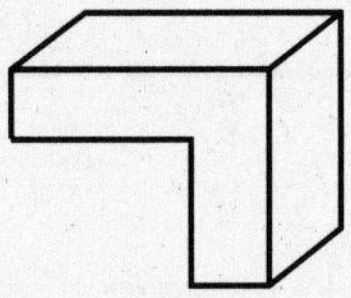 is to 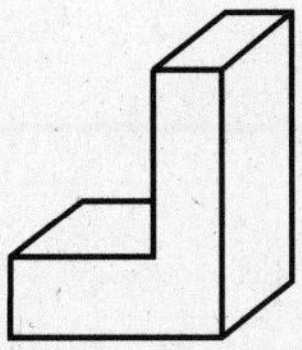 as 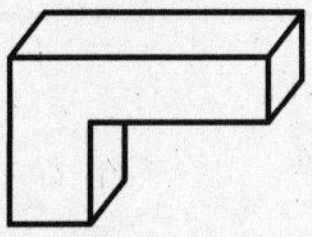 is to ______

a.

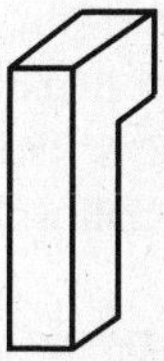

b.

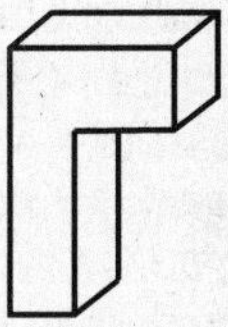

c.

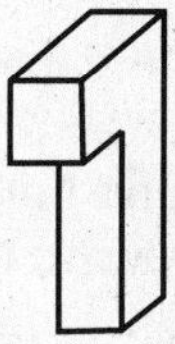

d.

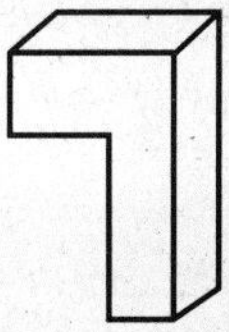

e.

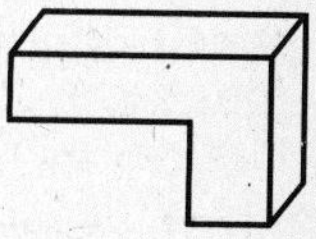

f.

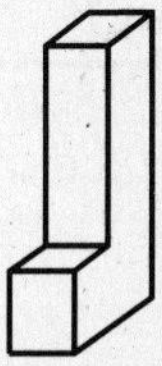

Teacher Notes

Use with
Objective 105
pages 378–381

Focus
Visual Thinking
Visual Patterns

Materials
3-dimensional shapes similar to those in the problems
Visual Thinking transparency (optional)

Overview
Students recognize the relationship between two figures of a *visual pattern* and use this same relationship to complete the pattern.

Teaching Suggestions
Discuss the concept of a pivot-point or axis; you may use a spinning globe as a model. Draw one of the objects found below on the board, showing the three possible axes through the object.

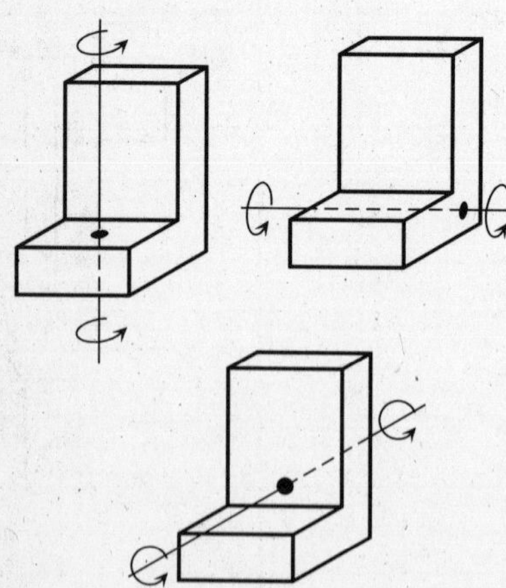

Question: *How many ways can the object turn?* [Six. Two directions around each axis]

Students should consider the first pair of drawings in Problem 1. Point out that they are two views of the same object. ***Questions:*** *How does the the second drawing differ from the first?* [It is turned sideways.] *How far is it turned?* [One-fourth of the way around]

Students should now look at the third object in Problem 1. ***Questions:*** *Which figures represent this object turned one quarter?* **[a, c, e]** *Which one of these is turned in the same direction as Pair #1?* **[c]**

Students should complete the remaining problems individually.

Alternate Approach: Use 3-dimensional shapes similar to those in the problems to show the axes and turns.

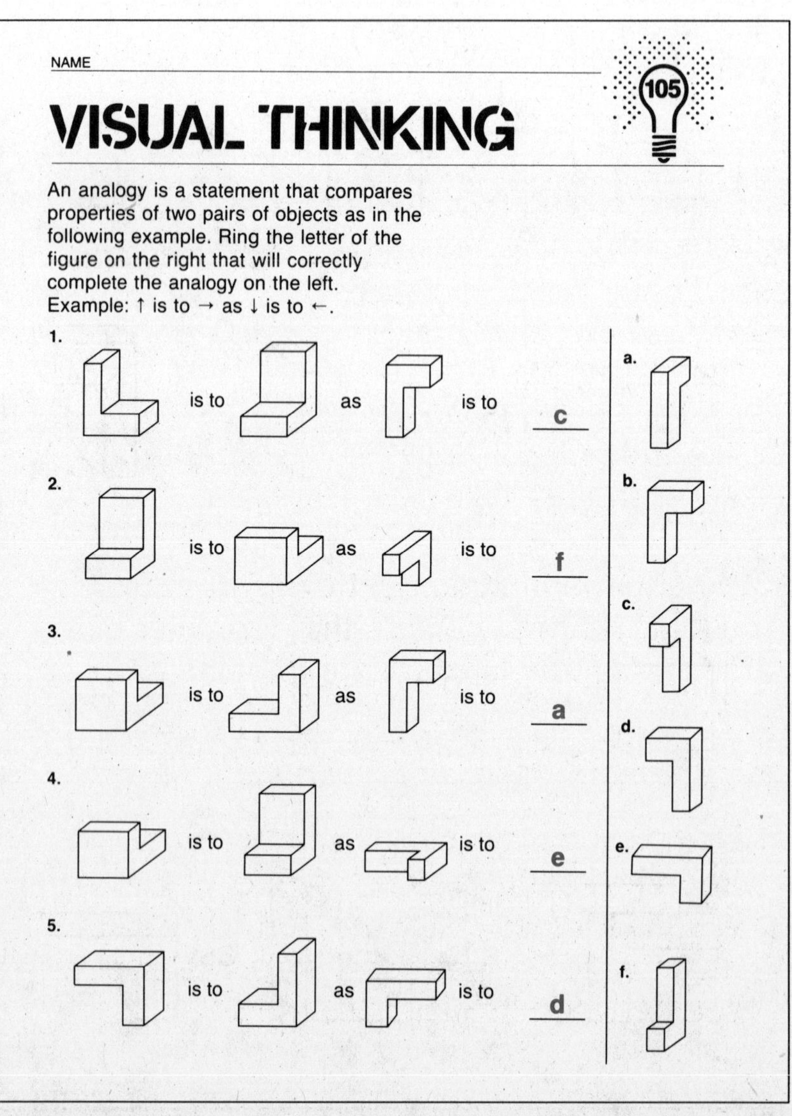

NAME

VISUAL THINKING

105

An analogy is a statement that compares properties of two pairs of objects as in the following example. Ring the letter of the figure on the right that will correctly complete the analogy on the left.
Example: ↑ is to → as ↓ is to ←.

1. is to as is to c
2. is to as is to f
3. is to as is to a
4. is to as is to e
5. is to as is to d

a.
b.
c.
d.
e.
f.

NAME ______________________________

CRITICAL THINKING

Notice in the picture that Square B has sides twice as long as those of Square A and Square C has sides three times as long as those of Square A.

Square	Top	Left	Right	Bottom
A	2	2	2	2
B	4	4	4	4
C	6	6	6	6

Find the perimeter of each square.

1. Square A _____ 2. Square B _____ 3. Square C _____

4. Find the ratio of a side of Square A to a side of Square B. ______________

5. Find the ratio of the perimeter of Square A to the perimeter of Square B. ______________

6. Are the ratios you found in Exercises 4 and 5 equal? ______________

7. What general statement can you make about what happens to the perimeter of a square when its sides are doubled?

____

8. Compare the sides and perimeters of Squares A and C as you did for Squares A and B. What statement can you make about what happens to the perimeter of a square when its sides are tripled?

____

Teacher Notes

Use with
Objective 106
pages 382–383

Focus
Critical Thinking
Making Generalizations

Overview
Students *make generalizations* about the effect of doubling or tripling the sides of a square on the perimeter.

Teaching Suggestions
Before students begin working on the problems, remind them that the numbers in a proportion must be written according to the order they were asked for in the problem.

If students have difficulty with Problem 7, have them concentrate on the relationship between the lengths of the sides and the perimeters, rather than the ratios. ***Questions:*** *How many times longer are the sides of Square B than the sides of Square A?* [Twice as long] *How are the perimeters of Square B and Square A related?* [The perimeter of Square B is twice the perimeter of Square A.]

You can use a similar approach for Problem 8. ***Questions:*** *What is the relationship between the lengths of the sides of Squares A and C?* [The sides of Square C are three times as long as the sides of Square A.] *What is the relationship between the perimeters of Squares A and C?* [The perimeter of Square C is three times as long as the perimeter of Square A.]

Alternate Approach: Have students find the perimeters for squares with side lengths of 1 unit, 2 units, and 3 units. Have students compute ratios between the side lengths and perimeters as in Problems 4 and 5. Have them do the same for squares with side lengths of 5 units, 10 units, and 15 units.

NAME ______________________

CRITICAL THINKING

Notice in the picture that Square B has sides twice as long as those of Square A and Square C has sides three times as long as those of Square A.

Square A: sides 2, 2, 2, 2 — Square B: sides 4, 4, 4, 4 — Square C: sides 6, 6, 6, 6

Find the perimeter of each square.

1. Square A **8** 2. Square B **16** 3. Square C **24**

4. Find the ratio of a side of Square A to a side of Square B. **$\frac{2}{4}$**

5. Find the ratio of the perimeter of Square A to the perimeter of Square B. **$\frac{8}{16}$**

6. Are the ratios you found in Exercises 4 and 5 equal? **yes**

7. What general statement can you make about what happens to the perimeter of a square when its sides are doubled?
Sides of a square are doubled, perimeter doubles.

8. Compare the sides and perimeters of Squares A and C as you did for Squares A and B. What statement can you make about what happens to the perimeter of a square when its sides are tripled?
Sides of a square are tripled, perimeter triples.

NAME ________________________________

CRITICAL THINKING

The Central States Conservation Association wanted to reproduce an existing prairie. The Association counted the prairie's plant specimens that it wanted to reproduce and tallied the results, shown at right.

The new prairie was planted over a larger area than the old prairie. Its plants should have been planted in the same proportion as the existing prairie, but the workers planted the wrong number of two plants. The new prairie plant numbers are shown at right.

OLD PRAIRIE

PLANT	NUMBER
Heath Aster	48
Shooting Star	36
Western Lily	22
Blue Hearts	76
Hairy Sunflower	112
Butterfly Weed	6
Common Sundrops	56

NEW PRAIRIE

PLANT	NUMBER
Heath Aster	120
Shooting Star	90
Western Lily	66
Blue Hearts	190
Hairy Sunflower	560
Butterfly Weed	15
Common Sundrops	140

1. Find the correct ratio of old plants to new plants. ____________

2. Which two prairie plants were planted in the wrong amount?

____

3. How many of each of the two plants in Problem two should there be in the new prairie?

____

4. Suppose the workers had one less of each kind of plant for the new prairie. Which prairie plant ratio do you think would be most affected by the change?

____

5. Which would be the least affected prairie plant ratio in this situation?

____

Teacher Notes

Use with
Objective 107
pages 384–387

Focus
Critical Thinking
Reasoning with Graphs and Charts

Overview
Students analyze data and form ratios to be used to determine the number of plants needed in a new, replicate prairie.

Teaching Suggestions
Ask students to describe plants and animals found in a prairie. Mention that the plants listed in the Old Prairie chart on the activity page are commonly found prairie plants. Discuss the concept of a balanced ecology. In an ecosystem, or environment, the proportion of each member must be balanced. Use a terrarium or an aquarium as an example.

Have students complete the activity page and discuss their answers.

***Questions:** Why is the ratio for Butterfly Weed most affected by the change in Problem 4?* [In the ratio of old prairie plants to new prairie plants, the ratio for Butterfly Weed has the smallest denominator.] *Why is the ratio for Hairy Sunflower least affected?* [In the ratio of old prairie plants to new prairie plants, the ratio for Hairy Sunflower has the largest denominator.]

Extension
Use your classroom's or school's aquarium or draw a model of an aquarium on the chalkboard. Count the number of each type of plant or decoration used that rests on the floor of the aquarium. Ask students to decide what would be needed in an aquarium that is to be decorated identically, but is three times as long and two times as wide.

NAME ______________________

CRITICAL THINKING

The Central States Conservation Association wanted to reproduce an existing prairie. The Association counted the prairie's plant specimens that it wanted to reproduce and tallied the results, shown at right.

The new prairie was planted over a larger area than the old prairie. Its plants should have been planted in the same proportion as the exising prairie, but the workers planted the wrong number of two plants. The new prairie plant numbers are shown at right.

OLD PRAIRIE

PLANT	NUMBER
Heath Aster	48
Shooting Star	36
Western Lily	22
Blue Hearts	76
Hairy Sunflower	112
Butterfly Weed	6
Common Sundrops	56

NEW PRAIRIE

PLANT	NUMBER
Heath Aster	120
Shooting Star	90
Western Lily	66
Blue Hearts	190
Hairy Sunflower	560
Butterfly Weed	15
Common Sundrops	140

1. Find the correct ratio of old plants to new plants. $\frac{2}{5}$

2. Which two prairie plants were planted in the wrong amount?
   Lily and Sunflower

3. How many of each of the two plants in Problem two should there be in the new prairie?
   Lily: 55, Sunflower: 280

4. Suppose the workers had one less of each kind of plant for the new prairie. Which prairie plant ratio do you think would be most affected by the change?
   Butterfly Weed

5. Which would be the least affected prairie plant ratio in this situation?
   Hairy Sunflower

NAME ______________________________

CRITICAL THINKING

The graph below shows the changes in the supply of printer ribbons stocked at the Words in Print Type-n-Comp Store over several weeks.

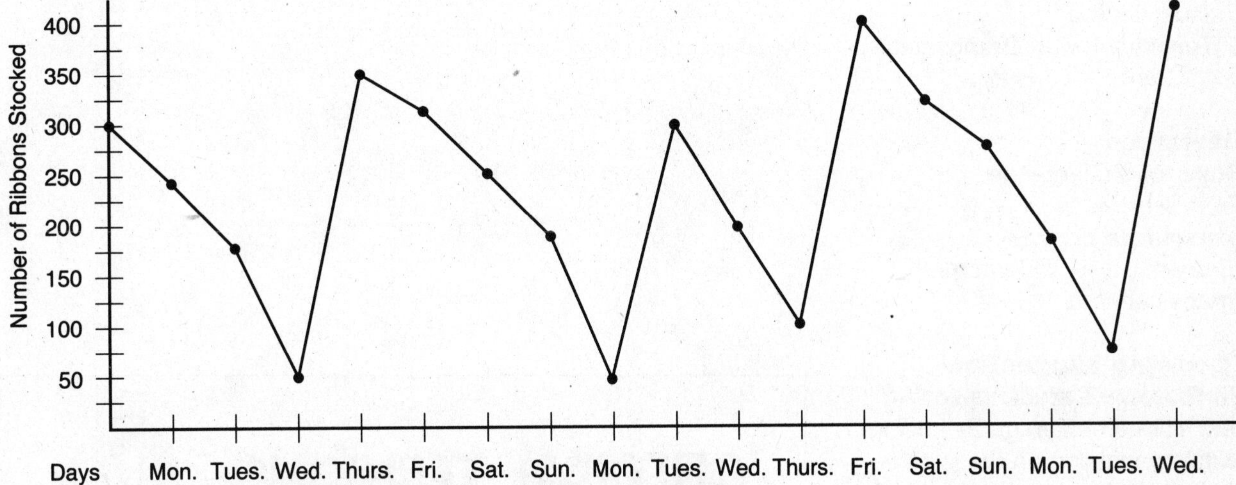

1. What are the greatest and least number of ribbons stocked during the time period shown above? Greatest: _____ Least: _____

2. Estimate the average number of ribbons stocked during this time. ____________________

3. What might have caused the increases in ribbons stocked, as shown by the graph?

____

4. Estimate the average increase in the number of ribbons stocked during this time. ____________________

5. If it takes 3 days for a new shipment of ribbons to arrive after it has been ordered, at about what number of stocked ribbons should the store order a new supply?

____

Teacher Notes

Use with
Objective 108
pages 390–391

Focus
Critical Thinking
Reasoning with Graphs and Charts

Materials
Ruler or straightedge

Overview
Students read and interpret graphical data.

Teaching Suggestions
In Problem 2, students can estimate the average by finding a horizontal line on the graph for which there are approximately as many data points above the line as below the line.

In Problem 4, make sure that students realize that what is asked for is the average of the increases shown. There are 4 increases shown on the graph, each indicated by an upward slanting line.

In Problem 5, students should realize that they should order ribbons in time to receive them before they run out. It follows that students should look for the largest three-day decrease in the number of ribbons. This occurs between the first Friday on the graph and the following Monday. The decrease is 275 ribbons.

NAME ______________________________

CRITICAL THINKING

108

The graph below shows the changes in the supply of printer ribbons stocked at the Words in Print Type-n-Comp Store over several weeks.

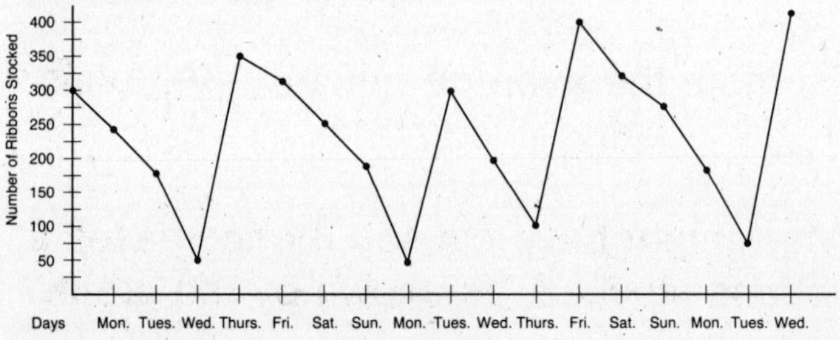

Number of Ribbons Stocked: 400, 350, 300, 250, 200, 150, 100, 50

Days: Mon. Tues. Wed. Thurs. Fri. Sat. Sun. Mon. Tues. Wed. Thurs. Fri. Sat. Sun. Mon. Tues. Wed.

1. What are the greatest and least number of ribbons stocked during the time period shown above? Greatest: **400** Least: **50**

2. Estimate the average number of ribbons stocked during this time. **About 225 ribbons**

3. What might have caused the increases in ribbons stocked, as shown by the graph?
A new shipment of ribbons arrived.

4. Estimate the average increase in the number of ribbons stocked during this time. **About 300 ribbons**

5. If it takes 3 days for a new shipment of ribbons to arrive after it has been ordered, at about what number of stocked ribbons should the store order a new supply?

____

NAME ____

VISUAL THINKING

Complete each figure so that the dotted line becomes a vertical line of symmetry.

a.

b.

c.

d.

e.

f.

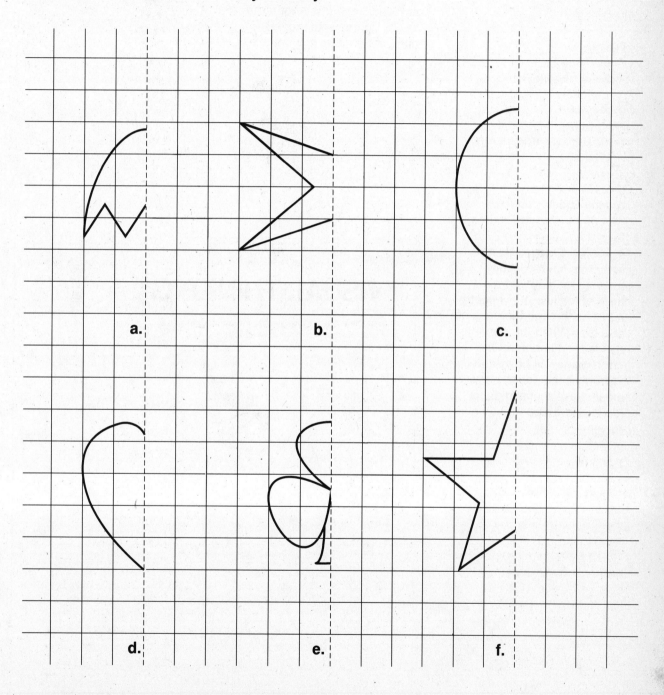

1. Which figures have more than 1 line of symmetry? ____________________

2. Draw in these lines on the figures above.

Teacher Notes

Use with
Objective 109
pages 392–395

Focus
Visual Thinking
Spatial Perception

Materials
Graph paper
Visual Thinking transparency (optional)

Overview
Students identify lines of symmetry in various figures.

Teaching Suggestions
If students have difficulty, suggest that they fold the paper at the line of symmetry and trace through the back of the paper. When the paper is unfolded, an imprint of the mirror image will be visible on the front of the paper. Have students use these folds to help in answering the problems.

Extension
Have students use graph paper and challenge one another to create figures with increasing numbers of lines of symmetry.

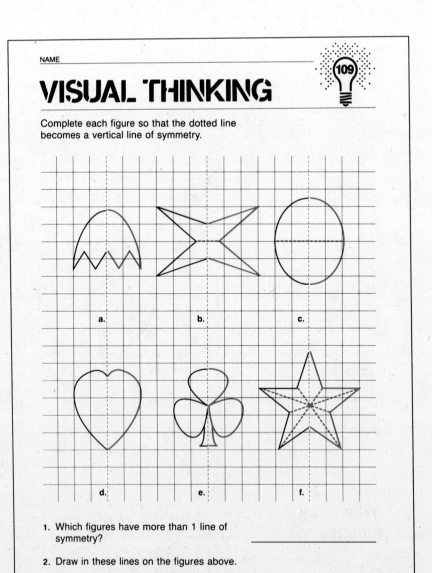

NAME

109

VISUAL THINKING

Complete each figure so that the dotted line becomes a vertical line of symmetry.

a. b. c.

d. e. f.

1. Which figures have more than 1 line of symmetry?
2. Draw in these lines on the figures above.

NAME ______________________________

PROBLEM SOLVING

Shannon made up the following puzzle for a school contest. The first person to solve the puzzle would win a pizza.

Puzzle for Win-a-Pizza Contest

List these five basketball players from shortest to tallest and give their heights.

Matt is $2\frac{1}{2}$ inches taller than Rick.

Steve is $3\frac{1}{4}$ inches shorter than Matt.

Rick is 1 inch taller than Andy, but 4 inches shorter than Jason.

The tallest player is 5 feet $11\frac{1}{2}$ inches tall.

1. Draw a diagram to arrange the players according to height.

______________________|______________________ Tallest

Rick

2. Label the height of the tallest player. Then use the information above to find the height of each of the other players.

Player	Height
Jason	____________
Matt	____________
Rick	____________
Steve	____________
Andy	____________

Teacher Notes

Use with
Objective 110
pages 396–397

Focus
Problem Solving
Use Logical Reasoning
Draw a Diagram

Overview
Students determine the heights of basketball players using given clues.

Teaching Suggestions
In order to prepare for Problem 1, students should study the statements concerning each player's height and picture a line representing these heights. The first statement indicates that Matt is 2-1/2 inches taller than Rick, so Matt's height would appear to the right of Rick's on the line. An expression that relates Matt's height to Rick's is $R + 2\text{-}1/2$. Have the students show Matt's position on the line in Problem 1 and label it with his name and $R + 2\text{-}1/2$.

The second statement tells the students that Steve is 3-1/4 inches shorter than Matt. ***Questions:*** *How much shorter is Steve than Rick?* [3-1/4 in. – 2 1/2 in. = 3/4 in.] *What expression relates Steve's height to Rick's?* [R – 3/4] Then have the students show Steve's position on the line.

The third statement tells that Andy is 1 inch shorter than Rick (R – 1) and that Jason is 4 inches taller than Rick (R + 4).

Since Jason's height is given, students can find Rick's height [5 ft 10-1/2 in. – 4 in. = 5 ft 6-1/2 in.] and from this, each of the other heights.

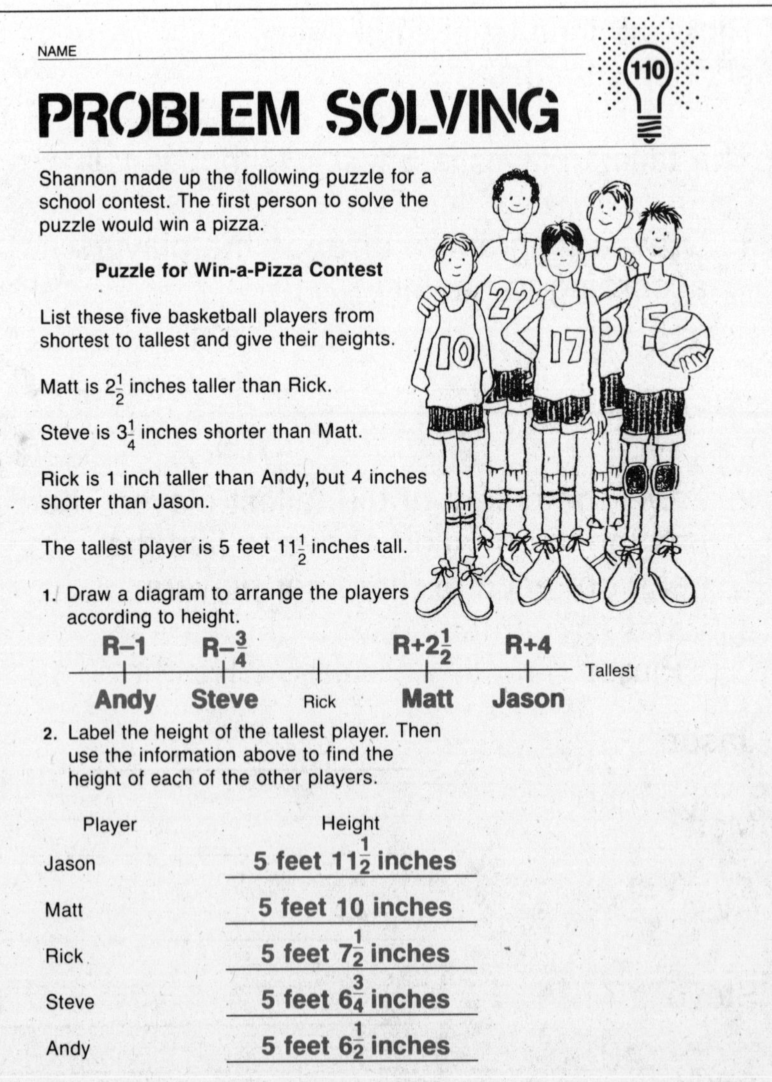

NAME

PROBLEM SOLVING

110

Shannon made up the following puzzle for a school contest. The first person to solve the puzzle would win a pizza.

Puzzle for Win-a-Pizza Contest

List these five basketball players from shortest to tallest and give their heights.

Matt is $2\frac{1}{2}$ inches taller than Rick.

Steve is $3\frac{1}{4}$ inches shorter than Matt.

Rick is 1 inch taller than Andy, but 4 inches shorter than Jason.

The tallest player is 5 feet $11\frac{1}{2}$ inches tall.

1. Draw a diagram to arrange the players according to height.

2. Label the height of the tallest player. Then use the information above to find the height of each of the other players.

Player	Height
Jason	**5 feet $11\frac{1}{2}$ inches**
Matt	**5 feet 10 inches**
Rick	**5 feet $7\frac{1}{2}$ inches**
Steve	**5 feet $6\frac{3}{4}$ inches**
Andy	**5 feet $6\frac{1}{2}$ inches**

NAME ____________________

DECISION MAKING

Margie collects figurines of horses. Maurice, Marcie, and Maureen would like to add to Margie's collection on her birthday.

Maurice, Marcie and Maureen have a total of $19 to spend on Margie's birthday gift.

1. Complete the table to list the possible combinations of figurines that could be purchased with *up to* $19, and how much money would be left after each purchase.

Large	Medium	Small	Money Left

2. What should they buy if they want to spend the most money possible? ____________________

3. What should they buy if they want to buy the most items? ____________________

4. What might they buy? Explain.

____

____

Teacher Notes

Use with
Objective 111
pages 398–399

Focus
Decision Making

Overview
Students compare prices of figurines in order to make decisions on the purchase of a birthday gift.

Teaching Suggestions
Introduce the activity by asking the following. ***Questions:*** *How many of you have some kind of collection?* [Many possible answers] *Do you have a difficult time deciding what to buy to add to your collection?* [Many possible answers]

Have a student volunteer read the opening statements on the activity sheet. Tell students that for this activity, it is possible to make combinations that include more than one item of the same size.

After the activity, discuss the students' responses as a group. Reinforce the fact that several answers are "correct" for Problem 4.

Alternate Approach: Pair up the students and assign one as the "buyer" and one as the "seller." Ask a student volunteer to read the directions on the activity sheet, and as a class fill in the first blank in Problem 1.

For each additional blank to be filled in, it is the responsibility of the "buyer" to decide the different combinations possible to purchase, and it is the job of the "seller" to determine the amount of money left after each purchase. To complete Problems 2–4, have the partners work together to decide answers.

NAME

DECISION MAKING

Margie collects figurines of horses. Maurice, Marcie, and Maureen would like to add to Margie's collection on her birthday.

Maurice, Marcie and Maureen have a total of $19 to spend on Margie's birthday gift.

1. Complete the table to list the possible combinations of figurines that could be purchased with *up to* $19, and how much money would be left after each purchase.

Large	Medium	Small	Money Left
1	0	0	$ 4
1	0	1	$ 0
0	1	0	$10
0	1	1	$ 6
0	1	2	$ 2
0	0	1	$15
0	0	2	$11
0	0	3	$ 7
0	0	4	$ 3

2. What should they buy if they want to spend the most money possible? **1 large and 1 small**

3. What should they buy if they want to buy the most items? **4 small**

4. What might they buy? Explain.
Possible answer: 1 medium and 2 small; it is the best combination of expense and number of items.

NAME

PROBLEM SOLVING

Interstellar Stella flew her spaceship from Substation Alpha back home to Earth. When she left Substation Alpha, she had 54 Galaxy Tollgate tokens; some were beta tokens, and some were delta tokens. The ratio of beta tokens to delta tokens was 4 to 5. On her trip, she passed through 3 Galaxy Tollgates. She paid 7 beta tokens at Tollgate 1, 10 delta tokens at Tollgate 2, and 2 beta tokens at Tollgate 3. When she arrived home, the ratio of beta tokens to delta tokens was 3 to 4.

1. Use the ratio 3 to 4 to list the possible numbers of tokens Stella had when she arrived home.

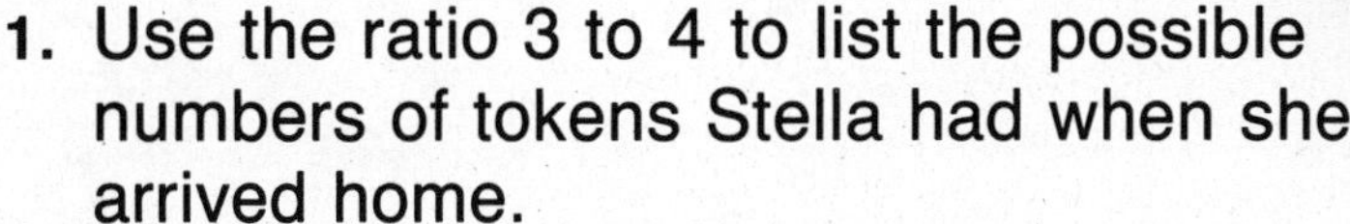

Beta	3					
Delta	4					

2. In the table below, add the number of tokens paid at the tollgates to each number of tokens in the table above.

Beta						
Delta						

3. How many beta and delta tokens did Interstellar Stella have when she left Substation Alpha?

____

Teacher Notes

Use with
Objective 112
pages 400–401

Focus
Problem Solving
Make a Table
Work Backward

Overview
Students construct tables of ratios and use data to solve a problem.

Teaching Suggestions
To begin this activity, students should read the page completely.

Question: *What are some possible numbers of tokens Stella may have had when she arrived home?* [Any ratios equivalent to 3/4 are acceptable. Possible answers may be 12/16, 18/24, and so on.] Instruct students to list the ratios in order from least to greatest to complete the table in Problem 1.

Tell students they will need to *work backward* to arrive at an answer to Problem 3.

Extension
Students should use the data from the tables to derive further information. For example, have them figure how many beta tokens Stella had after leaving Tollgate 2. [17] Then have them figure how many of each type of token Stella had when she arrived home. [15 beta, 20 delta tokens]

Students may also extend the table for additional trips. For example you may have them figure how many of each type of token Stella will have upon arrival at Substation Alpha if she makes an immediate return trip. [6 beta, 10 delta tokens]

NAME ______

PROBLEM SOLVING

112

Interstellar Stella flew her spaceship from Substation Alpha back home to Earth. When she left Substation Alpha, she had 54 Galaxy Tollgate tokens; some were beta tokens, and some were delta tokens. The ratio of beta tokens to delta tokens was 4 to 5. On her trip, she passed through 3 Galaxy Tollgates. She paid 7 beta tokens at Tollgate 1, 10 delta tokens at Tollgate 2, and 2 beta tokens at Tollgate 3. When she arrived home, the ratio of beta tokens to delta tokens was 3 to 4.

1. Use the ratio 3 to 4 to list the possible numbers of tokens Stella had when she arrived home.

Beta	3	6	9	12	15	18
Delta	4	8	12	16	20	24

2. In the table below, add the number of tokens paid at the tollgates to each number of tokens in the table above.

Beta	12	15	18	21	24	27
Delta	14	18	22	26	30	34

3. How many beta and delta tokens did Interstellar Stella have when she left Substation Alpha?

24 beta and 30 delta tokens

NAME ________________

VISUAL THINKING

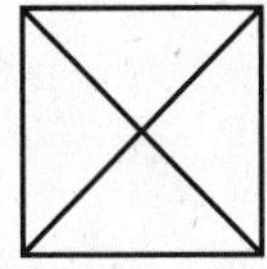

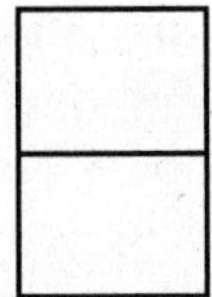
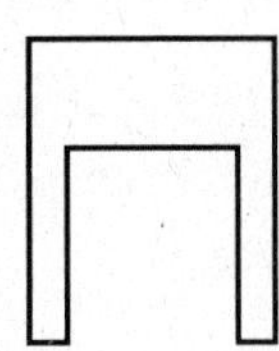
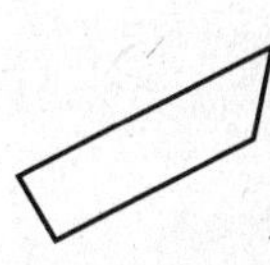

a. b. c. d. e.

One of the simple figures above is hidden in each of the complex figures below. Write the letter of the correct simple figure in each blank.

1. 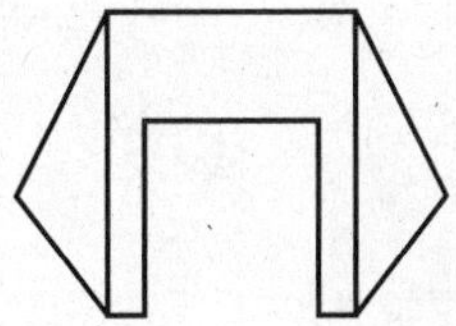 ______

2. 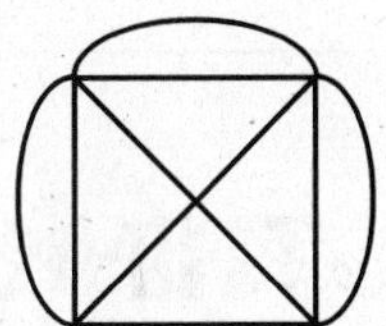 ______

3.  ______

4. 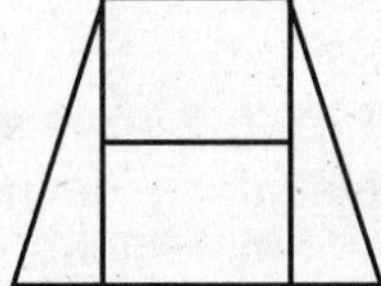 ______

5. 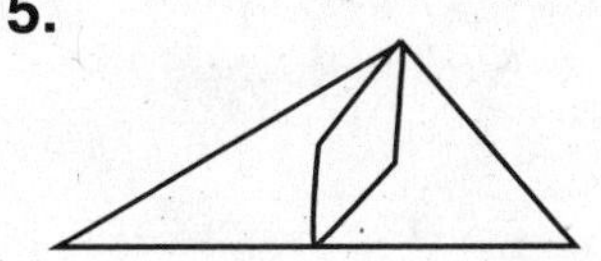 ______

6. 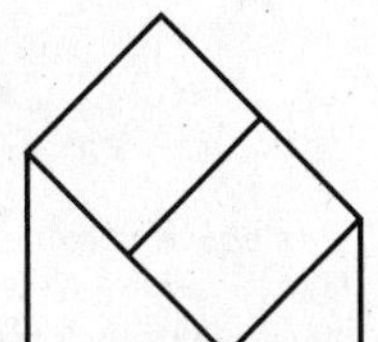 ______

7. 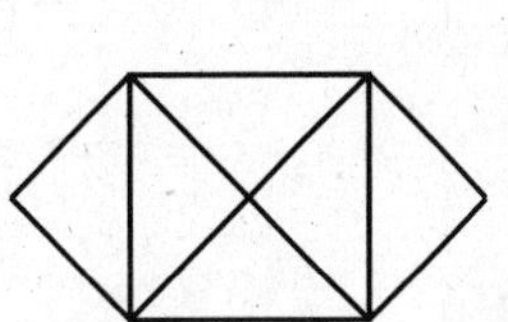 ______

8. 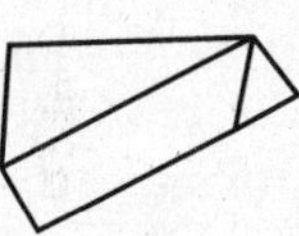 ______

9. 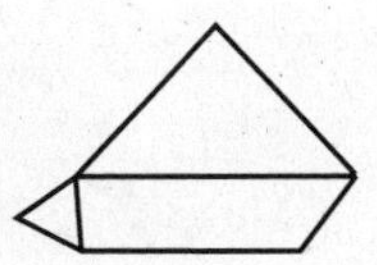 ______

10. 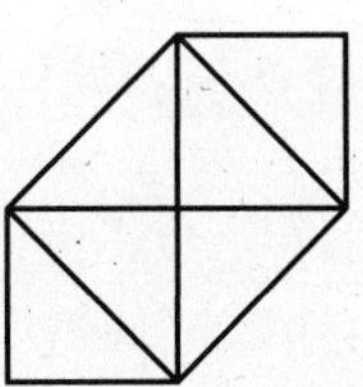 ______

11. 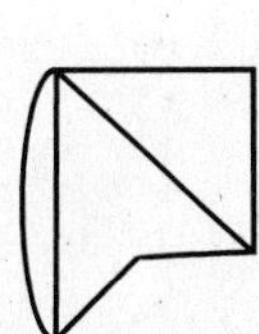 ______

12. 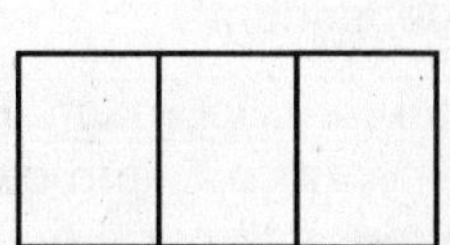 ______

13.  ______

14. 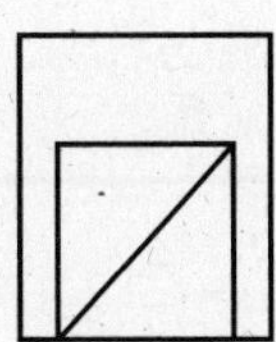 ______

15. 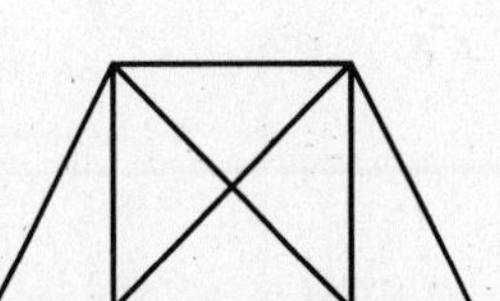 ______

16. 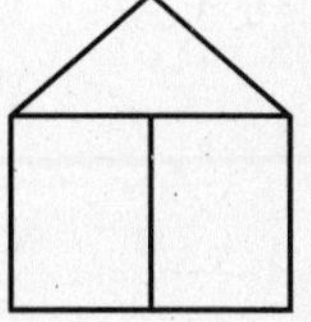 ______

Teacher Notes

Use with
Objective 113
pages 416–417

Focus
Visual Thinking
Spatial Perception

Materials
Scissors
Visual Thinking transparency (optional)

Overview
Students identify a simple figure concealed within a complex figure.

Teaching Suggestions
Have students define in words each of the 5 figures at the top of the page. For example: Figure **a** is a square with 2 diagonals. Explain that if they do not immediately see the hidden figure, they should look at the 5 figures one at time and check the complex figure to see if they can recognize the simple figure in it. Remind them that the simple figure may be rotated in the complex figure. Then have them complete the page independently.

Alternate Approach: Have students copy and cut out figures **a** through **e** and hold each one against the more complex figures in order to determine if it is contained there.

Extension
For each of the simple figures **a–e,** have students construct a complex figure containing it. Have students trade and check their solutions.

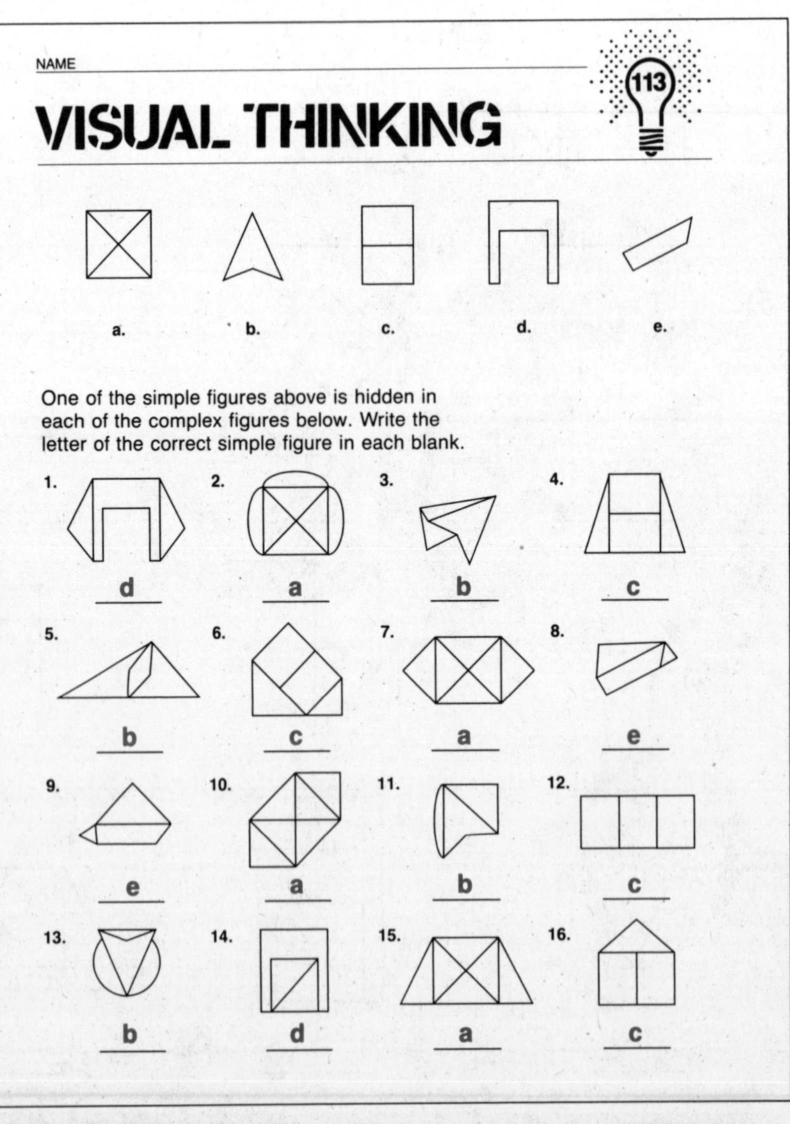

NAME ______________________________

CRITICAL THINKING

A baseball player's batting average is computed by dividing the number of times a player gets a hit by the number of times a player is at bat, and expressing the quotient to the nearest thousandth. Complete the following table to solve the problems.

Player	Hits	At Bats	Average
Lefty Toscano	21	70	.300
Knuckles Kloske	6	25	.240
Hurler Haus	3	18	
Catfish Kingfish	14	65	
Digger Morasco	10	37	
Charlie Rustle	2	9	

1. If Lefty Toscano gets 3 hits in his next 16 at bats, what do you estimate will happen to his batting average? Explain.

____

2. Catfish Kingfish gets 4 hits in his next 12 times at bat. What do you estimate will happen to his batting average? Explain.

____

3. Hurler Haus gets 1 hit in his next 6 times at bat, and Digger Morasco gets 4 hits in his next 9 times at bat. First estimate, then calculate, the changes in their batting average.

____

____

Use after pages 418–419.

Teacher Notes

Use with
Objective 114
pages 418–419

Focus
Critical Thinking
Evaluating Evidence and Conclusions
Making and Testing Predictions

Overview
Students compute batting averages, predict how batting averages will be affected by future performance, and test some of the predictions.

Teaching Suggestions
After students have read the first paragraph silently, have volunteers show how Lefty's and Knuckles's averages were computed. Remind students to round to the nearest thousandth. Have students work independently to complete the table.

Explain that Problem 2 requires two steps. The first step is to find the batting average for the next number of times at bat given. Then students can compare that number to the batting average in the chart and estimate whether that average will go up or go down.

In Problem 3, students complete the same steps as for Problem 2 and test their predictions by calculating the batting average for a larger number of times at bat.

Questions: What information from the table will you need to use to calculate Hurler's new average? [His hit and bat records] *How can you calculate his new batting average?* [Add previous hits to new hits and divide by previous at bats plus new at bats.]

Extension
Have students figure out how many hits each player would need in his next 20 times at bat to have at least a 300 batting average, basing their calculations on the information in the chart on the activity page. [Lefty, 6; Knuckles, 8; Hurler, 9; Catfish, 12; Digger, 8; Charlie, 7]

NAME ____________________

CRITICAL THINKING

114

A baseball player's batting average is computed by dividing the number of times a player gets a hit by the number of times a player is at bat, and expressing the quotient to the nearest thousandth. Complete the following table to solve the problems.

Player	Hits	At Bats	Average
Lefty Toscano	21	70	.300
Knuckles Kloske	6	25	.240
Hurler Haus	3	18	**.167**
Catfish Kingfish	14	65	**.215**
Digger Morasco	10	37	**.270**
Charlie Rustle	2	9	**.222**

1. If Lefty Toscano gets 3 hits in his next 16 at bats, what do you estimate will happen to his batting average? Explain.
   Go down; since $\frac{3}{16}$ or .188 < .300

2. Catfish Kingfish gets 4 hits in his next 12 times at bat. What do you estimate will happen to his batting average? Explain.
   Go up; since $\frac{4}{12}$ or .333 > .215

3. Hurler Haus gets 1 hit in his next 6 times at bat, and Digger Morasco gets 4 hits in his next 9 times at bat. First estimate, then calculate, the changes in their batting average.
   Haus stays same; new average $\frac{4}{24}$ = .167
   Morasco goes up; new average $\frac{14}{46}$ = .304

NAME ____________________

PROBLEM SOLVING

At Sharon's dress shop, the most expensive prom dress is priced so that the profit is 20% of the selling price. If Sharon raises the price \$20, the resulting profit is $\frac{1}{3}$ of the price of the dress.

1. Write an equation showing the percentage relationship of the profit P to the cost C. ____________________

2. Write an equation to show the relationship between the profit P and the cost C using the other information provided above. ____________________

3. How can you use the result in Problem 1 to help you solve the equation in Problem 2?

____

4. What was the original price of the dress? ____________________

Use with
Objective 115
pages 420–421

Focus
Problem Solving
Write an Equation

Overview
Students use simultaneous equations to solve a percentage problem with two variables and determine the original price of a dress.

Teaching Suggestions
If students have difficulty in relating the terms in the paragraph to the terms in problems, tell them that Problem 1 refers to the first sentence in the paragraph. ***Question:*** *To what term in the first sentence does the word* cost *refer?* [Selling price] Tell students that in order to solve Problem 2, they need to *write an equation* in which the variables *P* and *C* stand for exactly the same thing as variables *P* and *C* in the first equation. ***Questions:*** *How much of the $20 is profit?* [All of it] *How can we show the new profit in terms of P?* [P + 20] Have students complete Problem 2 independently.

For Problem 3, remind students that they will be able to solve the second equation only if they make it into an equation with one variable. Have them look ahead to Problem 4 to determine which variable they want to solve for. Have students complete Problems 3 and 4 independently.

Alternate Approach: Review converting percentages to decimals by taking off the percentage sign and moving the decimal point two places to the left. Remind students that when converting word problems to equations, an equal sign can usually be substituted for the word *is* and a multiplication sign can be substituted for the word *of.* Have students work in pairs to complete the page.

NAME ______________________

PROBLEM SOLVING

At Sharon's dress shop, the most expensive prom dress is priced so that the profit is 20% of the selling price. If Sharon raises the price $20, the resulting profit is $\frac{1}{3}$ of the price of the dress.

1. Write an equation showing the percentage relationship of the profit *P* to the cost *C*. **$P = 0.2C$**
2. Write an equation to show the relationship between the profit *P* and the cost *C* using the other information provided above. **$P + 20 = \frac{(C + 20)}{3}$**
3. How can you use the result in Problem 1 to help you solve the equation in Problem 2? **Substitute 0.2*C* for *P*: $0.2C + 20 = \frac{C + 20}{3}$**
4. What was the original price of the dress? **$100**

NAME ______________________________

VISUAL THINKING

In each row, ring the letter of the figure on the right that can be formed by putting together the pieces on the left. The pieces can be flipped or turned, but they cannot overlap, and there cannot be gaps.

1.

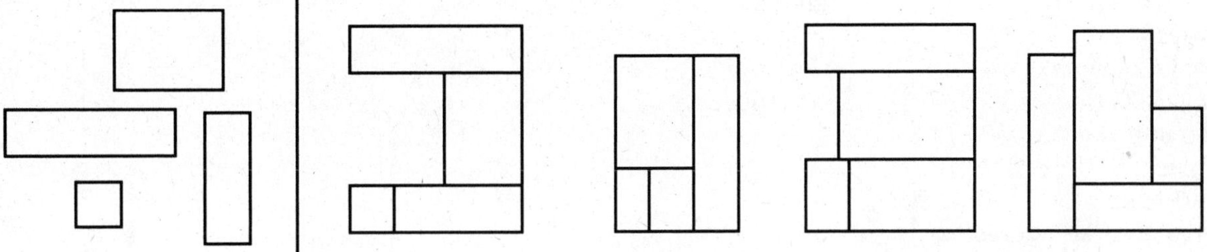

a. b. c. d.

2.

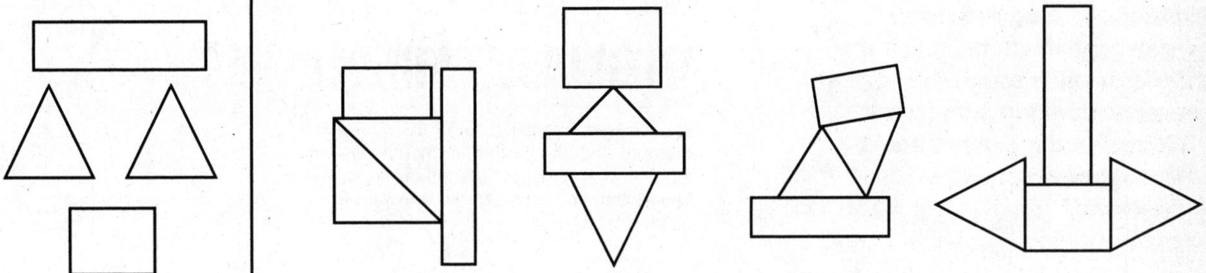

a. b. c. d.

3.

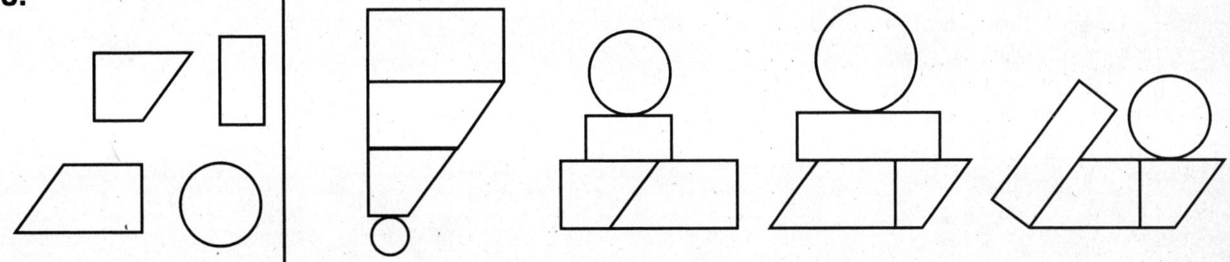

a. b. c. d.

4.

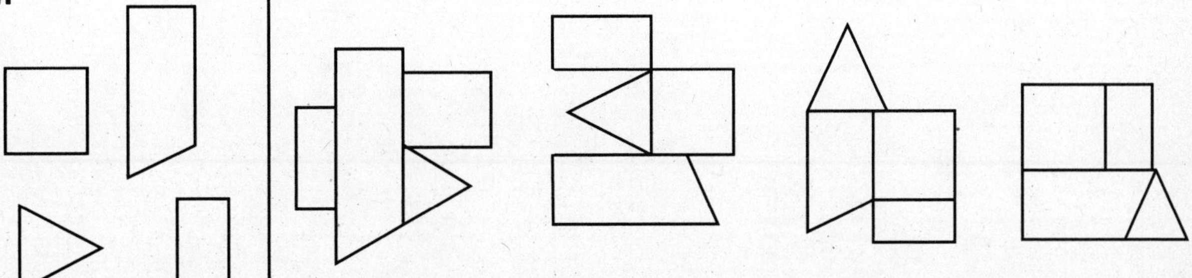

a. b. c. d.

Teacher Notes

Use with
Objective 116
pages 422–425

Focus
Visual Thinking
Visual Patterns

Materials
Tangrams (optional)
Visual Thinking transparency (optional)

Overview
Students analyze figures to identify which one is made of four given geometric shapes.

Teaching Suggestions
Make sure students notice that the division lines in the assembled figures show the outlines of the shapes from which they are made.

Alternate Approach: Have students verbally identify each shape by its geometric name and size. For example, for Problem 1, there is 1 short wide rectangle, 1 long narrow rectangle, 1 medium narrow rectangle, and 1 small square. Then have them examine one figure at a time, marking each part of the figure that corresponds exactly to an individual piece until either they make a match or they come to piece that does not match. Have them complete the page independently.

Extension
Distribute tangram sets. Have students make a figure and outline it. Have them trade outlines with a partner and have the partner try to fill in the outline with the appropriate shapes.

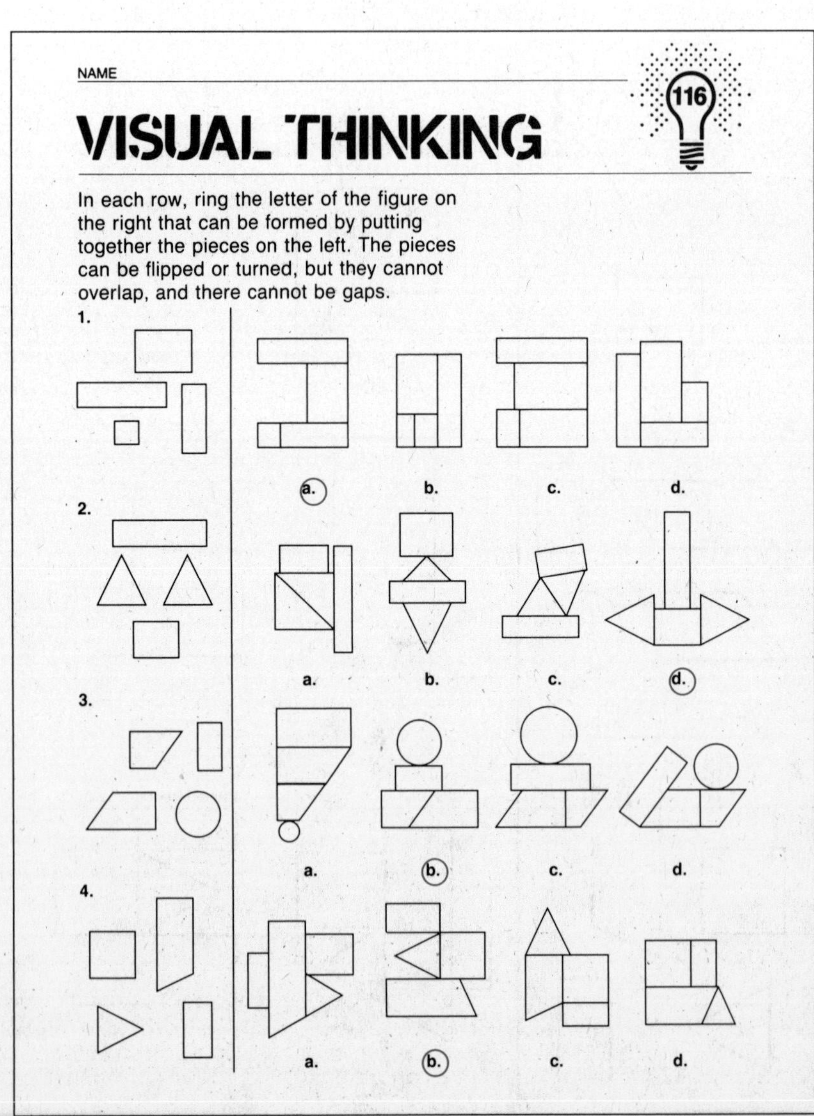
NAME
116
VISUAL THINKING
In each row, ring the letter of the figure on the right that can be formed by putting together the pieces on the left. The pieces can be flipped or turned, but they cannot overlap, and there cannot be gaps.
1.
a. b. c. d.
2.
a. b. c. d.
3.
a. b. c. d.
4.
a. b. c. d.

NAME ______________________________

CRITICAL THINKING

Replace each letter in the following puzzle with a number from 0 through 9 to make the computation correct. In each problem, the same letter must have the same value, and different letters must have different values.

Suppose you let E equal 1. Then O must equal 2 because 1 + 1 = 2. T must be equal to 4 if there is no regrouping from the tens to the hundreds place, or 5 if there is regrouping.

```
  O N E
+ O N E
-------
  T W O

  2 _ 1
+ 2 _ 1
-------
  _ _ 2
```

Now finish the puzzle on your own.

1. Find two other solutions for this puzzle.

```
  _ _ _        _ _ _
+ _ _ _      + _ _ _
-------      -------
  _ _ _        _ _ _
```

Find one solution for each of the following puzzles below.

2.

```
  T W O
+ T W O
-------
F O U R

  _ _ _
+ _ _ _
-------
_ _ _ _
```

3.

```
  T H R E E
+   F O U R
-----------
  S E V E N

  _ _ _ _ _
+   _ _ _ _
-----------
  _ _ _ _ _
```

4.

```
  F O U R
+ F O U R
---------
E I G H T

  _ _ _ _
+ _ _ _ _
---------
_ _ _ _ _
```

Teacher Notes

Use with
Objective 117
pages 428–429

Focus
Critical Thinking
Using Logic
Drawing Conclusions
Making and Testing Predictions

Overview
Students *use logic* to predict and test alternative solutions to match puzzles.

Teaching Suggestions
Make sure students understand the rules for the activity. Then read the second paragraph and have a volunteer explain each sentence. Record each successive conclusion on the chalkboard as follows.

Sentence 1	Sentence 2
_ _ 1	2 _ 1
_ _ 1	2 _ 1
_ _ _	_ _ 2

Sentence 3		Sentence 4
2 _ 1		2 _ 1
2 _ 1		2 _ 1
4 _ 2	or	5 _ 2

Point out that *T, N,* and *W* must still be assigned values. Two possible values for *T* have been determined, but this does not mean that both will necessarily work. Tell students they should test one value at a time. Complete the puzzle on the chalkboard as you receive answers to the following.

***Questions:** Suppose that $T = 4$. What conclusion can you draw about N?* [N must be less than 5] *What values in that category are already used?* [1, 2, 4] *If $N = 3$, what value can be used for W?* [6] *If $T = 5$, what must be true about $N + N$?* [$N + N \geq 10$] *What must be true about N?* [$N \geq 5$] *Can it be 5?* [No] *Why not?* [5 has already been assigned to *T*.]

Have students test the values 6–9 and analyze each possibility. [6 does not work because *W* would have to be 2; if $N = 7$, $W = 4$; if $N = 8$, $W = 6$; if $N = 9$, $W = 8$.]

NAME ________________________

CRITICAL THINKING

Replace each letter in the following puzzle with a number from 0 through 9 to make the computation correct. In each problem, the same letter must have the same value, and different letters must have different values.

Suppose you let E equal 1. Then O must equal 2 because 1 + 1 = 2. T must be equal to 4 if there is no regrouping from the tens to the hundreds place, or 5 if there is regrouping.

Now finish the puzzle on your own.

```
  O N E
+ O N E
  T W O

  2 3 1
+ 2 3 1
  4 6 2
```

2, 4, 6, 8, WHO DO WE APPRECIATE?

1. Find two other solutions for this puzzle.

Possible answers:

```
  4 3 2      2 3 6
+ 4 3 2    + 2 3 6
  8 6 4      4 7 2
```

Find one solution for each of the following puzzles below.

```
2.   T W O     3.   T H R E E     4.   F O U R
   + T W O        +   F O U R        + F O U R
   F O U R          S E V E N        E I G H T

     7 6 5          6 2 3 1 1          5 3 9 2
   + 7 6 5        +   9 5 0 3        + 5 3 9 2
   1 5 3 0          7 1 8 1 4        1 0 7 8 4
```

NAME ______________________________

VISUAL THINKING

Use the figure below to solve the problems. There are no hidden spaces. Each cube rests on another cube, unless shown otherwise.

1. How many separate cubes did it take to construct the entire figure above?

____

2. Complete the table on the right to determine the number of painted surfaces that will result if all of the outside surfaces of the entire figure are painted red.

Total number of red surfaces: __________

Number of Red Surfaces on a Cube	Number of Cubes with Red Surfaces
4	
3	
2	
1	
0	

3. If each edge of a cube measures 1 inch, what is the total surface area of the figure?

____

Teacher Notes

Use With
Objective 118
pages 430–431

Focus
Visual Thinking
Spatial Perception

Materials
50 small cubes for each student

Overview
Students analyze a 2-dimensional picture of a structure made of cubes to draw conclusions about the 3-dimensional figure it represents.

Teaching Suggestions
Make sure students understand that the picture represents a 3-dimensional figure which has cubes that they cannot see. ***Questions:*** *How many cubes are in the first row which is 1 cube high?* [5] *How many cubes can you see in the second row which is 2 cubes high?* [6] *How many cubes that you cannot see must be there?* [4] *How many cubes high is the third row?* [3] *How many total cubes are in the third row?* [15] Repeat the questions for the fourth row. Then have students answer Problem 1. For Problem 2 have students identify where in the picture the cubes are that show each of the number of faces indicated. Then have them complete the table.

For Problem 3, remind students about the formula for finding the area of a square [$A = s \times s$]. If necessary, also remind them that the whole surface area for one side of the figure equals the sum of the areas of all faces showing on that side.

Alternate Approach: Have students agree that you will call the side of the figure toward the sitting painter "right," the one near the painter on the ladder "left," and the others "top," "bottom," "front," and "back." Have them determine the number of red sides by determining the number of cube faces showing on each of the six named sides. [Right, 10; left, 10; top, bottom, front, and back, 20 each]

NAME ____________________

VISUAL THINKING

Use the figure below to solve the problems. There are no hidden spaces. Each cube rests on another cube, unless shown otherwise.

1. How many separate cubes did it take to construct the entire figure above?
   50 cubes

2. Complete the table on the right to determine the number of painted surfaces that will result if all of the outside surfaces of the entire figure are painted red.

   Total number of red surfaces: **100**

Number of Red Surfaces on a Cube	Number of Cubes with Red Surfaces
4	**4**
3	**12**
2	**17**
1	**14**
0	**3**

3. If each edge of a cube measures 1 inch, what is the total surface area of the figure?
   100 square inches

NAME

PROBLEM SOLVING

Luke read this newspaper ad and said, "Wow! 25% off if I pay cash."

TWO STYLES – Touring & Racing
$150
REGULAR PRICE
EACH STYLE SAME PRICE!
Sale! 20% OFF THE REGULAR PRICE!
5% OFF SALE PRICE for CASH!

1. What is the price of the bicycle with a 20% discount? ______

2. What is the price of the bicycle with a 20% discount followed by a 5% discount for paying in cash? ______

3. Is the 20% discount minus a 5% discount for cash the same as a 25% discount? Explain. Was Luke correct?

______

4. Is a 25% increase in price, minus a 10% decrease the same as a 15% increase? Explain by giving an example.

______

______

______

Teacher Notes

Use with
Objective 119
pages 432–433

Focus
Problem Solving
Write an Equation
Try and Check

Overview
Students compare final costs of a bicycle when changes in the price are made either all at once or in consecutive operations.

Teaching Suggestions
You may want to review finding the discount price when the original price and the percent of discount are given. For Problem 1, have students *write an equation* ($0.20 \times 150 = n$) to find 20% of \$150. Then students should subtract the amount of discount from the original price to find the discount price.

Students should follow a similar procedure for Problem 2, but the 5% discount applies to the \$120.

To make the comparison in Problem 3, students will need to find the price for a discount of 25% and compare this answer to the price found in Problem 2.

For Problem 4, students should *try and check* to determine the answer.

Suggest that they use an original price of \$100.00. You may wish to have students *try and check* other original prices to confirm that a 25% increase followed by a 10% decrease is always less than a 15% increase.

Extension
Have students determine the actual percentage of discount for the two consecutive discounts in Problem 3. They should find the amount of the discount [\$36] by subtracting the final price from the original price. Then they should find what percent 36 is of 150. [24%]

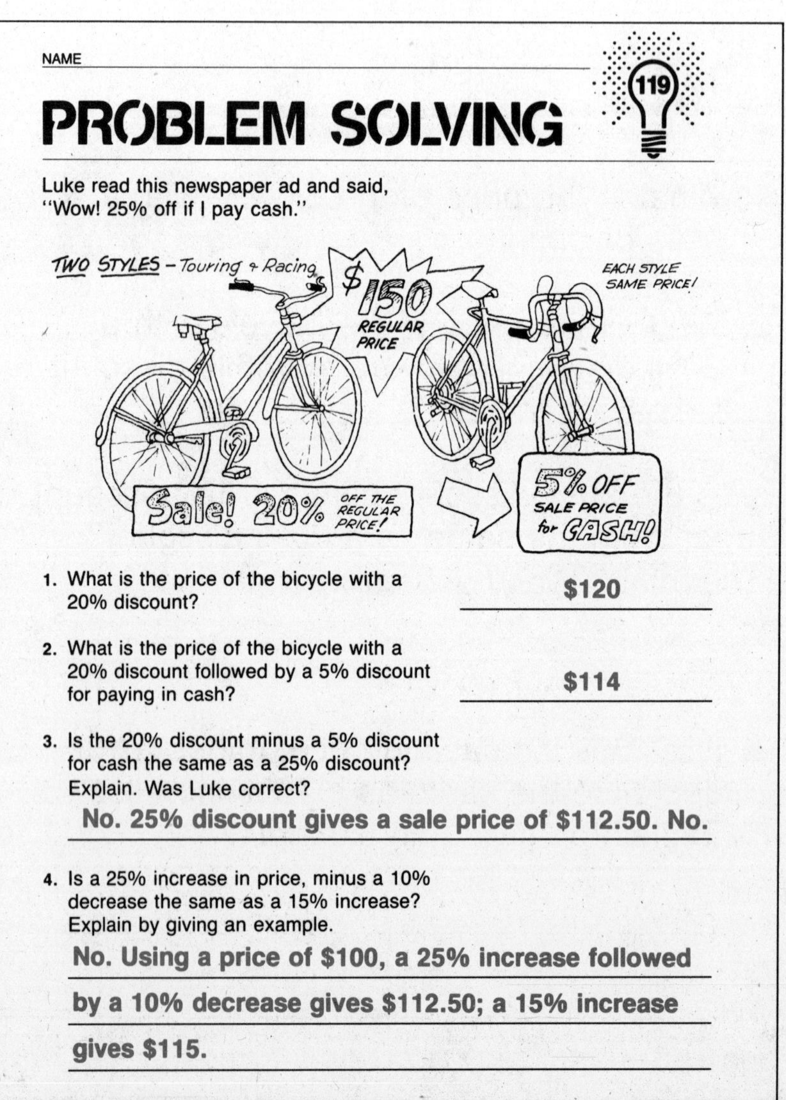

NAME ______________________

PROBLEM SOLVING

Luke read this newspaper ad and said, "Wow! 25% off if I pay cash."

1. What is the price of the bicycle with a 20% discount? **\$120**

2. What is the price of the bicycle with a 20% discount followed by a 5% discount for paying in cash? **\$114**

3. Is the 20% discount minus a 5% discount for cash the same as a 25% discount? Explain. Was Luke correct?
No. 25% discount gives a sale price of \$112.50. No.

4. Is a 25% increase in price, minus a 10% decrease the same as a 15% increase? Explain by giving an example.
No. Using a price of \$100, a 25% increase followed by a 10% decrease gives \$112.50; a 15% increase gives \$115.

NAME ______________________________

DECISION MAKING

Jaime, Charles, Robert, Kris, and Nick are going to a baseball game at Quigley Field. They decided to put all of their money together in order to get tickets for the best seats possible. Together they have $19.00. The higher-priced seats are better than the lower-priced seats.

Charles and Robert are best friends and would prefer to sit together in the best seats available. Robert and Kris would prefer not to sit together. Jaime wants the very best seat possible and does not mind sitting alone. Nick will sit anywhere as long as he can sit with at least one of the other boys.

1. On another sheet of paper, list all of the possible combinations of 5 tickets that the boys can buy for $19.

2. How might the boys buy their tickets? Explain your answer.

____

____

____

____

____

Teacher Notes

Use with
Objective 120
pages 434–437

Focus
Decision Making

Overview
Students identify the restrictions on how 5 boys can satisfy certain requirements for cost and seating when buying tickets for a baseball game.

Teaching Suggestions
Have students read the two introductory paragraphs silently. ***Questions:** What are the two kinds of restrictions in this problem?* [Available money and seating] *Which restrictions should be dealt with first and why?* [Money; because there is only $19 to spend] For Problem 1, suggest that students make a table to help list all possibilities for combinations of 5 tickets that cost no more than $19. This table lists all the possible combinations.

Number of seats in			
Bleachers ($3)	Grand-stand ($4)	Box seats ($5)	Total cost
1	4	0	$19
2	2	1	$19
3	0	2	$19
3	1	1	$18
3	2	0	$17
4	0	1	$17
4	1	0	$16
5	0	0	$15

For Problem 2, have students use their tables plus the stated preferences to determine an option that best fulfills the requirements. Some students may suggest putting Jaime, Charles, Robert, and Nick in the grandstand and Kris in the bleachers as the alternative that provides the best seats for the most people since that is the goal stated in the first paragraph on the activity sheet.

Extension
Have students work in pairs to design another decision-making problem with an absolute restriction about available money and preferences about how to spend it. Possible topics include buying concert tickets, purchasing pizzas, or planning a class party. Have the pairs trade problems and discuss possible solutions.

NAME ______________________________

DECISION MAKING

Jaime, Charles, Robert, Kris, and Nick are going to a baseball game at Quigley Field. They decided to put all of their money together in order to get tickets for the best seats possible. Together they have $19.00. The higher-priced seats are better than the lower-priced seats.

Charles and Robert are best friends and would prefer to sit together in the best seats available. Robert and Kris would prefer not to sit together. Jaime wants the very best seat possible and does not mind sitting alone. Nick will sit anywhere as long as he can sit with at least one of the other boys.

1. On another sheet of paper, list all of the possible combinations of 5 tickets that the boys can buy for $19.

2. How might the boys buy their tickets? Explain your answer.

Possible answer: Jaime in box seat (best seat possible), Charles and Robert in grandstands (best friends in best seats available together), Kris and Nick in bleachers (Kris away from Robert, Nick sitting with another boy)

NAME ______________________________

PROBLEM SOLVING

Vicky has ten percent cards labeled as shown. She deals them out following these six steps.

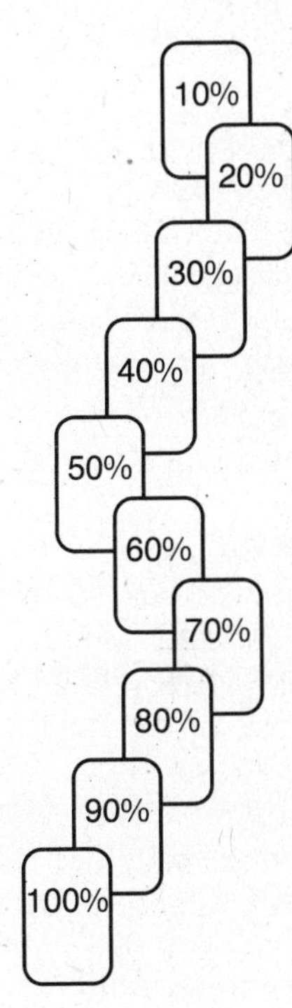

Step 1 She holds the ten cards face down in a deck.

Step 2 She moves the top card, face down, to the bottom of the deck.

Step 3 She places the next card, face up, on the table.

Step 4 She moves the next card, face down, to the bottom of the deck.

Step 5 She places the next card, face up, on the table to the right of the previously-placed card.

Step 6 She repeats steps 2–5 until all the cards are lined up on the table.

1. Vicky arranges the cards, face down, from the top of the deck to the bottom in this order: 10%, 20%, 30%, . . . , 100%. After Vicky follows the six steps, in what order will the cards appear from left to right on the table?

2. Vicky can do a special trick. She can follow the six steps and have the cards appear on the table from left to right in this order: 10%, 20%, 30%, . . . , 100%. In what order must Vicky arrange the cards in the deck, from top to bottom, before she starts Step 1?

Teacher Notes

Use with
Objective 121
pages 438–439

Focus
Problem Solving
Try and Check
Use Logical Reasoning
Work Backward

Materials
10 index cards for each student

Overview
Students investigate the effects of performing repeated operations on a deck of ten cards.

Teaching Suggestions
Have each student make a set of the percent cards by writing 10%, 20%, and so on, on individual index cards. You may want to demonstrate the procedure to the class.

For Problem 2, some students may *try and check* to find the arrangement that works. Others may use *logical reasoning* to incorporate the results from Problem 1 in their work for Problem 2 by thinking of the cards in Problem 1 in terms of the place where they appeared in the deck, so that 10% is the 1st card, 20% is the 2nd card, and so on. ***Questions:** For Problem 1, what is the order of the cards on the table using their position names?* [2nd, 4th, 6th, 8th, 10th, 3rd, 7th, 1st, 9th, 5th] *How can you use this information to arrange the cards?* [Put the cards face up in the desired order, which is 10%, 20%, and so on, from left to right.

Then put the cards face-down into a deck using the position name listed above. For example, the card for 80% would be the first card in the deck, the card for 10% would be the second card in the deck, the card for 60% would be the third card, and so on.] Students may also arrange the cards in the desired order and *work backward* to reverse the dealing procedure. That is, they should pick up the 100% card.

Then they should pick up the 90% card and put it on top of the deck. Move the bottom card in the deck to the top, and so on, until all the cards are picked up, ending with the bottom card of the entire deck being moved to the top.

Alternate Approach: Some students may find the percent signs with the numbers confusing. Have these students work with the numbers 1–10 instead.

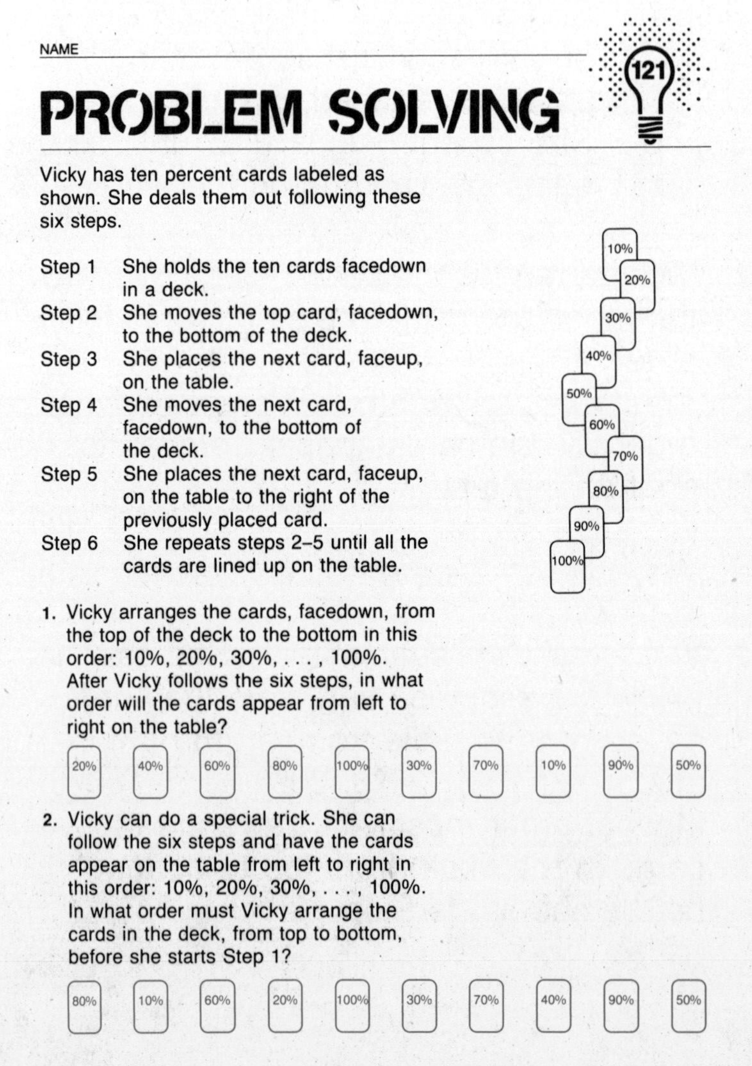
NAME

PROBLEM SOLVING

121

Vicky has ten percent cards labeled as shown. She deals them out following these six steps.

Step 1 She holds the ten cards facedown in a deck.
Step 2 She moves the top card, facedown, to the bottom of the deck.
Step 3 She places the next card, faceup, on the table.
Step 4 She moves the next card, facedown, to the bottom of the deck.
Step 5 She places the next card, faceup, on the table to the right of the previously placed card.
Step 6 She repeats steps 2–5 until all the cards are lined up on the table.

1. Vicky arranges the cards, facedown, from the top of the deck to the bottom in this order: 10%, 20%, 30%, . . . , 100%. After Vicky follows the six steps, in what order will the cards appear from left to right on the table?

20% 40% 60% 80% 100% 30% 70% 10% 90% 50%

2. Vicky can do a special trick. She can follow the six steps and have the cards appear on the table from left to right in this order: 10%, 20%, 30%, . . . , 100%. In what order must Vicky arrange the cards in the deck, from top to bottom, before she starts Step 1?

80% 10% 60% 20% 100% 30% 70% 40% 90% 50%

NAME ______

VISUAL THINKING

In each row, the figure on the left shows a box that is to be unfolded. Ring the letter of the figure on the right that shows the unfolded box.

1.

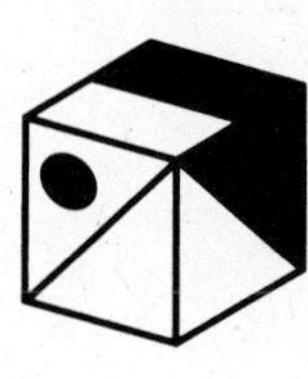

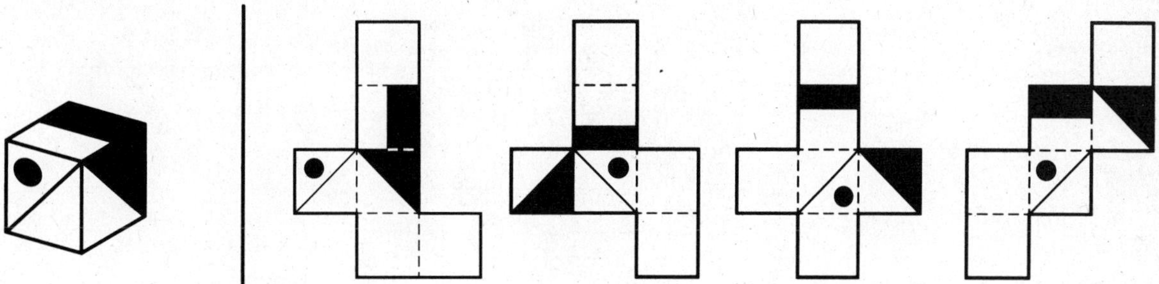

a. b. c. d.

2.

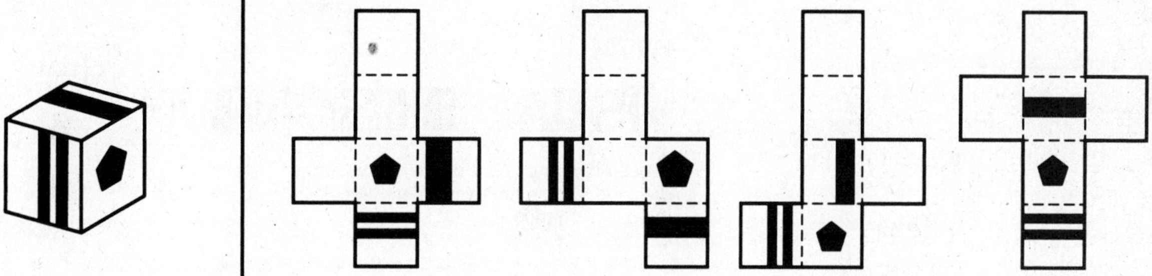

a. b. c. d.

3.

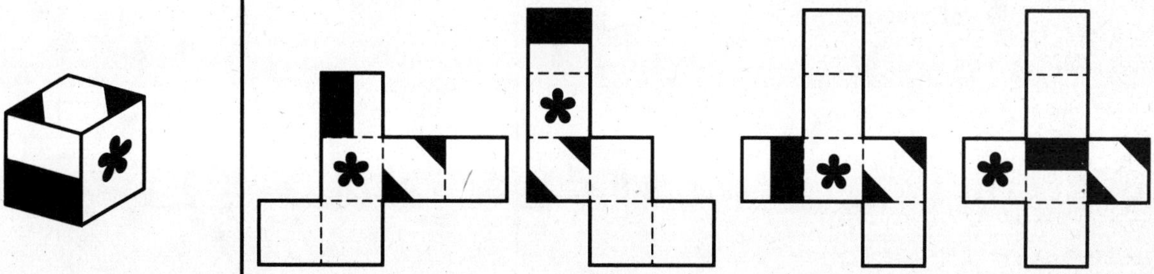

a. b. c. d.

4.

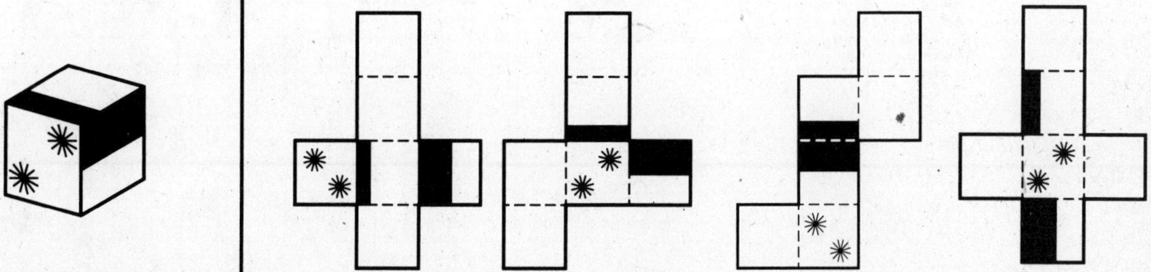

a. b. c. d.

Teacher Notes

Use with
Objective 122
pages 450–451

Focus
Visual Thinking
Spatial Perception

Materials
Sheets of cardboard
Scissors
Visual Thinking transparency (optional)

Overview
Students match a folded box with an unfolded box.

Teaching Suggestions
Explain to students that they need only pay attention to the configuration of the three shaded or marked squares. A strategy the students may want to use is this: Look at which portions of the squares join each other. In Problem 1, in the square to the left, the right triangle with the dot touches the unshaded half of the square it joins, and the triangle without the dot touches the unshaded triangle of the square it joins. Have students look among the unfolded boxes for a choice which represents these junctions. Only choice **a** does.

Alternate Approach: For each problem, have students make three separate cardboard squares, each with the design of one of the sides of the boxes in the left column. Have students arrange the squares to match the configurations given in the answer choices and fold them into a half box to see which answer choice is correct.

Extension
Have students draw the box represented by each incorrect choice.

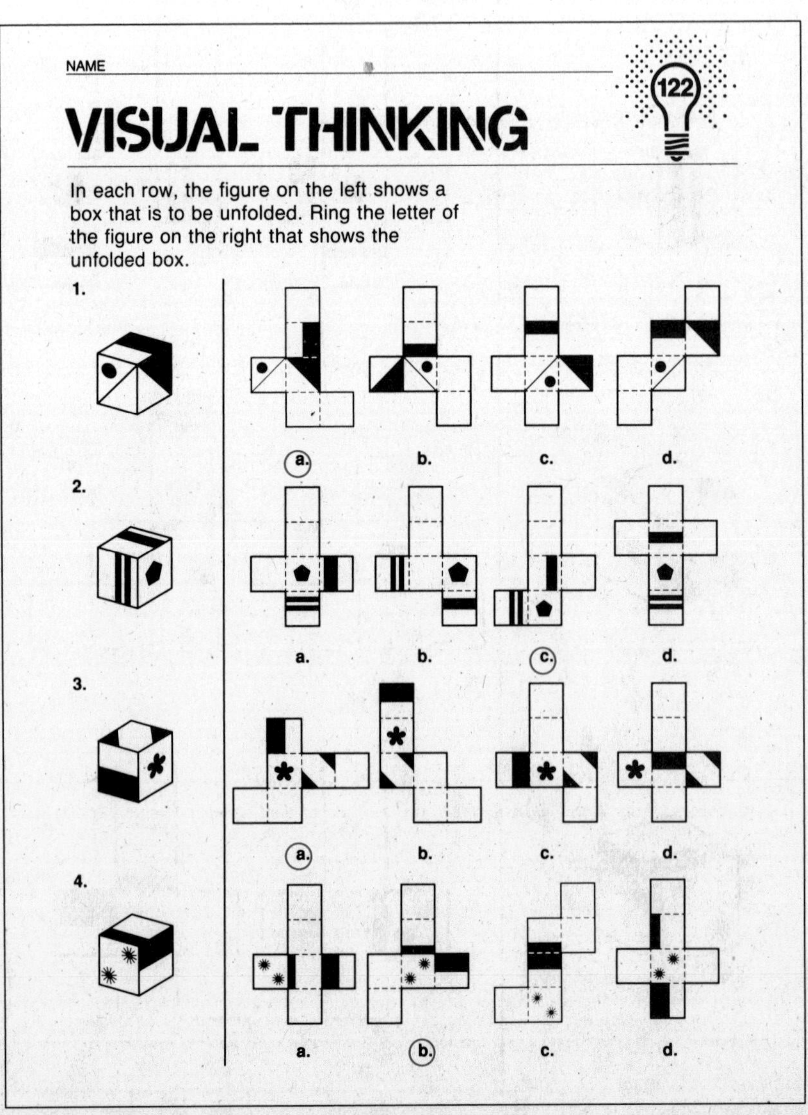

NAME ______________________________

PROBLEM SOLVING

1. Suppose you guessed each answer. Since there are 3 choices for each answer, you would expect to guess about one third of the questions correctly. How many questions is that?

____

TRIVIA TEST

For each question, only one answer is correct. Circle the correct answer.

1. The Zip Code for Guanica is
   a. 00632. b. 00653. c. 00670.
2. Stan Jok played for the
   a. Browns. b. Red Sox. c. White Sox.
3. The 88th word in Gettysburg Address is
   a. lives. b. their. c. that.
4. The capital of the Republic of Nauru is
   a. Renay. b. Yaren. c. Areyn.
5. The 7th highest volcano in Japan is
   a. Kirisima. b. Azuma. c. On-take.
6. The capybara lives primarily in
   a. Africa. b. S. America. c. Asia.
7. Augustus was the 1st Roman Emperor in
   a. 27 B.C. b. 31 B.C. c. 13 A.D.
8. The unit of money in Mauritius is the
   a. dirhan. b. rand. c. rupee.
9. The height of the Skykjefos Waterfall is
   a. 550 m. b. 125 m. c. 250 m.
10. Hannah Van Buren's maiden name was
    a. Hoes. b. Smith. c. Denton.
11. The 1920 Olympic Games were held in
    a. Athens. b. Antwerp. c. London.
12. The Prime Minister of Canada in 1900 was
    a. Laurier. b. Trudeau. c. MacDonald.

2. Take the test and check your answers with your teacher. How many questions did you answer correctly? ______________________________

3. What is the total number of correct answers for all the students in your class? What is the average number of correct answers per student? How does this result compare to that in Problem 1?

____

Teacher Notes

Use with
Objective 123
pages 452–453

Focus
Problem Solving
Use Logical Reasoning
Try and Check

Materials
One coin per student

Overview
Students test the laws of probability with a 12-question trivia test.

Teaching Suggestions
Explain to students that probability indicates only what is likely to occur, not what must occur. ***Question:*** *Since we are checking the outcome of pure guessing on the trivia test, how would our research be affected if a student knew the answer to one or more questions?* [That student's score would not reflect the results of guessing. This means the results for students who know one or more of the answers should not be included.]

Have students take the test. Then give the correct answers. [1b; 2c; 3c; 4b; 5a; 6b; 7a; 8c; 9c; 10a; 11b; 12a] Have students solve Problem 2. ***Questions:*** *How many students had exactly four questions correct?* [Answers will vary.] *How many students got more or fewer than four correct answers?* [Answers will vary.] Draw a two-column chart on the chalkboard. Have each student record the number of his or her correct answers in the chart. Have students solve Problem 3.

Discuss why the average number of correct answers per test is near 4, even though not every student got close to four correct answers.

Extension
Give each student a coin. Inform students that according to probability, a flipped coin should land heads and tails the same number of times. Have each student flip the coin twice. How many students had these results? Have students keep track of thirty flips and discuss the results. [With more flips the results should approach the predicted results.]

NAME ______________________

PROBLEM SOLVING

1. Suppose you guessed each answer. Since there are 3 choices for each answer, you would expect to guess about one third of the questions correctly. How many questions is that?
4 questions

TRIVIA TEST

For each question, only one answer is correct. Circle the correct answer.

1. The Zip Code for Guanica is
a. 00632. (b.) 00653. c. 00670.
2. Stan Jok played for the
a. Browns. b. Red Sox. (c.) White Sox.
3. The 88th word in Gettysburg Address is
a. lives. b. their. (c.) that.
4. The capital of the Republic of Nauru is
a. Renay. (b.) Yaren. c. Areyn.
5. The 7th highest volcano in Japan is
(a.) Kirisima. b. Azuma. c. On-take.
6. The capybara lives primarily in
a. Africa. (b.) S. America. c. Asia.
7. Augustus was the 1st Roman Emperor in
(a.) 27 B.C. b. 31 B.C. c. 13 A.D.
8. The unit of money in Mauritius is the
a. dirhan. b. rand. (c.) rupee.
9. The height of the Skykjefos Waterfall is
a. 550 m. b. 125 m. (c.) 250 m.
10. Hannah Van Buren's maiden name was
(a.) Hoes. b. Smith. c. Denton.
11. The 1920 Olympic Games were held in
a. Athens. (b.) Antwerp. c. London.
12. The Prime Minister of Canada in 1900 was
(a.) Laurier. b. Trudeau. c. MacDonald.

2. Take the test and check your answers with your teacher. How many questions did you answer correctly?
Answers will vary.

3. What is the total number of correct answers for all the students in your class? What is the average number of correct answers per student? How does this result compare to that in Problem 1?
Answers will vary, but average should be close to 4.

NAME ______________________________

VISUAL THINKING

Write the letter of the figure on the right that is formed by folding the figure on the left along its line of symmetry.

1. ______

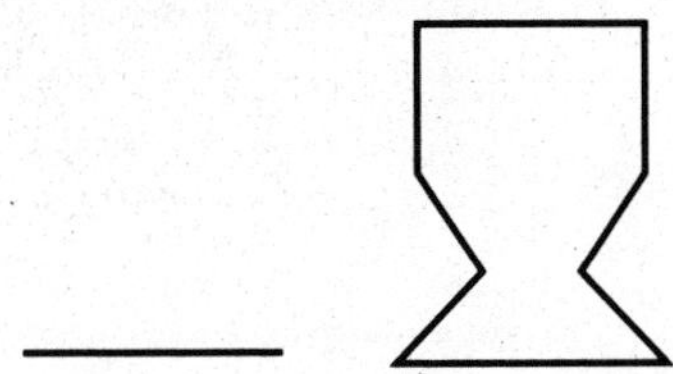

a. 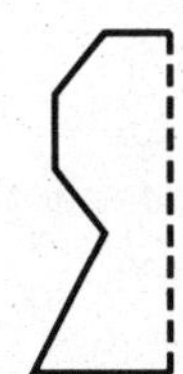

2. ______

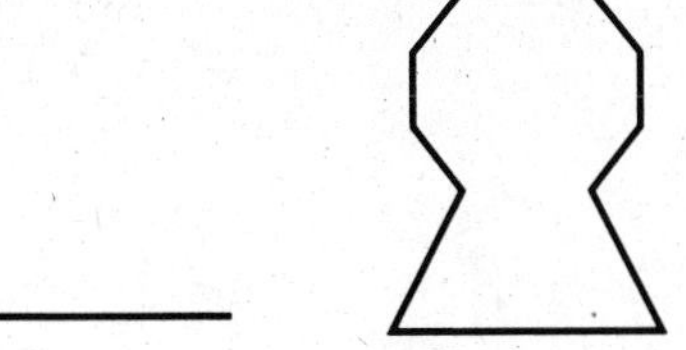

b. 

3. ______

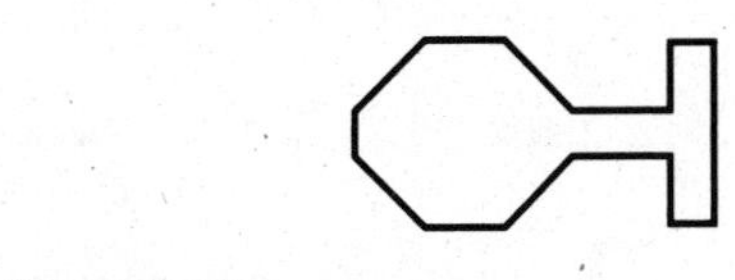

c. 

4. ______

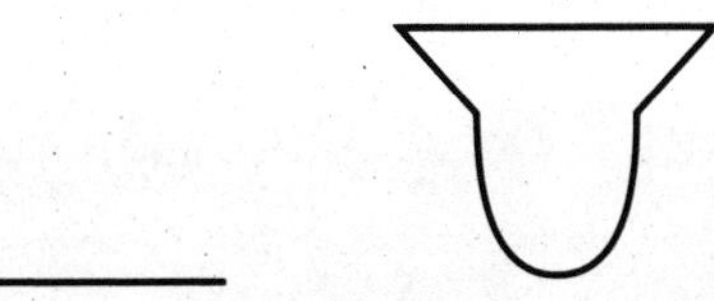

d. 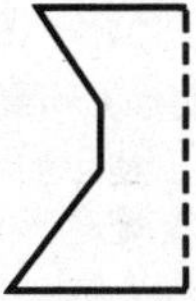

5. ______

e. 

6. ______

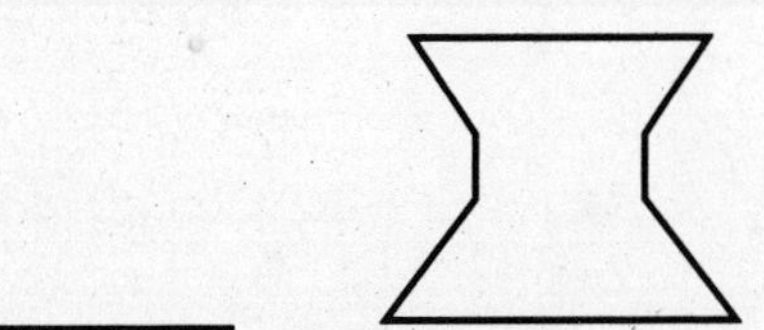

f. 

7. ______

g. 

Teacher Notes

Use with
Objective 124
pages 454–457

Focus
Visual Thinking
Spatial Perception

Materials
Small index card
Flexible plastic mirror
Visual Thinking transparency (optional)

Overview
Students match an unfolded view of a figure with the view of that figure folded along one line of symmetry.

Teaching Suggestions
Have students look at the figures in the column on the right. ***Question:*** *Are the figures with vertical lines of symmetry* (**a, c, d, f**) *folded to the left or the right?* [They are all folded to the left.] Have students place the edge of an index card along the line of symmetry for the figures in Problems 1, 2, 5, and 7, so that the right half of the figure is covered. Then have students find the folded figure on the right that is identical to the figure to the left of the index card. Then have students do Problems 3, 4, and 6, noting the direction of the fold and placing their index card horizontally along the line of symmetry.

Alternate Approach: Have students work backward and start with the column on the right. Have students place a mirror along the edge of each figure in the column on the right and match the figure the mirror creates with a figure in the column on the left.

Extension
Have students create figures with two lines of symmetry. Then have students draw figures formed by folding them along both lines of symmetry.

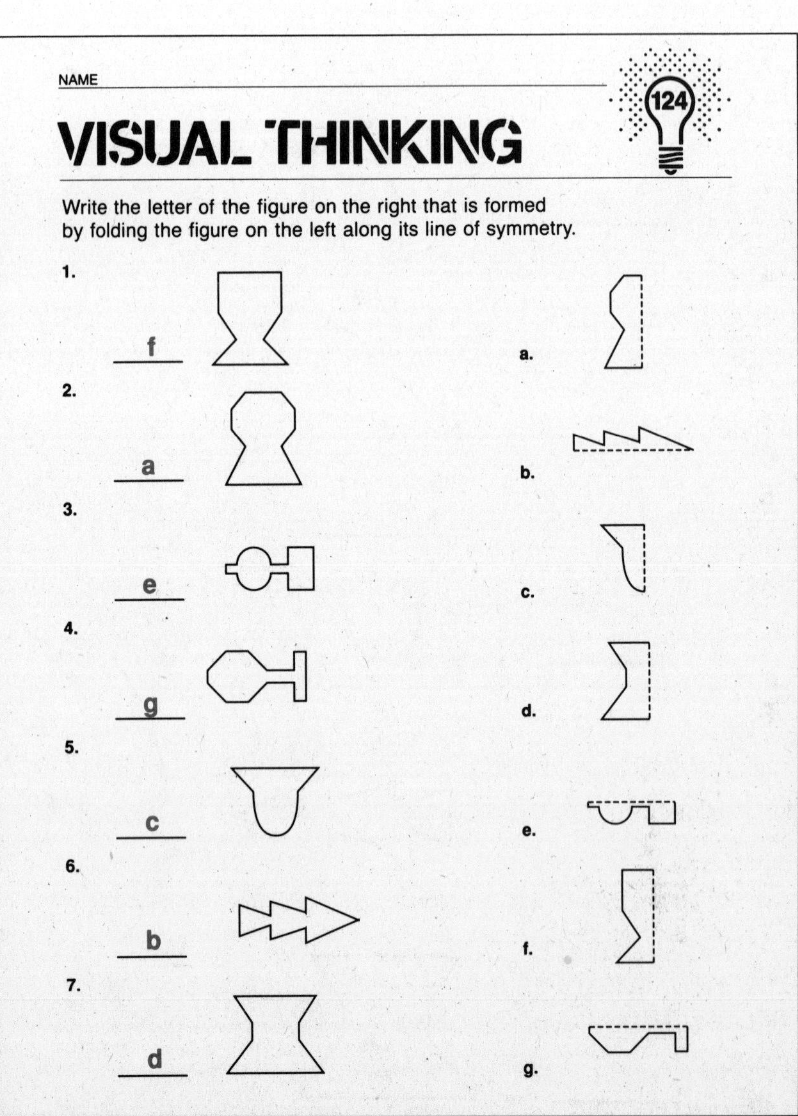
NAME
124
VISUAL THINKING
Write the letter of the figure on the right that is formed by folding the figure on the left along its line of symmetry.
1. f
2. a
3. e
4. g
5. c
6. b
7. d
a.
b.
c.
d.
e.
f.
g.

NAME ______________________________

PROBLEM SOLVING

At Howard School, Line 1 in the lunchroom serves certain meals on certain days, as shown below. Charles gets in Line 1, but forgets to look at the menu.

1. What is the chance that Charles will be served pizza? ______________

2. What is the chance that he will be served a hamburger? ______________

3. What is the chance he will be served a bowl of chili? ______________

4. Suppose the school year is 36 weeks long. If Charles always gets in Line 1, how many times will he be served each meal during the entire school year?

Pizza: ____________ Hamburger: ________ Chili: ____________

Teacher Notes

Use with
Objective 125
pages 458–459

Focus
Problem Solving
Use Logical Reasoning

Overview
Students *use logical reasoning* and a weekly menu to figure out the likelihood of a particular meal being served.

Teaching Suggestions
Inform students that since we do not know which day it is, and since only one meal is served per day, Problem 1 can be restated as "What is the chance that the day Charles gets in Line 1 is a Monday or a Wednesday?" ***Questions:*** *How many days is the lunchroom open?* [5] *What is the chance that the day Charles gets in Line 1 is a Monday or Wednesday?* [2/5] Have students do Problems 2 and 3 independently.

For Problem 4, students should note that the sum of their answers should be 180. ***Questions:*** *Since 5 meals are served every week, how many meals are served in a year?* [5 × 36 = 180] *What must the sum of the answers to Problem 4 equal?* [180] Students can use this fact to check if their answers for Problem 4 are reasonable.

Extension
Copy the following charts on the chalkboard or overhead. Assume that each day Charles chooses one line at random. Then have students solve Problems 1–3. [Pizza 4/15; hamburgers 4/15; chili 1/5]

LINE 2	LINE 3
Mon. & Tues.	Mon. & Fri.
PIZZA	FISH STICKS
Wed. & Thurs.	Tues. & Thurs.
HAMBURGERS	HOT DOGS
Fri. CHILI	Wed. CHILI

Have students find out how many times Charles will be served each type of food (pizza, hamburgers, chili, fish sticks, hot dogs) during the school year. [Pizza, 48; hamburgers, 48; chili, 36; fish sticks, 24; hot dogs, 24]

NAME
125
PROBLEM SOLVING
At Howard School, Line 1 in the lunchroom serves certain meals on certain days, as shown below. Charles gets in Line 1, but forgets to look at the menu.
Mon. and Wed.
PIZZA
Tues. and Thurs.
HAMBURGERS
Fri - CHILI
LINE
1
1. What is the chance that Charles will be served pizza? 2/5
2. What is the chance that he will be served a hamburger? 2/5
3. What is the chance he will be served a bowl of chili? 1/5
4. Suppose the school year is 36 weeks long. If Charles always gets in Line 1, how many times will he be served each meal during the entire school year?
Pizza: 72 Hamburger: 72 Chili: 36

NAME ______________________________

DECISION MAKING

An ambulance traveling from the fire station to the school can choose two different paths.

A: Grand Ave. to Oak St. to Hamilton St.
B: Grand Ave. to Highway 16 to Hamilton St.

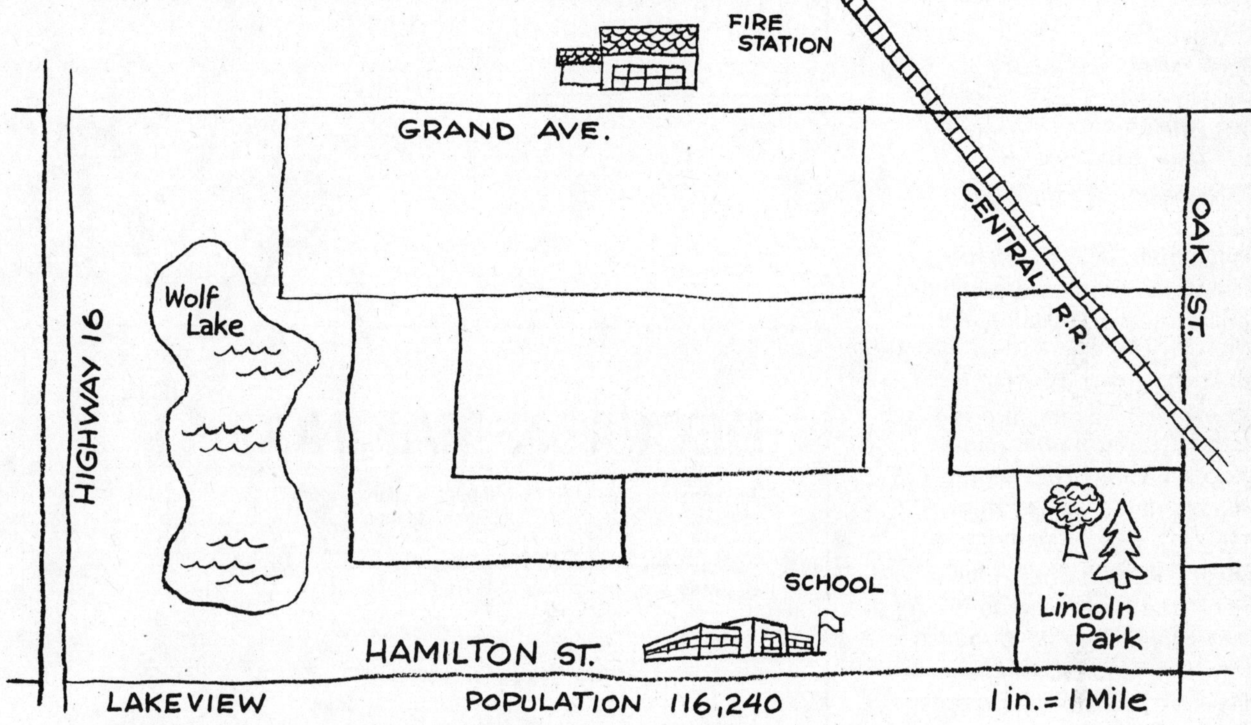

1. Estimate the distances along paths A and B.

   Path A: ______________________ Path B: ______________________

2. When the ambulance must travel to school, what are the advantages of using Path A? Path B?

   Path A: ____

   Path B: ____

3. Which path would you recommend? Why?

   ____

Teacher Notes

Use with
Objective 126
pages 460–461

Focus
Decision Making

Materials
Ruler for each student

Overview
Students measure the distances of two different paths, assess their advantages, and recommend one of them as a more suitable route for an ambulance.

Teaching Suggestions
Have students measure the distances along both paths with a ruler. Instruct students in the use of the scale. Then have students solve Problems 1 and 2. ***Questions:*** *How much of a disadvantage is it for an ambulance to have to stop at two railroad crossings?* [Possible answer: It is a great disadvantage. Having to wait for a train could seriously delay the ambulance.] *Would the greater distance of Path B probably be compensated for by the faster highway speed?* [Possible answer: Yes, considering that Path B is only a mile longer, that highway speed can be nearly double that of street speed, and that about 1/3 the distance of Path B is highway]

Extension
If the ambulance travels an average of 40 mph on the street and 60 mph on the highway, how many minutes would it take to travel Path A? [12.75 minutes] Path B? [12.75 minutes]

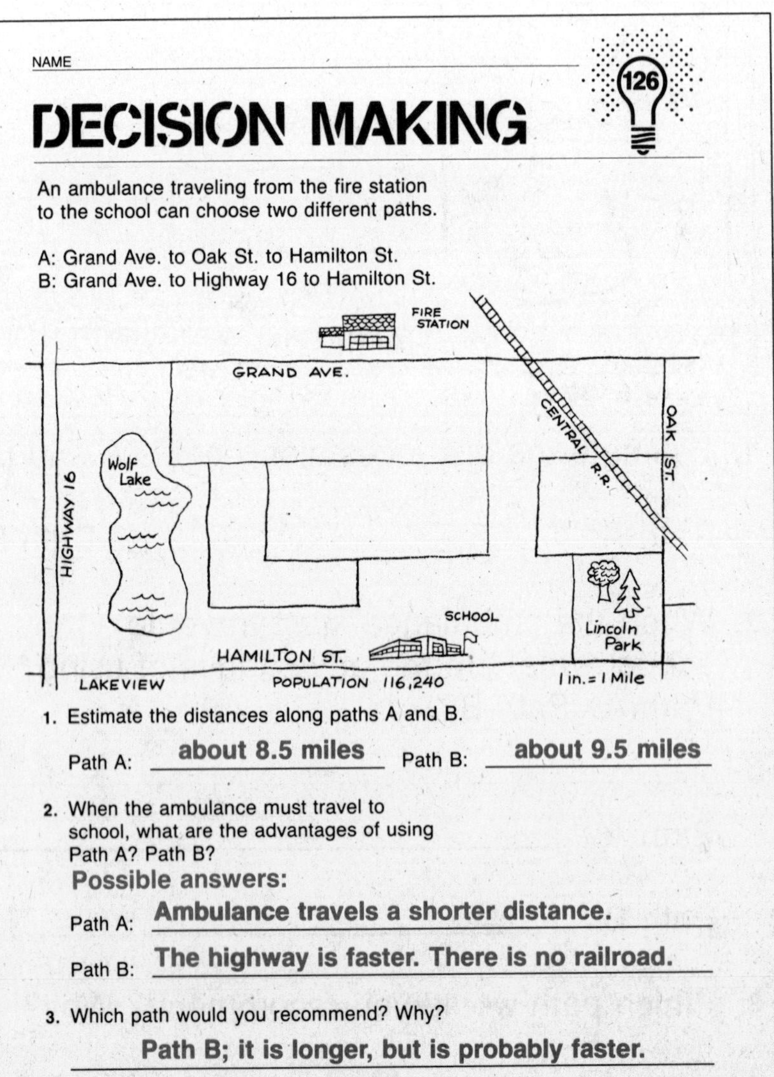

NAME ______

DECISION MAKING

126

An ambulance traveling from the fire station to the school can choose two different paths.

A: Grand Ave. to Oak St. to Hamilton St.
B: Grand Ave. to Highway 16 to Hamilton St.

1. Estimate the distances along paths A and B.

   Path A: **about 8.5 miles** Path B: **about 9.5 miles**

2. When the ambulance must travel to school, what are the advantages of using Path A? Path B?

   Possible answers:

   Path A: **Ambulance travels a shorter distance.**

   Path B: **The highway is faster. There is no railroad.**

3. Which path would you recommend? Why?

   Path B; it is longer, but is probably faster.

NAME ___

VISUAL THINKING

For each row, ring the letter of the percent of the figure that is shaded.

1.

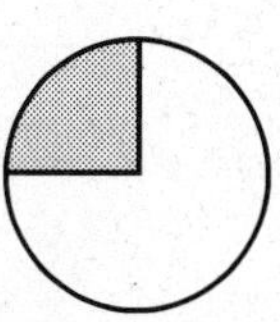

a.	b.	c.	d.
25%	35%	15%	45%

2.

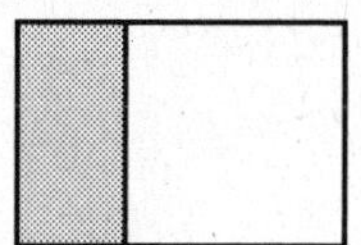

a.	b.	c.	d.
50%	20%	25.5%	33.3%

3.

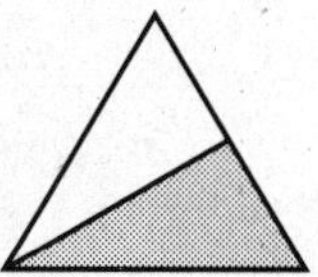

a.	b.	c.	d.
40%	50%	33.3%	25%

4.

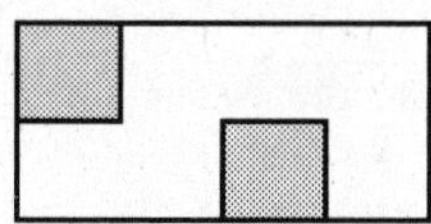

a.	b.	c.	d.
35%	10%	25%	15%

5.

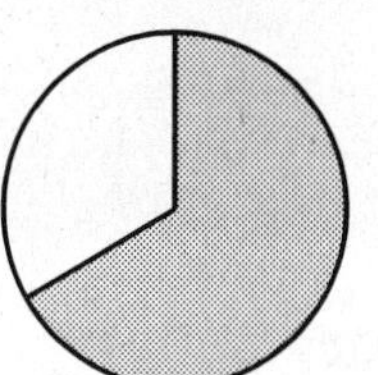

a.	b.	c.	d.
50%	75%	33.3%	66.6%

6.

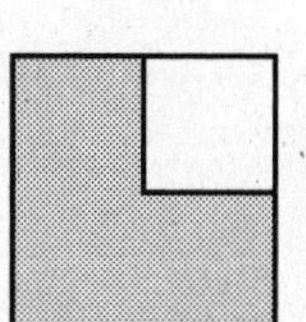

a.	b.	c.	d.
85%	75%	60%	50%

7.

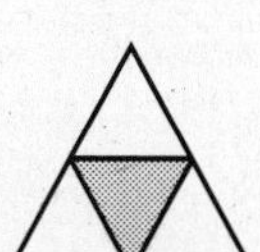

a.	b.	c.	d.
25%	66.6%	50%	40%

8.

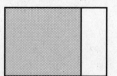

a.	b.	c.	d.
75%	30%	40%	50%

Use after pages 464–465.

Teacher Notes

Use with
Objective 127
pages 464–465

Focus
Visual Thinking
Spatial Perception

Materials
Ruler, protractor, and tracing paper for each student

Overview
Students estimate the percent of a figure represented by a shaded portion.

Teaching Suggestions
Encourage students to use visual estimation and the process of elimination. Some students will immediately see the relative size of some shaded portions, especially those in Problems 1, 2, 3, 6, and 7. In Problems 4, 5, and 8, some wrong answers can be easily eliminated. In Problem 8, for example, the shaded portion is clearly more than 50%, leaving only choice **a.**

Alternate Approach: If students have difficulty, suggest that they divide the entire figure into fractional parts equal to the shaded or unshaded portion (whichever is smaller). For example, in Problem 1, divide the remaining portion of the circle into fourths. For Problem 3, students might measure the sides of the shaded and unshaded triangles with a ruler.

Extension
For Problems 2, 3, 4, 6, 7, and 8, have students find the percent of the figure that is shaded using the formula for area. Students should measure the base and height with a ruler.

NAME ______________________

127

VISUAL THINKING

For each row, ring the letter of the percent of the figure that is shaded.

	a.	b.	c.	d.
1.	(a.) 25%	35%	15%	45%
2.	50%	20%	25.5%	(d.) 33.3%
3.	40%	(b.) 50%	33.3%	25%
4.	35%	10%	(c.) 25%	15%
5.	50%	75%	33.3%	(d.) 66.6%
6.	85%	(b.) 75%	60%	50%
7.	(a.) 25%	66.6%	50%	40%
8.	(a.) 75%	30%	40%	50%

(circled)

NAME ___

PROBLEM SOLVING

Katie enjoys riding in bike rallies. At the last rally she attended, the cross-country course was 20 miles long, with markers every 2 miles. At each marker, a timer recorded the time each biker passed. The picture at the right show's Katie's time for each 2-mile portion of the course.

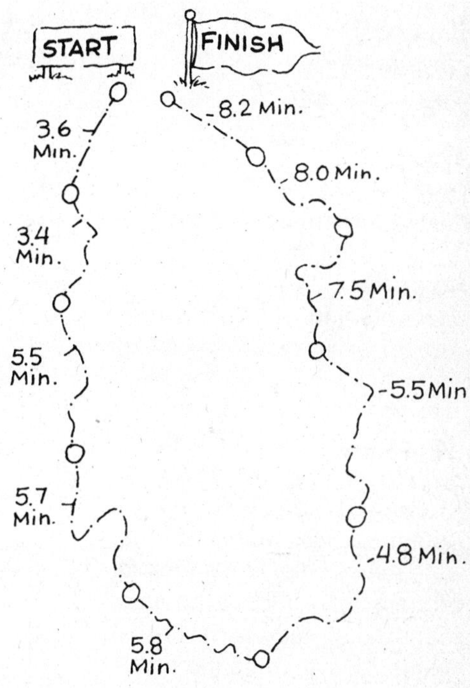

To find Katie's average rate, use the formula $d = r \times t$, where d is the distance in miles, r is the rate in miles per minute, and t is the time in minutes. Round your answers to the nearest hundredth.

1. What was Katie's total time for the rally? ___
2. How far did she ride? ___
3. What was her average rate for the rally? ___
4. What was her average rate for the first half of the course? ___
5. What was her average rate for the second half of the course? ___

Teacher Notes

Use with
Objective 128
pages 466–467

Focus
Problem Solving
Use a Formula

Overview
Students find a biker's average rate for an entire bike rally and for the two halves of the rally.

Teaching Suggestions
Tell students to look at the drawing of the course. ***Question:*** *How can you determine Katie's total time for the rally?* [By adding the times recorded at each two-mile marker] Have students answer Problems 1 and 2.

Show students that since $d = r \times t$, it follows that $r = d/t$. Have students solve Problem 3. ***Questions:*** *What was Katie's time for the first half of the rally?* [24 min] *What was Katie's time for the second half of the rally?* [34 min] *How can you quickly check if these half-course times are correct?* [They must add up to 58 min] *What is the distance of each half of the course?* [10 miles] Have students solve Problems 4 and 5.

Extension
Have students solve the following problems.

1. On the day of the rally, Joe, a marathon runner, ran the course with an average speed of a mile every 5 minutes. How long did it take him to cover the course? [1 hour and 40 minutes]
2. The same day, Jill drove the course in her car. It took her 2 hours. She drove at the same speed throughout the entire course. At what speed did she drive? [10 miles per hour]

NAME ______________________

128

PROBLEM SOLVING

Katie enjoys riding in bike rallies. At the last rally she attended, the cross-country course was 20 miles long, with markers every 2 miles. At each marker, a timer recorded the time each biker passed. The picture at the right show's Katie's time for each 2-mile portion of the course.

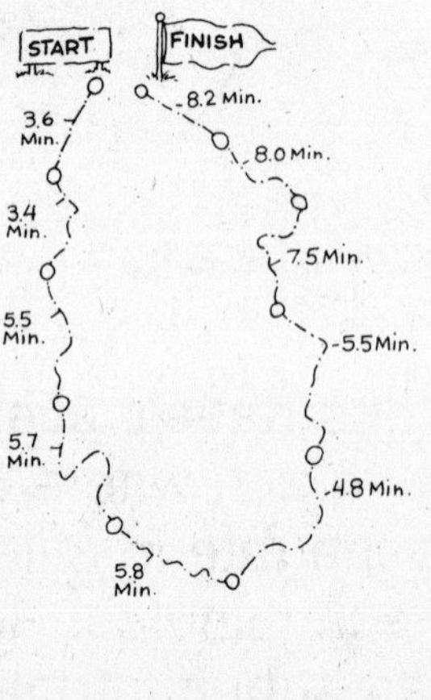

To find Katie's average rate, use the formula $d = r \times t$, where d is the distance in miles, r is the rate in miles per minute, and t is the time in minutes. Round your answers to the nearest hundredth.

1. What was Katie's total time for the rally? **58.0 minutes**
2. How far did she ride? **20 miles**
3. What was her average rate for the rally? **0.34 mile/minute**
4. What was her average rate for the first half of the course? **0.42 mile/minute**
5. What was her average rate for the second half of the course? **0.29 mile/minute**

NAME

CRITICAL THINKING

Septimus Siete loves the number 7. In fact, he loves it so much that he wants to use no other numbers.

Septimus needs to fill out a job application which asks for his age. He would like to represent his age, which is 43 years, using only the number 7.

What are 3 ways Septimus Siete might represent his age using only seven 7s and any mathematical operations?

Teacher Notes

Use with
Objective 129
pages 468–469

Focus
Critical Thinking
Using Number Sense

Overview
Students combine mathematical operations using only the number 7, to create 3 expressions that equal 43.

Teaching Suggestions
Inform students that since 43 is not a multiple of 7, they must find inventive ways to make their number sentences. You may want to remind them that fractions and exponents can be used. Then have students solve the problem.

Alternate Approach: As an introduction to the activity, have students find the values of the following:

$7 \times 7 = [49]$ $77/7 = [11]$
$7/7 = [1]$ $\left(\frac{7}{7}\right)^7 = [1]$

Extension
Have students write expressions using only sevens that equal each of the numbers 40–49. [Possible answers: $7 \times (7 - 7/7) - 7/7 - 7/7 = 40$; $7 \times (7 - 7/7) - 7/7 = 41$; $7 \times (7 - 7/7) = 42$; $7 \times (7 - 7/7) + 7/7 = 43$; $(7 - 7/7 - 7/7 - 7/7) \times (77/7) = 44$; $(7 + 7/7 + 7/7) \times (7 - 7/7 - 7/7) = 45$; $7 \times 7 - 7/7 - 7/7 - 7/7 = 46$; $(7 + 7/7) \times (7 - 7/7) - 7/7 = 47$; $(7 + 7/7) \times (7 - 7/7) = 48$; $7 \times 7 = 49$]

NAME ____________________

CRITICAL THINKING

Septimus Siete loves the number 7. In fact, he loves it so much that he wants to use no other numbers.

Septimus needs to fill out a job application which asks for his age. He would like to represent his age, which is 43 years, using only the number 7.

What are 3 ways Septimus Siete might represent his age using only seven 7s and any mathematical operations?

Possible answers: $7 + (7 \times 7) - 7 + \frac{7}{7} - 7$,

$\frac{(7 + 7 + 7)(7 + 7) + 7}{7}$, $7 \times (7 - \frac{7}{7}) + \left(\frac{7}{7}\right)^7$

NAME ____________________

PROBLEM SOLVING

In a carnival game you select one of the numbers 1 through 6. Then you spin 3 spinners, each numbered 1 through 6. If your number comes up once, you win a slide whistle. If your number comes up twice, you win a blue cap. If your number comes up all three times you win a model car.

1. If you picked the number 4, what are your chances of winning a model car? ____________________

2. What are your chances of winning a blue cap? A slide whistle? ____________________

3. If you played the game 432 times, how many model cars would you expect to win? How many blue caps? How many slide whistles?

____________________ ____________________ ____________________

4. Each play is $1.00. Model cars cost $5.00 each, blue caps cost $1.00 each, and slide whistles cost $0.50 each. How much profit can the carnival operator expect to make after 432 plays? ____________________

Teacher Notes

Use with
Objective 130
pages 480–481

Focus
Problem Solving
Use Logical Reasoning

Overview
Students make a prediction about the outcome of spinning 3 spinners.

Teaching Suggestions
Questions: *On a single spin, what are your chances of getting your number?* [1/6] *In Problem 1, how many times would you have to spin a 4?* [All three times] Be sure students recall that compound probabilities are found by multiplying the individual probabilities.

In Problem 2, help students see that their chosen number cannot be spun on one of the three spins if they win a blue cap. ***Questions:*** *To win a blue cap, what must your three spins be?* [Two 4s and one that is not 4] *What are the individual probabilities for each spin?* [1/6 for each 4; 5/6 for the spin that is not 4] *Does it matter which spinner does not show a 4?* [No] Help students to see that this allows for three arrangements of the spins that are 4: first and second spins are 4; second and third spins are 4; first and third spins are 4. Be sure students know to figure each of these individually (1/6 × 1/6 × 5/6) and then add the three results.

To find the chances of winning a slide whistle, use reasoning similar to that for the blue cap. There will be three probabilities of 1/6 × 5/6 × 5/6 = 25/216 to be added.

In Problem 3, be sure students know to multiply the probability of each outcome by the total number of times the game is played [432].

Questions: *In Problem 4, how many prizes of each type will the carnival operator expect to have given out after 432 plays?* [2 cars, 30 caps, and 150 whistles] *What is his cost for these prizes?* [(2 × $5) + (30 × $1) + (150 × $0.50) = $115] *Will the entire $432 collected be profit? Explain.* [No. The $115 cost of the prizes will have to be subtracted.]

NAME ____________________

PROBLEM SOLVING

In a carnival game you select one of the numbers 1 through 6. Then you spin 3 spinners, each numbered 1 through 6. If your number comes up once, you win a slide whistle. If your number comes up twice, you win a blue cap. If your number comes up all three times you win a model car.

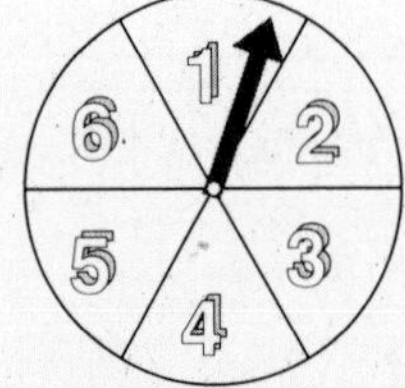

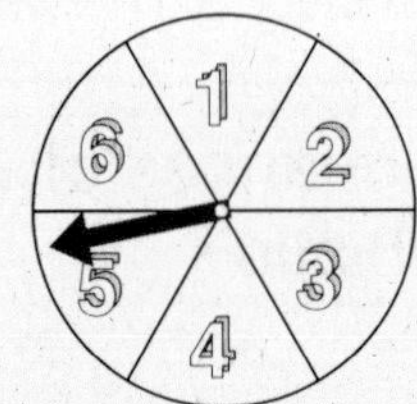

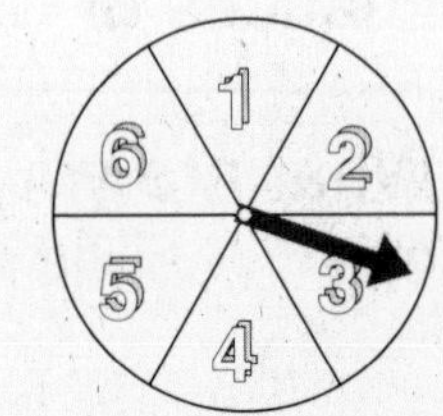

1. If you picked the number 4, what are your chances of winning a model car? **$\frac{1}{216}$**

2. What are your chances of winning a blue cap? A slide whistle? **$\frac{15}{216}$; $\frac{75}{216}$**

3. If you played the game 432 times, how many model cars would you expect to win? How many blue caps? How many slide whistles?

   2 model cars **30 blue caps** **150 slide whistles**

4. Each play is $1.00. Model cars cost $5.00 each, blue caps cost $1.00 each, and slide whistles cost $0.50 each. How much profit can the carnival operator expect to make after 432 plays? **$432 – $115 = $317**

NAME ____________________

CRITICAL THINKING

Surveys can be conducted either by asking questions of the total population of the group being studied, or by asking questions of only a few people in the group. Use the following survey to compare these two methods. Ask all your classmates to answer the survey questions on paper, and collect their responses.

	Total Population		Sample of 5	
Question	% Yes	% No	% Yes	% No
Have you seen a movie in the last 7 days?				
Did you watch less than 2 hours of TV last night?				
Did you drink milk with your breakfast today?				
Have you eaten pizza in the last 5 days?				
Have you read a book in the last 10 days?				

1. Complete the table by calculating the percents for the total population. Then shuffle all of the survey papers. Pull out 5 papers at random, and put their results in the sample column.

2. How did the results of the total population compare with those of the sample? Explain.

____

Teacher Notes

Use with
Objective 131
pages 482–483

Focus
Critical Thinking
Evaluating Evidence and Conclusions

Overview
Students compare a census survey to a random sample survey and make an evaluation of the usefulness of each.

Teaching Suggestions
Introduce the activity by discussing the U.S. national census done every 10 years. Discuss some of the uses of the information, such as predicting changing trends in population growth. Point out that in a census, everyone answers the questions on the survey.

A different type of survey is by use of a sample, where a group of people are chosen randomly. This type of survey is often used by pollsters to gather data. ***Question:*** *To determine the popularity of various television shows, which type of survey do you think is used, census or sample?* [Sample] Encourage students to discuss possible uses for each type of survey.

For Problem 1, students must find the percent of the total population that answered *Yes* and the percent that answered *No.* ***Question:*** *How do you find the percent that answered* Yes? [Divide the number of *Yes* answers by the total number of people that responded.] You may wish to tell students to round to the nearest whole percent.

To complete the Sample part of the table, let students take turns choosing 5 papers at random for their samples. Return these papers before other students make their choices. Remind students to divide by 5 when finding the Sample percents.

Extension
Have students take their survey questions home and question two adults. Then have the class pool their adult responses to form a new sample. Students should draw conclusions on what the average adult's responses would be, based on this new sample. Have the class compare the predicted adult responses to those of the class.

NAME ______________________

CRITICAL THINKING

Surveys can be conducted either by asking questions of the total population of the group being studied, or by asking questions of only a few people in the group. Use the following survey to compare these two methods. Ask all your classmates to answer the survey questions on paper, and collect their responses.

Answers will vary.

	Total Population		Sample of 5	
Question	% Yes	% No	% Yes	% No
Have you seen a movie in the last 7 days?				
Did you watch less than 2 hours of TV last night?				
Did you drink milk with your breakfast today?				
Have you eaten pizza in the last 5 days?				
Have you read a book in the last 10 days?				

1. Complete the table by calculating the percents for the total population. Then shuffle all of the survey papers. Pull out 5 papers at random, and put their results in the sample column.
2. How did the results of the total population compare with those of the sample? Explain.

Possible answer: Sample approximated total results.

NAME ______________________________

VISUAL THINKING

Each pair of figures on the left is related by a common property. In the space provided, write in the letter of the pair of figures on the right that is related by the same property.

1.

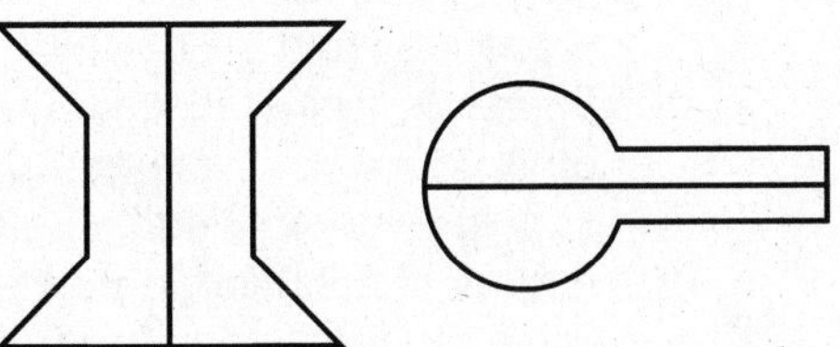

______

2.

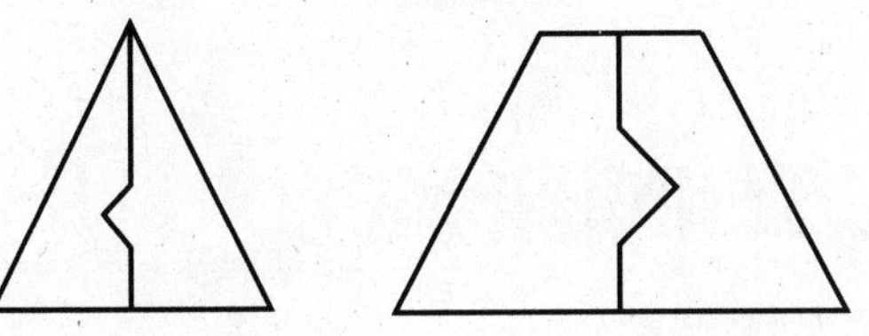

______

3.

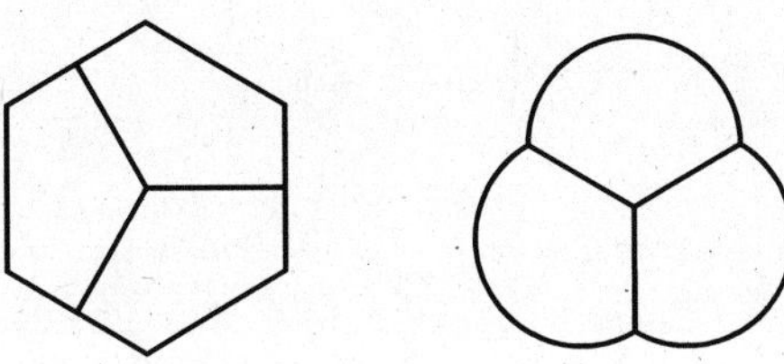

______

4.

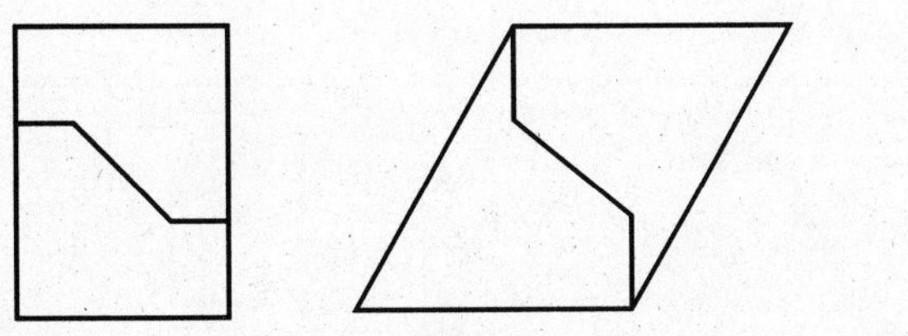

______

5.

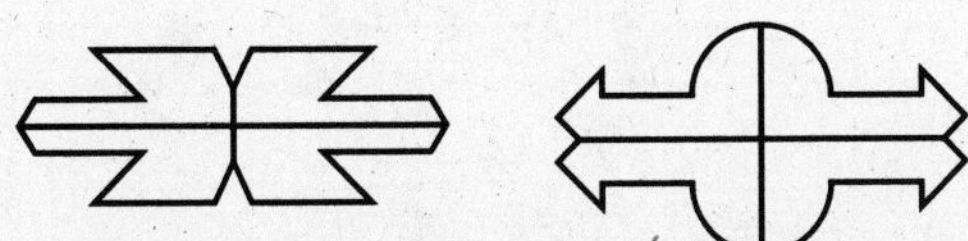

______

a.

b.

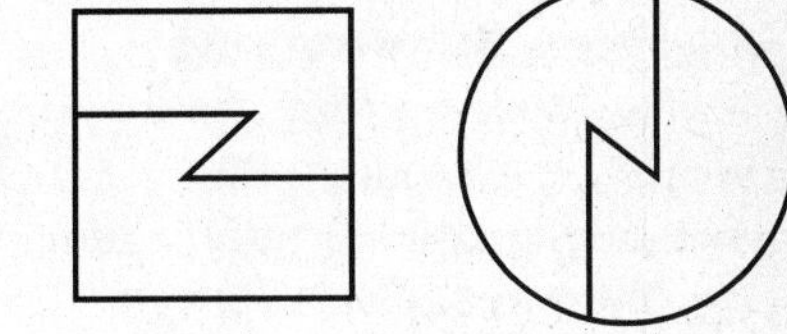

c.

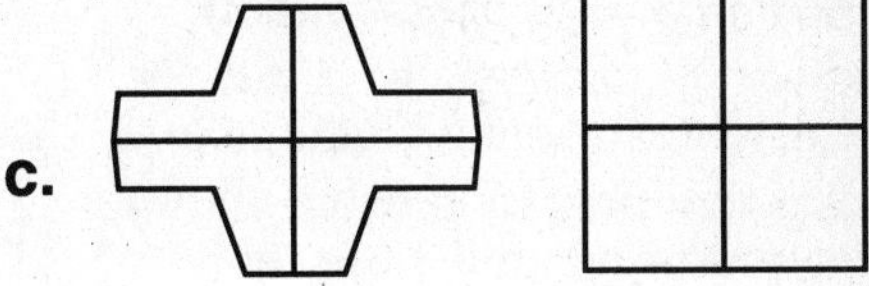

d.

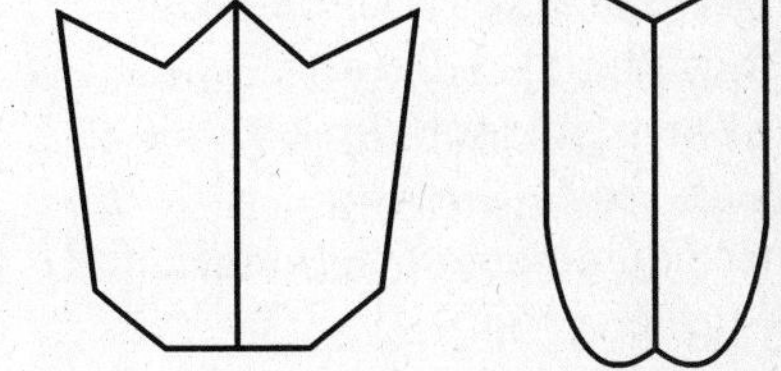

e.

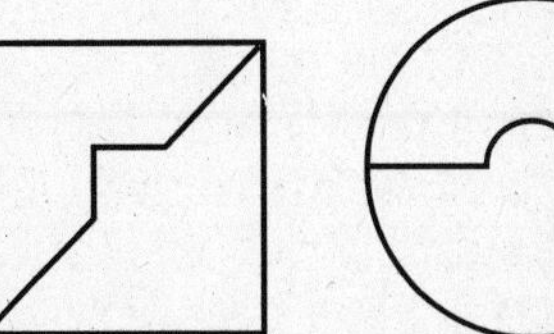

Teacher Notes

Use with
Objective 132
pages 484–487

Focus
Visual Thinking
Visual Patterns

Materials
Visual Thinking transparency (optional)

Overview
Students recognize the relationship in a visual pattern and use this same relationship to complete the pattern.

Teaching Suggestions
At first, students may have difficulty determining the relationship between the given pair of figures. ***Question:** In Problem 1, what is the same about the figures?* [Possible answer: They both have a line dividing them in half.]

In Problems 2 and 4, both pairs are divided but not by a straight line. Help students to see that the relationship shown in choice **e** is most like that shown in Problem 2.

Have students look at Problem 3. ***Question:** How do the figures seem to be divided?* [Into thirds]

Have students look at Problem 5. ***Question:** How do the figures seem to be divided?* [Into fourths]

Alternate Approach: Have students trace and cut out the figures. Have them cut each figure apart on the line(s) provided. Students may then examine the pieces and put the figures back together to better visualize the common property.

Extension
Students may work in small groups. Tell them to first cut out several figures of various shapes: circles, squares, trapezoids, triangles, and so forth. Have each student choose two figures. One student should divide the figures in a related way. The other students in the group should try to divide their figures in a similar manner. Have students compare results.

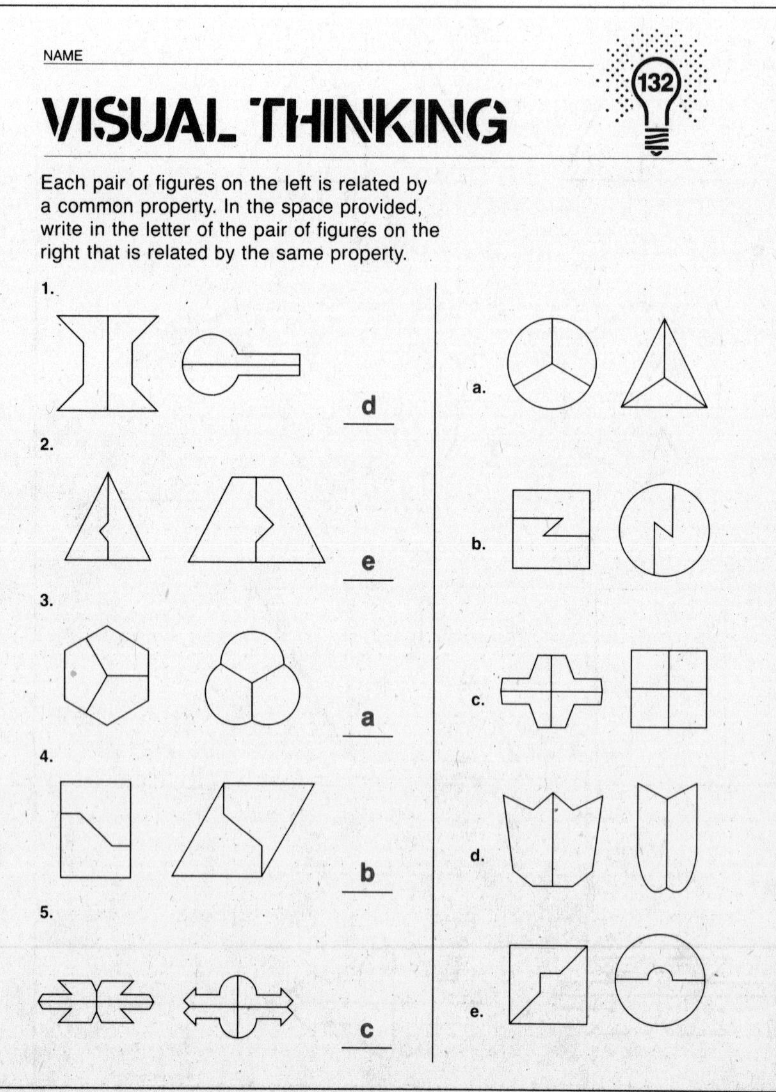

NAME ______________________

PROBLEM SOLVING

An ant found itself in the rectangular room shown in the picture. The room is 30 feet long, 12 feet wide, and 12 feet high. The ant was at A, at the center of one of the shorter walls and 1 foot from the ceiling. Its only way out of the room was a hole at B, at the center of the opposite wall and 1 foot from the floor. The ant took the shortest route to this space. The scale diagrams below show how the room could be opened to show a flat diagram of the ant's possible route.

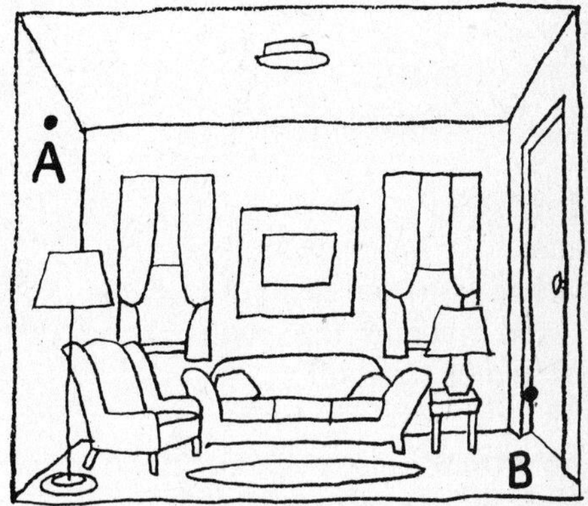

1. Ring the letter of the diagram that you think shows the shortest distance the ant had to travel.

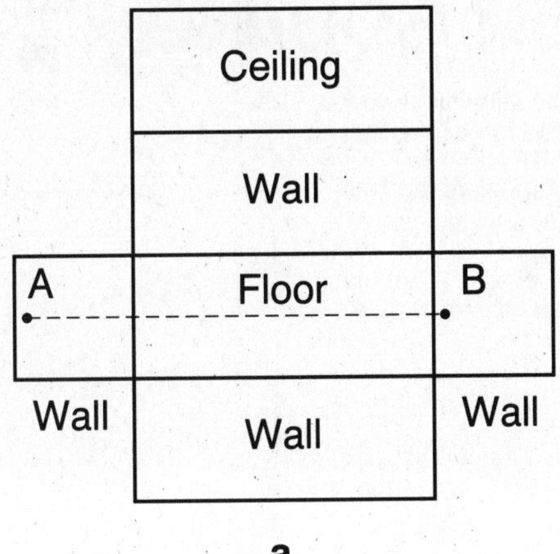

a.

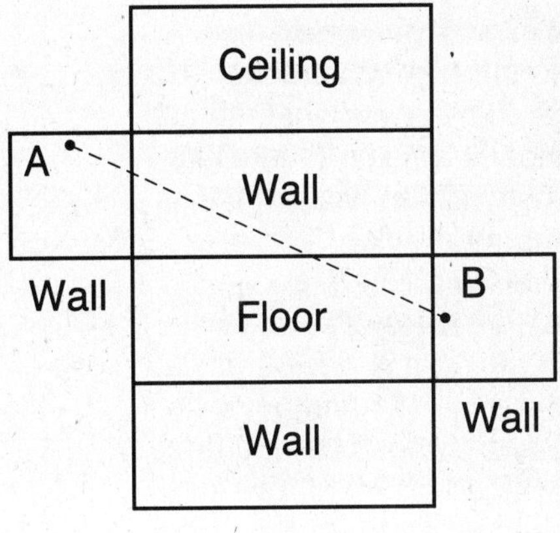

b.

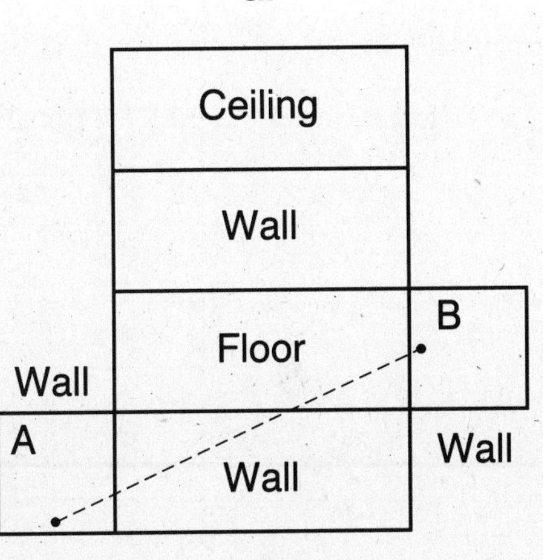

c.

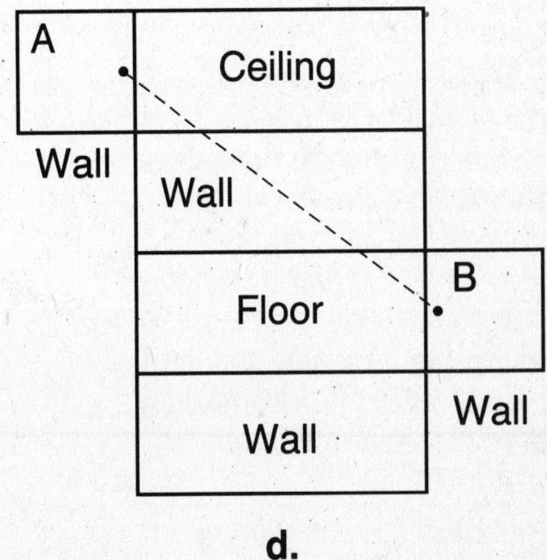

d.

2. How far did the ant have to travel? ______________________

Teacher Notes

Use with
Objective 133
pages 490–491

Focus
Problem Solving
Draw a Diagram

Materials
Ruler
Yardstick, meter stick, or tape measure (optional)
Calculator (optional)

Overview
Students use diagrams and proportions to determine the shortest path between two points.

Teaching Suggestions
You may wish to introduce this problem by saying that the ant cannot fly or jump to furniture. It must walk on walls, the ceiling, or the floor.

Refer to diagram **a.** ***Questions:*** *How far does the ant walk from* ***A*** *down the wall to the floor?* [11 feet] *How far is it across the floor?* [30 feet] *How far does the ant walk up the opposite wall to* ***B****?* [1 foot] *What is the total distance walked?* [11 + 30 + 1 = 42 feet]

In diagrams **b, c,** and **d,** students will have to use proportions to find the distance from **A** to **B.** ***Questions:*** *How could you use diagram* ***b*** *to determine the actual distance from* ***A*** *to* ***B****?* [Use a ruler to measure the distance and then use a proportion.] *In diagram* ***b,*** *what is the distance in inches from* ***A*** *to* ***B****?* [$1\frac{11}{16}$ inch] *In inches, what is the height of the wall in diagram* ***b****?* [$\frac{1}{2}$ inch]

Questions: *What is the actual height of the wall?* [12 feet] *What proportion could you use to find the actual distance from* ***A*** *to* ***B****?* $\left[\frac{\frac{1}{2}}{12} = \frac{1\frac{11}{16}}{n}\right]$ *What is the actual distance from* ***A*** *to* ***B****?* [$40\frac{1}{2}$ feet]

Have students use the same strategy to find the distances in diagrams **c** and **d**.

Extension
Have the class as a whole choose two points in the room on opposite walls. In small groups, have each group decide on the shortest route between the points and use measuring tools and string to find the distance along this route. Have groups compare their distances to find the shortest one.

NAME ______________________

PROBLEM SOLVING

An ant found itself in the rectangular room shown in the picture. The room is 30 feet long, 12 feet wide, and 12 feet high. The ant was at A, at the center of one of the shorter walls and 1 foot from the ceiling. Its only way out of the room was a hole at B, at the center of the opposite wall and 1 foot from the floor. The ant took the shortest route to this space. The scale diagrams below show how the room could be opened to show a flat diagram of the ant's possible route.

1. Ring the letter of the diagram that you think shows the shortest distance the ant had to travel.

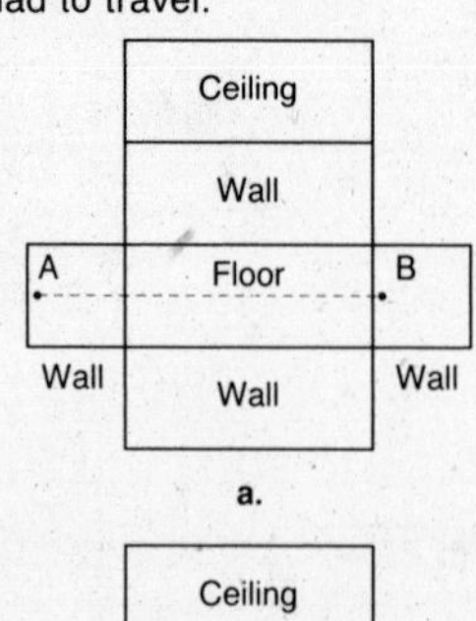

a.

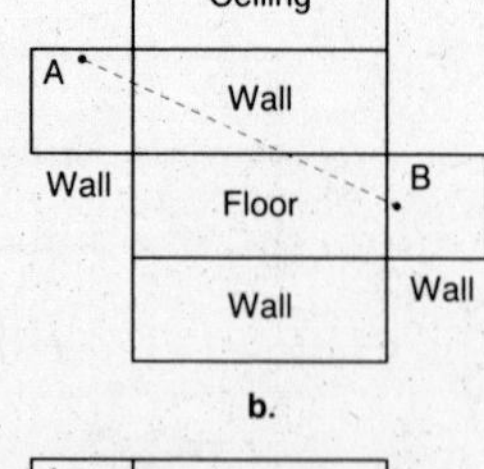

b.

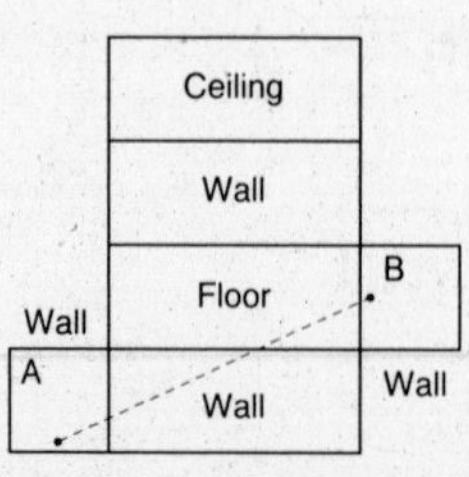

c.

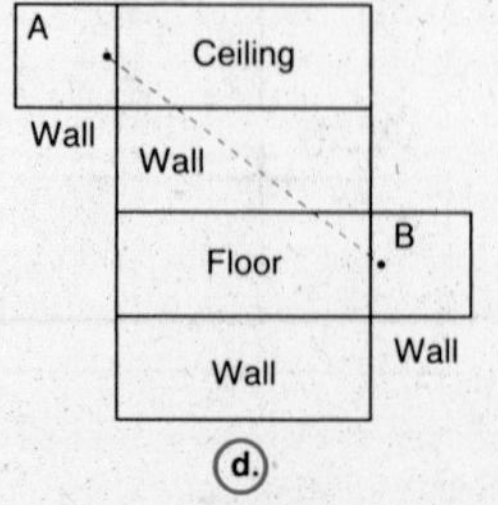

(d.)

2. How far did the ant have to travel? **40 feet**

NAME ______________________________

VISUAL THINKING

The first pair of figures in each row is related by a common property. In the column, write the letter of the figure from the column on the right that completes the second pair with the same property.

1. 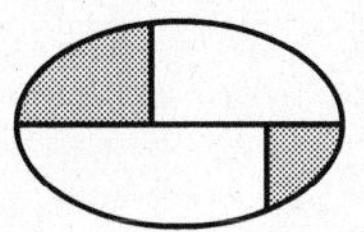 is to 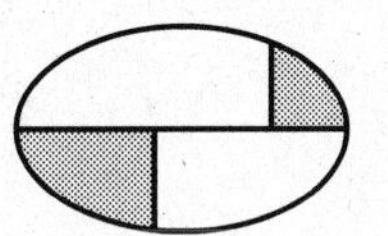 as 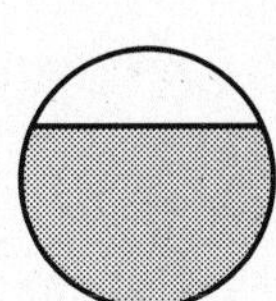 is to ____

2. 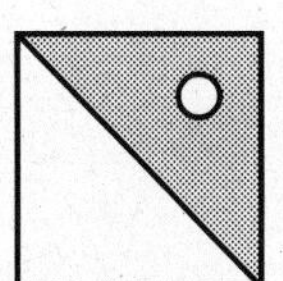 is to 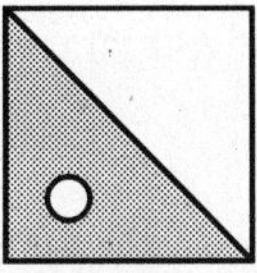 as 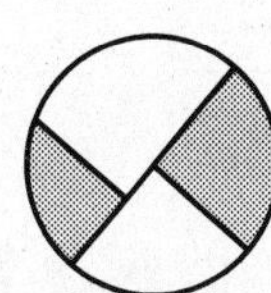 is to ____

3. 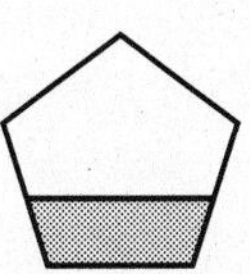 is to 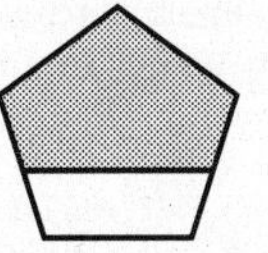 as 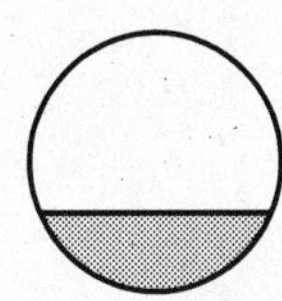 is to ____

4. 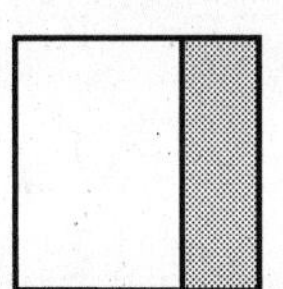 is to 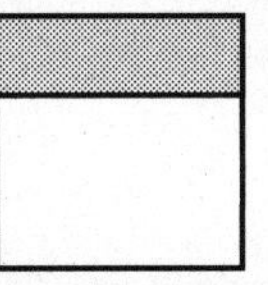 as 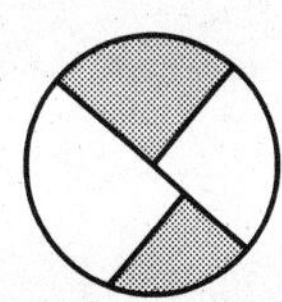 is to ____

5. 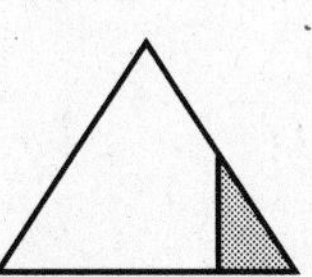 is to 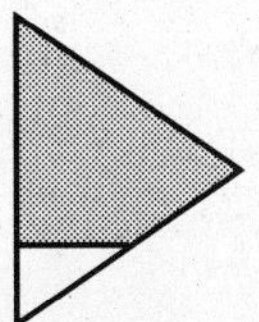 as 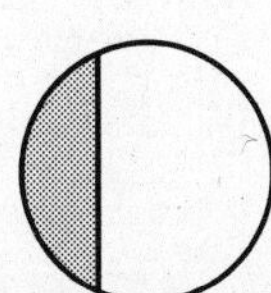 is to ____

6. 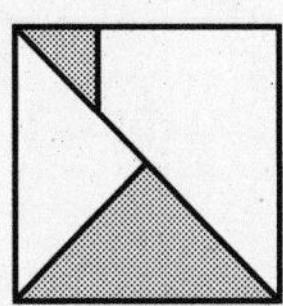 is to 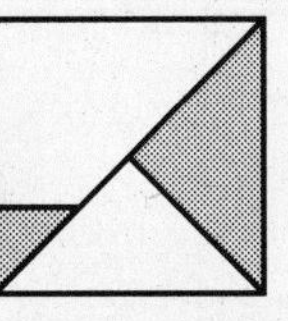 as 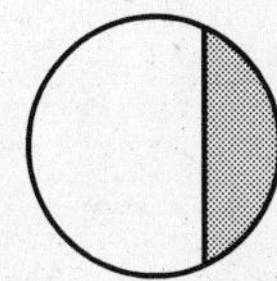 is to ____

a. 

b. 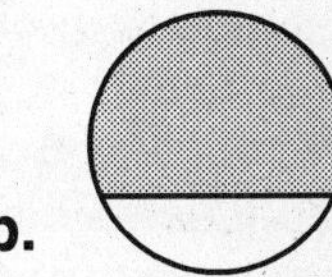

c. 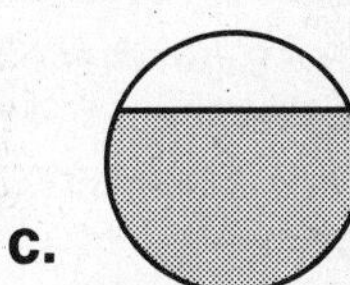 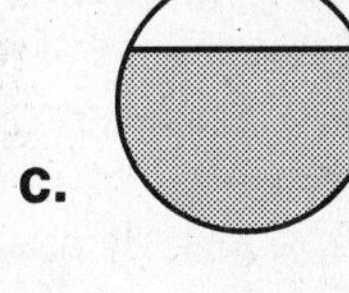

d. 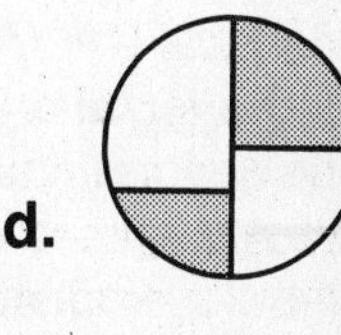

e. 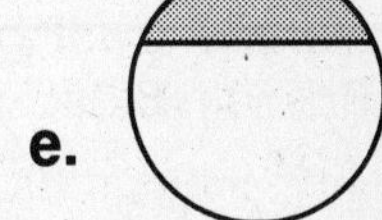

Use after pages 492–493.

Teacher Notes

Use with
Objective 134
pages 492–493

Focus
Visual Thinking
Visual Patterns

Materials
Visual Thinking transparency (optional)

Overview
Students recognize the relationship between two figures of a visual analogy and use this same relationship to complete the analogy.

Teaching Suggestions
If students have trouble with Problem 1, it may help to list the features each pair of figures have in common and the differences between the figures. ***Questions:*** *How are the figures alike?* [Possible answers: They are both ovals; they both have equal parts shaded.] *How are they different?* [Possible answer: The left one has been flipped top to bottom.]

Note that in each problem the figures in a pair are identical except for the shading and orientation. In Problem 2, the second figure in a pair is flipped across the diagonal line. In Problem 3, the shading in the second figure is opposite that of the first figure. In Problem 4, the second figure in a pair is rotated. In Problem 5, the second figure is rotated and the shading is opposite. In Problem 6, the second figure is rotated.

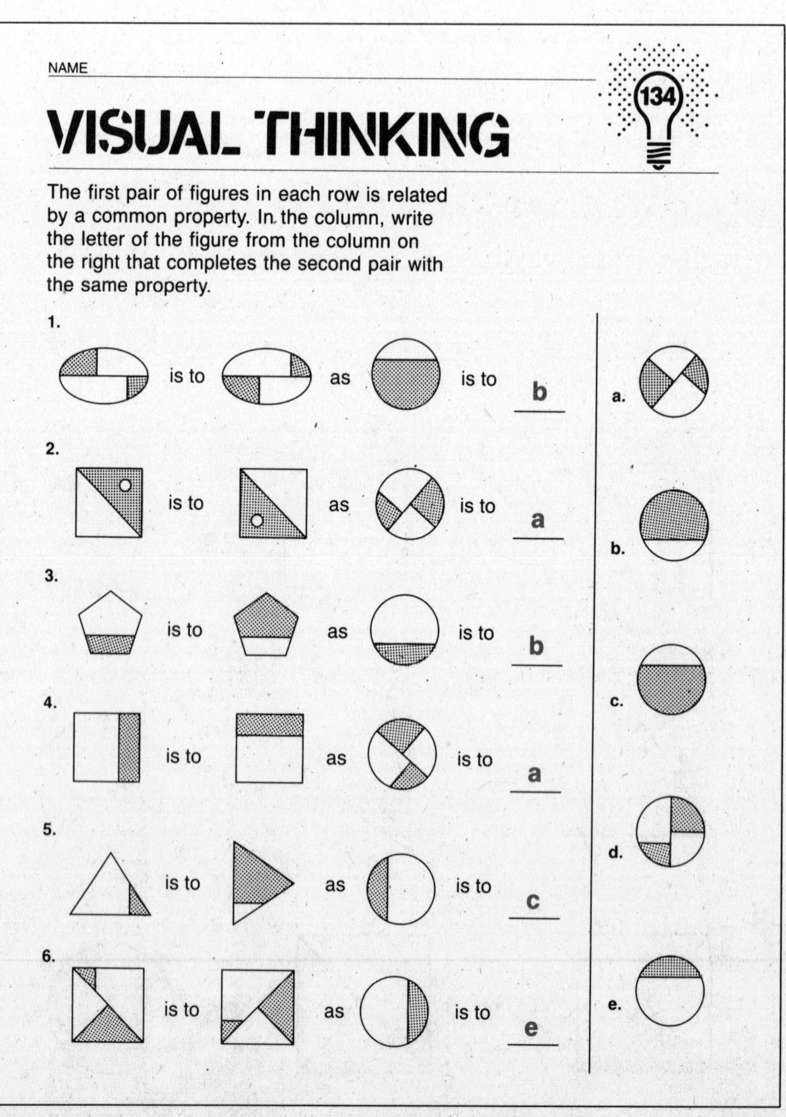

NAME ______________________________

DECISION MAKING

In a baseball batting lineup, the players are arranged in a certain order. The manager generally puts the fastest runners with the highest batting averages in the 1st and 2nd positions. The best home run hitters are usually in the 3rd, 4th, and 5th positions in the lineup. The 6th- and 7th-place batters tend not to be as fast as the other players and do not hit as many home runs. The 8th-place batter is usually the weakest hitter (except for the pitcher). The pitcher usually bats last.

Use the following information and the table below to create a batting lineup on the right for the Northfield Condors.

MORE BASEBALL LINEUP FACTS:

- Fast runners steal the most bases.
- Strong hitters usually have the most runs batted in (hits that score another player already on base).
- Good hitters tend to get more walks.

Condors' lineup	
1st	______
2nd	______
3rd	______
4th	______
5th	______
6th	______
7th	______
8th	______
9th	______

Name	Bat. Ave.	Strike-Outs	Walks	Home Runs	Runs Bat. In	Stolen Bases
Bacon	.285	32	14	23	36	1
Carnes	.303	11	45	19	61	11
Dulles	.295	17	20	2	52	6
Eaglen	.250	25	9	12	40	4
Prego	.197	35	12	3	27	2
Grant	.286	20	30	12	35	8
Hart	.255	8	10	5	17	6
Wenzel	.291	27	20	17	26	1
Orr (pitcher)	.165	10	1	1	3	0

Use after pages 494–495.

Teacher Notes

Use with
Objective 135
pages 494–495

Focus
Decision Making

Overview
Students use information about baseball players and batting order to create their own batting lineup.

Teaching Suggestions
Students may need an explanation of the baseball statistics listed in the chart. Ask volunteers to explain these terms and write the definitions on the chalkboard. Then have students complete the activity. Emphasize to students that many answers are possible, and that there is no "right" answer. After they have created a lineup, have them give reasons for their choices.

Alternate Approach: Suggest to students that they categorize the players according to individual traits, then see whose name occurs in the desired categories for each position.

Extension
In a newspaper or sports periodical look up the statistics of a local professional baseball team if possible. Have students make up a lineup for this team. Compare student lineups with the actual lineups used.

Have each student write a character trait (such as dependable, organized, funny) on a slip of paper. Write ten fictitious names on the board. For each name, draw three traits and write them down. Have the class assign each character to committees in charge of various tasks, such as planning a party or writing a report. Discuss which character traits were best for each job.

NAME

DECISION MAKING

In a baseball batting lineup, the players are arranged in a certain order. The manager generally puts the fastest runners with the highest batting averages in the 1st and 2nd positions. The best home run hitters are usually in the 3rd, 4th, and 5th positions in the lineup. The 6th- and 7th-place batters tend not to be as fast as the other players and do not hit as many home runs. The 8th-place batter is usually the weakest hitter (except for the pitcher). The pitcher usually bats last.

Use the following information and the table below to create a batting lineup on the right for the Northfield Condors.

MORE BASEBALL LINEUP FACTS:
- Fast runners steal the most bases.
- Strong hitters usually have the most runs batted in (hits that score another player already on base).
- Good hitters tend to get more walks.

Possible answers:

Condors' lineup	
1st	Grant
2nd	Dulles
3rd	Carnes
4th	Bacon
5th	Wenzel
6th	Eaglen
7th	Hart
8th	Prego
9th	Orr

Name	Bat. Ave.	Strike-Outs	Walks	Home Runs	Runs Bat. In	Stolen Bases
Bacon	.285	32	14	23	36	1
Carnes	.303	11	45	19	61	11
Dulles	.295	17	20	2	52	6
Eaglen	.250	25	9	12	40	4
Prego	.197	35	12	3	27	2
Grant	.286	20	30	12	35	8
Hart	.255	8	10	5	17	6
Wenzel	.291	27	20	17	26	1
Orr (pitcher)	.165	10	1	1	3	0

NAME ____________________

PROBLEM SOLVING

Tracy cannot find her bank credit card. She needs to know the account number in order to cancel the lost card and order a new one. Unfortunately, the list of account numbers she keeps at home has faded, and she can only read the two digits shown. She does remember, however, that the sum of any three consecutive digits in her account number is 18.

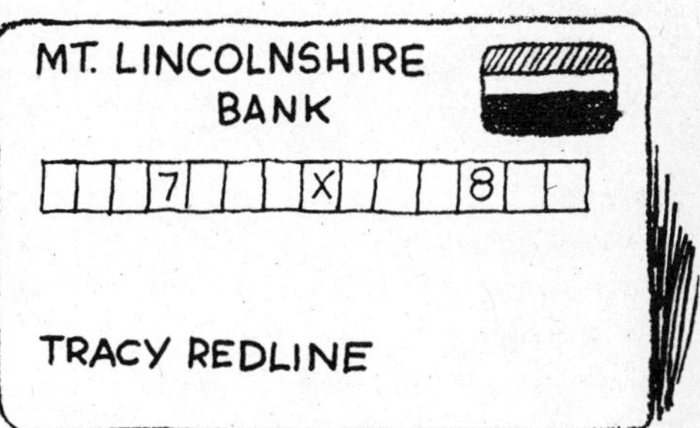

1. What is the value of the digit *X*? ____________________

2. What is Tracy's account number?

____

Use after pages 496–497.

Teacher Notes

Use with
Objective 136
pages 496–497

Focus
Problem Solving
Try and Check
Use Logical Reasoning

Materials
3 different colors of disks (5 of each color per student)

Overview
Students have to determine a 14-digit number where only two of the digits are given and they know that the sum of any three consecutive digits is 18.

Teaching Suggestions
Have students carefully read the problem. ***Questions:*** *What does the sum of the two digits to the right of 7 have to be?* [11] *What, then, must the digit to the left of* **X** *be?* [7] Be sure students see that since the digit to the left of **X** must add with the two digits to the right of 7 to total 18, it must also be 7. ***Questions:*** *What must the two digits to the left of 8 total?* [10] *What, then, must the digit to the right of* **X** *be?* [8]

Once the above digits have been determined, students should be able to find the rest of the digits. Remind them that each set of three consecutive digits must have a sum of 18.

Alternate Approach: Give each student 15 disks (5 of each color). Place 3 disks, one of each color, in a row—for example, red, blue, yellow. Explain that red + blue + yellow = 18.

Have students figure out what disk must be to the right of the yellow disk so that the blue plus the yellow plus the unknown disk equals 18. [Red] Repeat this for consecutive disks to the right until a pattern is seen. [The same order of disks is repeated.] Then have students use the disks to complete the activity.

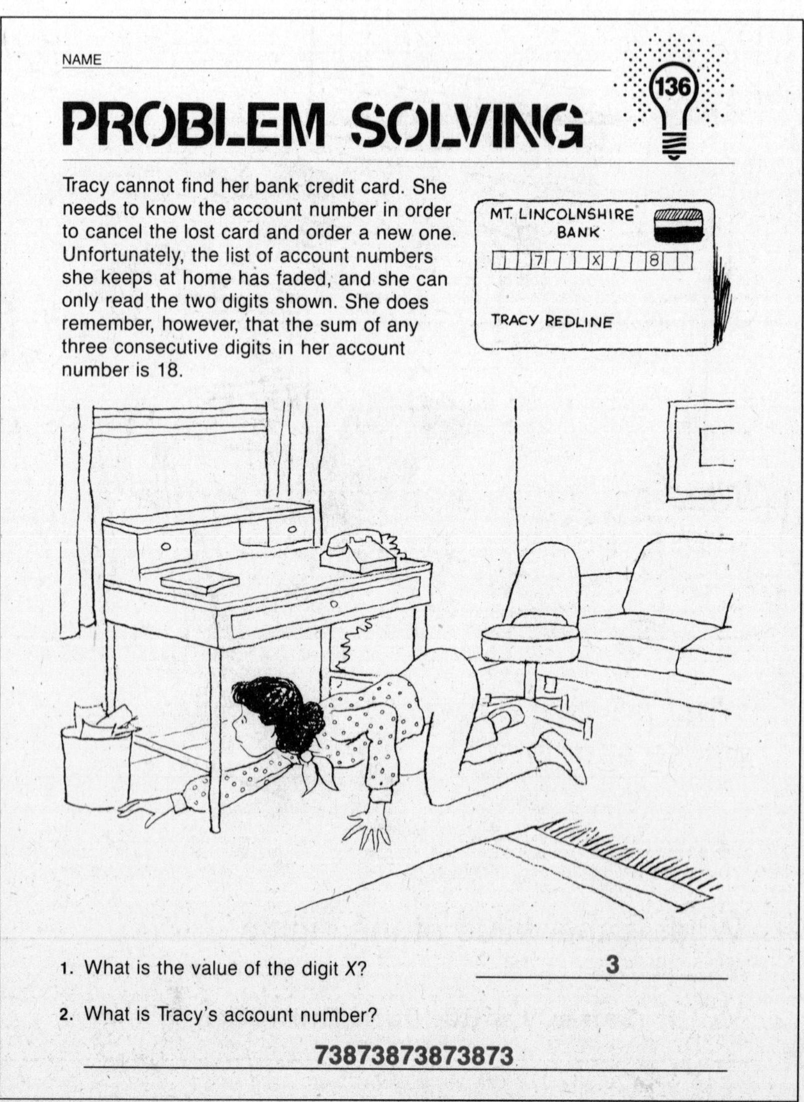
NAME ____________

136

PROBLEM SOLVING

Tracy cannot find her bank credit card. She needs to know the account number in order to cancel the lost card and order a new one. Unfortunately, the list of account numbers she keeps at home has faded, and she can only read the two digits shown. She does remember, however, that the sum of any three consecutive digits in her account number is 18.

1. What is the value of the digit *X*? **3**
2. What is Tracy's account number?
73873873873873

NAME ______________________________

PROBLEM SOLVING

Bertoldo has a large bag of peanuts that he wants to distribute among seven of his friends. He knows that each person will probably want a different amount of peanuts. Bertoldo wonders if he can find seven different unit fractions whose sum is 1 for any bag of peanuts he might have, leaving no peanuts left over. Bertoldo has found this way to determine two unit fractions whose sum is a third unit fraction.

$$\frac{1}{a} = \frac{1}{(a+1)} + \frac{1}{a(a+1)} \text{ for } a \neq 0, -1$$

For example:

$$\frac{1}{4} = \frac{1}{5} + \frac{1}{4(5)} = \frac{1}{5} + \frac{1}{20}$$

1. What are three different unit fractions whose sum is 1?

____

2. What are five different unit fractions whose sum is 1?

____

3. What are seven different unit fractions whose sum is 1?

____

Teacher Notes

Use with
Objective 137
pages 508–509

Focus
Problem Solving
Solve a Simpler Problem

Overview
Students generalize to determine different unit fractions whose sum is one.

Teaching Suggestions
Motivate student interest by asking a less complicated problem. ***Question:*** *What are two unit fractions whose sum is 1?* [1/2 + 1/2] Have students complete Problem 1. Encourage them to look for relationships among the three fractions.

Write on the board these examples to demonstrate the generalizations found by Bertoldo.

1/3 = 1/(3 + 1) + 1/3(3 + 1)
1/3 = 1/4 + 1/12

Let the students discuss their interpretations of this generalization.

Alternate Approach: Have students cut a sheet of paper in half. They should put one of the halves aside. Then challenge students to take the other half and determine two unit fractions whose sum is this half. Write on the board these equations to represent the concepts the students are developing.

1/2 + 1/2 = 1
1/2 = 1/? + 1/?

Fill in the unknowns in the equation on the board by writing the following.

1/2 = 1/(2 + 1) + 1/2(2 + 1)
1/2 = 1/3 + 1/6

Have students work in small groups to complete the activity sheet.

Extension
Suppose Bertoldo has 840 peanuts in his bag. Determine the number of peanuts each student would receive according to your answer to Problem 3. [Possible answers: 420, 168, 42, 70, 105, 15, 20]

NAME ______________________

PROBLEM SOLVING

Bertoldo has a large bag of peanuts that he wants to distribute among seven of his friends. He knows that each person will probably want a different amount of peanuts. Bertoldo wonders if he can find seven different unit fractions whose sum is 1 for any bag of peanuts he might have, leaving no peanuts left over. Bertoldo has found this way to determine two unit fractions whose sum is a third unit fraction.

$\frac{1}{a} = \frac{1}{(a+1)} + \frac{1}{a(a+1)}$ for $a \neq 0, -1$

For example:

$\frac{1}{4} = \frac{1}{5} + \frac{1}{4(5)} = \frac{1}{5} + \frac{1}{20}$

1. What are three different unit fractions whose sum is 1?
   Possible answer: $\frac{1}{2} + \frac{1}{3} + \frac{1}{6} = 1$

2. What are five different unit fractions whose sum is 1?
   Possible answer: $\frac{1}{2} + \frac{1}{4} + \frac{1}{12} + \frac{1}{7} + \frac{1}{42}$

3. What is one way for Bertoldo to distribute a bag of peanuts in different unit fractions leaving no peanuts left over?
   Possible answer: $\frac{1}{2} + \frac{1}{5} + \frac{1}{20} + \frac{1}{12} + \frac{1}{8} + \frac{1}{56} + \frac{1}{42} = 1$

NAME ______________________________

DECISION MAKING

Use the map below to make your decisions.

1. Complete the table to find the distances and times between each city on each type of road.

Toll road
Highway
Rural

Speed limits (mph): Toll road; 65; Highway, 55; Rural, 45
Distances marked on map are in miles

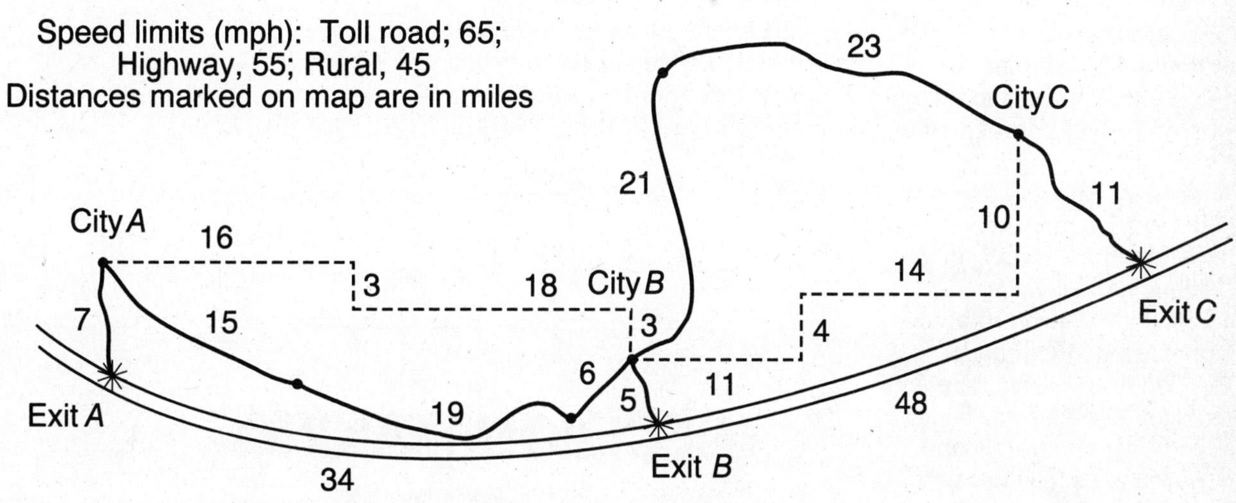

Route	Road	Distance	Time
City *A* to City *B*	Rural Highway Toll Road		
City *A* to City *C*	Rural Highway Toll Road		
City *B* to City *C*	Rural Highway Toll Road		

2. Which route is best from City A to City C? Why?

____

3. Which route is best from City A to City B? Why?

Teacher Notes

Use with
Objective 138
pages 510–511

Focus
Decision Making

Overview
Students study a map to decide which routes to take when traveling between cities.

Teaching Suggestions
Make sure students understand the map symbols. Discuss how traveling conditions differ on rural roads, highways, and toll roads. Mention how toll roads require payment but allow for faster speeds, and highways and rural roads usually have more congestion and stops. Remind students that a highway must be traveled before reaching the toll road. ***Questions:*** *How is travel time computed?* [Divide the distance traveled by the speed to get the number of hours.] *How can a travel time given in hours be converted to minutes?* [Multiply by 60, since 60 minutes equals 1 hour.] *How can a large amount of minutes be converted into hours?* [Divide by 60.]

Extension
Ask students to find out the average cost for a gallon of gasoline and the average number of miles traveled per gallon of gas for a typical automobile. Have them use this information to determine the difference in cost to travel from City *A* to City *C* using the highway versus using the rural roads.

NAME ______________________________

DECISION MAKING

Use the map below to make your decisions.

Toll road
Highway
Rural

1. Complete the table to find the distances and times between each city on each type of road.

Speed limits (mph): Toll road; 65; Highway, 55; Rural, 45
Distances marked on map are in miles

City *A* 16 3 18 City *B* 3 21 23 City *C* 10 11 14 4 11 7 15 6 5 19 34 48 Exit *A* Exit *B* Exit *C*

Route	Road	Distance	Time
A to *B*	Rural	**40 miles**	**53 min**
	Highway	**40 miles**	**44 min**
	Toll Road	**46 miles**	**44 min**
A to *C*	Rural	**79 miles**	**1 h 45 min**
	Highway	**84 miles**	**1 h 32 min**
	Toll Road	**100 miles**	**1 h 36 min**
B to *C*	Rural	**39 miles**	**52 min**
	Highway	**44 miles**	**48 min**
	Toll Road	**64 miles**	**61 min**

Possible answers:

2. Which route is best from *A* to *C*? Why?
Toll Road; less chance of delays due to traffic

3. Which route is best from *A* to *B*? Why?
Highway; as fast as Toll Road, no tolls to pay

NAME ______________________________

VISUAL THINKING

Tina has a 3 by 4 block of 12 stamps, as shown at right. She wants to give 4 stamps to Arlette, all joined together. Each should share at least one of its sides with another stamp.

1. Show the different arrangements of four stamps that Tina can make. (Note: congruent shapes are considered to be the same arrangement.)

2. How many different combinations of the four stamps are possible? ______________________________

Teacher Notes

Use with
Objective 139
pages 512–515

Focus
Visual Thinking
Spatial Perception

Materials
Visual Thinking transparency (optional)

Overview
Students determine all of the different combinations of four connecting squares.

Teaching Suggestions
Ask a student volunteer to read the directions and first problem. ***Question:** What is a definition for congruent shapes?* [Possible answer: The shapes that are the same when superimposed] Remind students that congruent shapes and arrangements with only corner attachments cannot be used when making combinations.

To help students complete Problem 2, suggest that different combinations can be obtained by sliding, rotating, and flipping arrangements on the block of stamps.

Alternate Approach: Have students cut out twelve identical square boxes from a sheet of paper. These boxes are to represent the block of stamps in the activity. Have students make different combinations of four stamps. Have them record all the various arrangements they can make.

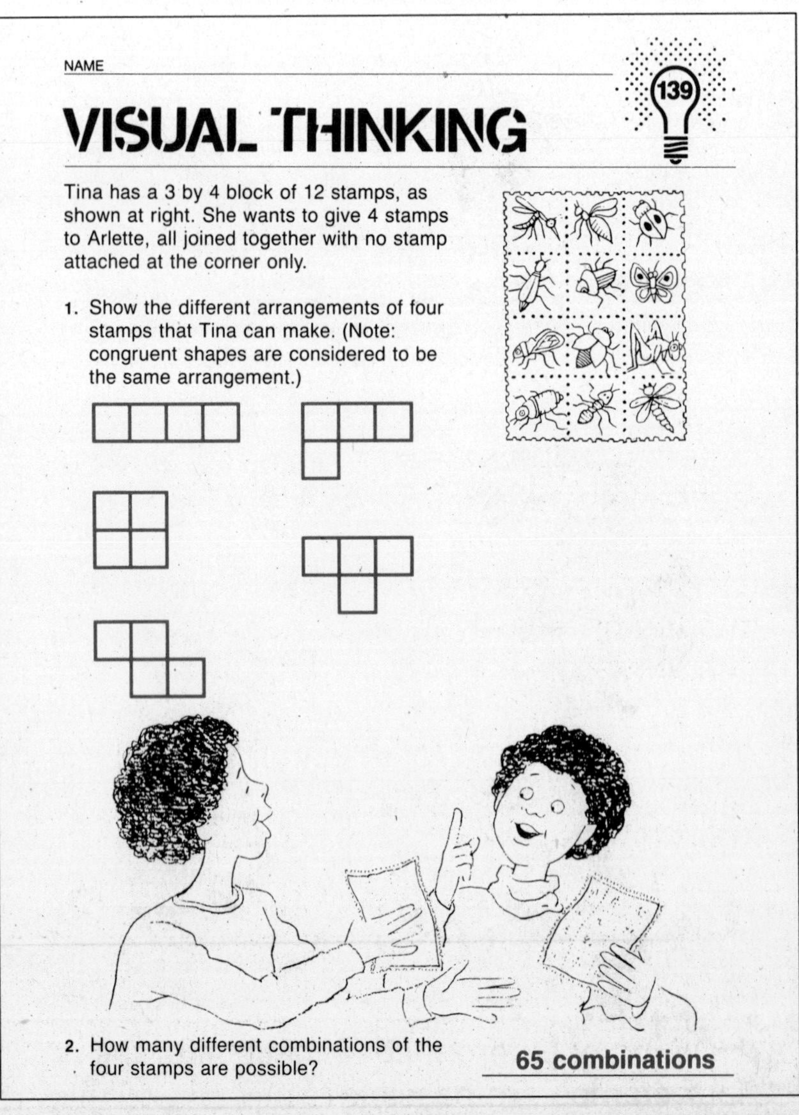
NAME
139
VISUAL THINKING
Tina has a 3 by 4 block of 12 stamps, as shown at right. She wants to give 4 stamps to Arlette, all joined together with no stamp attached at the corner only.
1. Show the different arrangements of four stamps that Tina can make. (Note: congruent shapes are considered to be the same arrangement.)
2. How many different combinations of the four stamps are possible?
65 combinations

NAME ____________________

PROBLEM SOLVING

The diagram at right represents the various routes along ski trails that may be taken down a hill. A skier may only ski downhill following these trails.

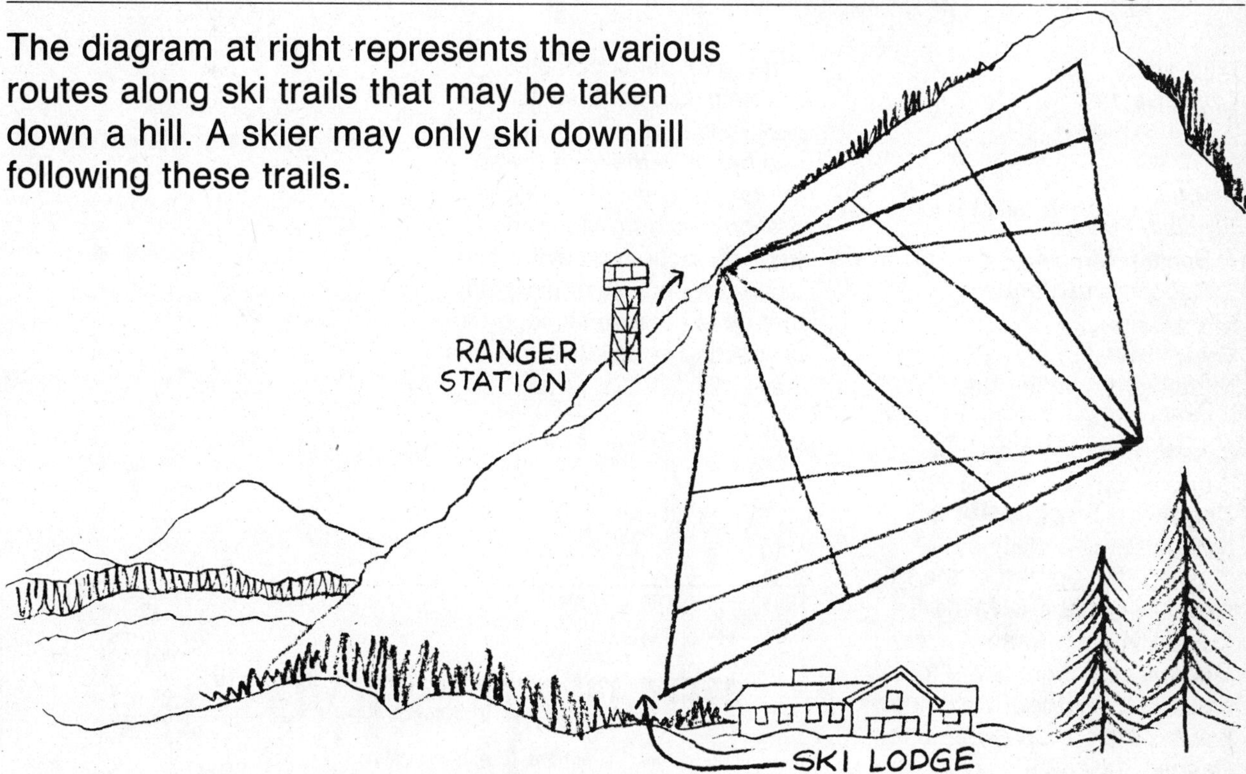

1. How many different paths downhill are there from the top of the ski slope to the ranger station? ____________________

2. On the diagram, write in the number of different paths from the top of the hill to each intersection point on the trails.

3. How many different paths are there from the top of the ski slope to the ski lodge at the bottom of the hill? ____________________

4. What pattern can you find in the number of paths at each intersection of the ski trails on the hill?

____

____

____

Teacher Notes

Use with
Objective 140
pages 516–517

Focus
Problem Solving
Solve a Simpler Problem
Choose an Operation

Overview
Students determine the number of possible paths down a system of ski trails.

Teaching Suggestions
Introduce the activity by drawing the top part of the ski slope on the board. Mark the top of the hill with an **X**. ***Questions:*** *Where is the top of the slope?* [At the **X**] *What path would be the most direct to the Ranger Station?* [Possible answer: The straight line path from the **X** to the Ranger Station] *How many different paths to the Ranger Station involve using only 2 turns at intersections?* [4]

Have students complete Problem 1. ***Question:*** *What pattern do you see in the number of paths from the top to the points above the Ranger Station?* [Adding the paths to the intersections above a point gives the number of paths to that point.] This technique can be used to complete Problems 2 and 3.

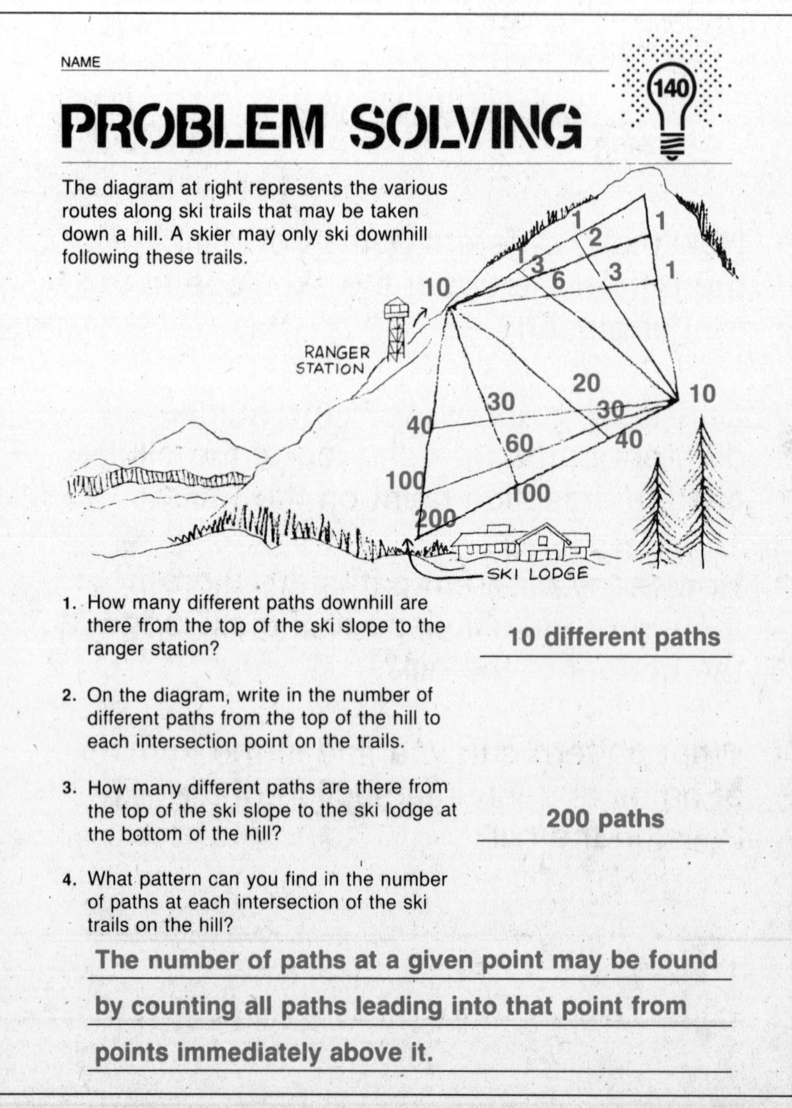

NAME ______________________

PROBLEM SOLVING

140

The diagram at right represents the various routes along ski trails that may be taken down a hill. A skier may only ski downhill following these trails.

1. How many different paths downhill are there from the top of the ski slope to the ranger station? **10 different paths**

2. On the diagram, write in the number of different paths from the top of the hill to each intersection point on the trails.

3. How many different paths are there from the top of the ski slope to the ski lodge at the bottom of the hill? **200 paths**

4. What pattern can you find in the number of paths at each intersection of the ski trails on the hill?

The number of paths at a given point may be found by counting all paths leading into that point from points immediately above it.

NAME ________________________________

CRITICAL THINKING

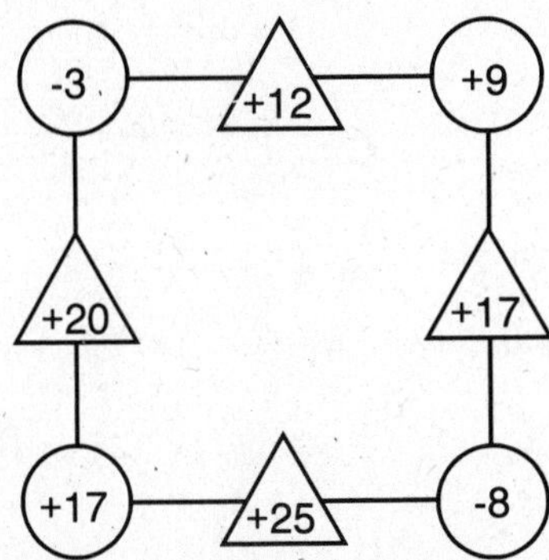

In the square above, the number in each triangle is the difference of the circled integers on either side of the triangle. The lesser integer is subtracted from the greater.

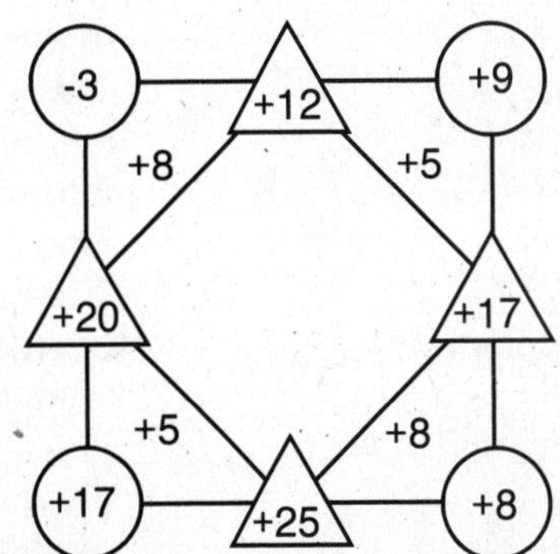

Next, the triangles are connected to form a new square inside the original square. The differences are again written on each side of the new square.

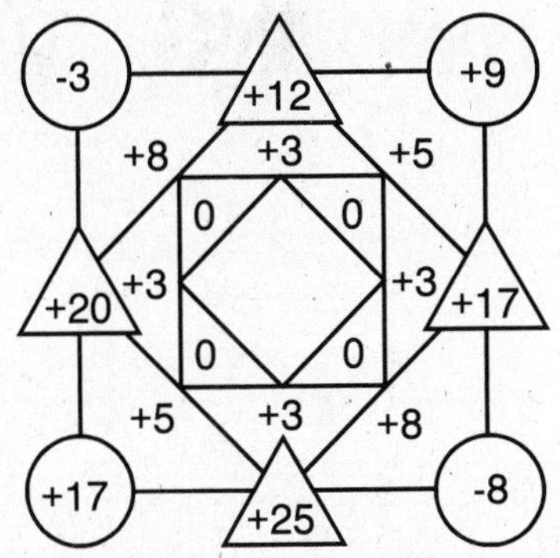

The third picture shows that when this process is repeated four times, all the differences are zero.

1. Use the above procedure with another set of four different integers. Did you eventually end with a common difference of zero? ________________

2. Does it always take 4 steps to get a common difference of zero? Complete more sets to test your answer. ________________

3. Try to find a set of four starting integers that require 7 subtractions to get a common difference of zero.

____

Teacher Notes

Use with
Objective 141
pages 518–521

Focus
Critical Thinking
Finding/Extending/Using Patterns
Using Number Sense

Overview
Students compute successive differences for pairs of integers. They continue to *find and extend patterns.*

Teaching Suggestions
Make sure all students understand that the term *difference* in this activity refers to the result of subtracting the lesser of two integers from the greater integer. Go over the procedure for computing the differences for adjacent pairs of integers at the vertices of the square. Complete the second, third, and fourth cycles, ending when the common difference is zero.

There is nothing special about the four integers selected. Any four integers will eventually give a common difference of zero. For Problem 1, have students count the number of cycles required to achieve a common difference of zero. To solve Problems 2 and 3 students should try several sets of numbers. If all four numbers are identical, only one cycle is required. Some sets of numbers require more than 4 cycles to reach a common difference of zero.

Extension
Have students assign the same set of numbers in different orders to the corners of the square to see how many cycles are required. For example, 1, 2, 4, and 8 require 7 cycles, and 1, 4, 2 and 8 require only 4 cycles. Students could also try using fractions or decimals. [Examples: 1/2, 2-1/4, 1-1/2, 1-3/4 results in 4 cycles; 0.06, 0.13, 0.18, 0.04 has 5 cycles.]

NAME ______

CRITICAL THINKING

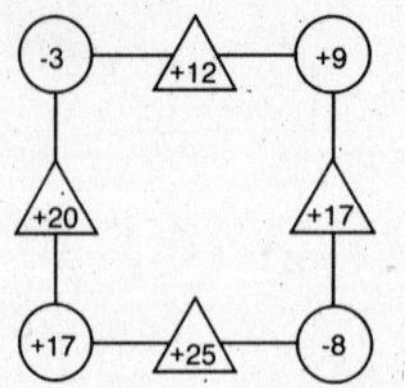

In the square above, the number in each triangle is the difference of the circled integers on either side of the triangle. The lesser integer is subtracted from the greater.

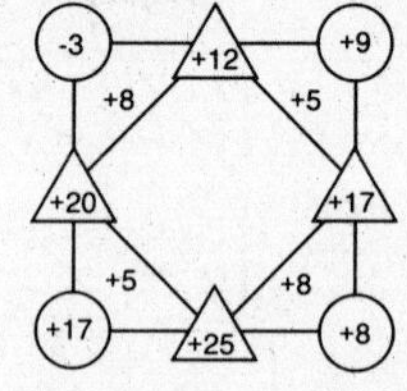

Next, the triangles are connected to form a new square inside the original square. The differences are again written on each side of the new square.

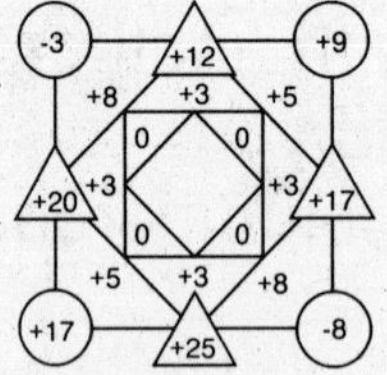

The third picture shows that when this process is repeated four times, all the differences are zero.

1. Use the above procedure with another set of four different integers. Did you eventually end with a common difference of zero? **Yes**

2. Does it always take 4 steps to get a common difference of zero? Complete more sets to test your answer. **No**

3. Try to find a set of four starting integers that require 7 subtractions to get a common difference of zero.

Possible answer: 1, 2, 4, 8

NAME ___________________________________

PROBLEM SOLVING

Many ships use radar to help them locate objects. At right is a picture of a radar screen. A point of light appears on the radar screen if there is an object within range. The ship is at the center of the circle.

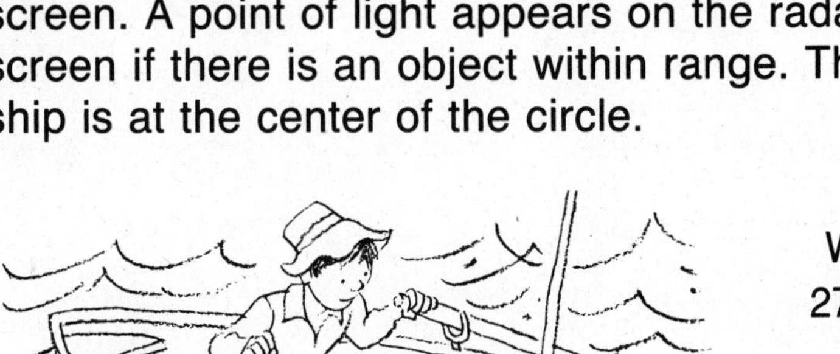

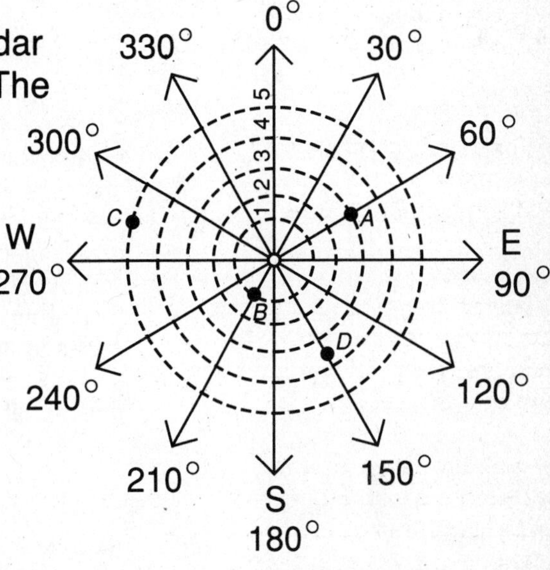

1. The circles mark the distance from the center in kilometers. How many kilometers from the center is point *A*? ____________

2. The numbers around the circle mark degrees. How many degrees from North is point *A*? ____________

3. Ordered pairs are used to name the location of points. The number of kilometers is named first, followed by the number of degrees. Write the position of the ship at point *A* as an ordered pair. ____________

4. Use ordered pairs to name the location of points *B, C* and *D* on the radar screen.

   B: ____________ *C:* ____________ *D:* ____________

Mark the location of the following objects on the radar screen.

5. Buoy marker: *E* (2, 90°)
6. Radio tower: *G* (4, 45°)
7. Ship: *F* (3, 180°)
8. Lighthouse: *H* (4.5, 270°)

Teacher Notes

Use with
Objective 142
pages 524–525

Focus
Problem Solving
Make a Graph

Overview
Students locate points on a picture of a radar screen using ordered pairs of numbers.

Teaching Suggestions
Ask a student volunteer to read the opening instructions. ***Questions:*** *How far away from the ship is the first circle?* [1 kilometer] *What is the general range of distance seen by the radar?* [Just beyond 5 kilometers] Have students complete Problem 1 and share answers. Suggest that they estimate the distance when the point lies between circles.

In Problem 2, have students note that North is 0°. As one moves clockwise, the measure of the angle increases. Point *A* is 60° from North. ***Question:*** *Point B is how many degrees from North?* [210°]

In Problem 3, students should realize that an ordered pair of numbers is used to locate points on this graph. The distance is always named first and the angle measure second. Students should then locate the three points indicated in Problem 4. Point out the notation used to write the ordered pair (____, ____).

Have students plot the points for Problems 5–8.

Extension
Take the class to an open area such as a gym or a playground. Place an **X** in the center of the open area and place objects in various locations around the **X.** Have students determine the ordered pair that gives the location for each object. The first coordinate can be determined by counting the number of paces to the object and the second coordinate by use of a directional compass.

NAME ____________________ 142

PROBLEM SOLVING

Many ships use radar to help them locate objects. At right is a picture of a radar screen. A point of light appears on the radar screen if there is an object within range. The ship is at the center of the circle.

N 0°, 30°, 60°, E 90°, 120°, 150°, S 180°, 210°, 240°, W 270°, 300°, 330°

1. The circles mark the distance from the center in kilometers. How many kilometers from the center is point *A*? **3 kilometers**

2. The numbers around the circle mark degrees. How many degrees from North is point *A*? **60°**

3. Ordered pairs are used to name the location of points. The number of kilometers is named first, followed by the number of degrees. Write the position of the ship at point *A* as an ordered pair. **(3, 60°)**

4. Use ordered pairs to name the location of points *B*, *C* and *D* on the radar screen.

B: **(1, 210°)** *C:* **(5, 285°)** *D:* **(3.5, 150°)**

Mark the location of the following objects on the radar screen.

5. Buoy marker: *E* (2, 90°)
6. Radio tower: *G* (4, 45°)
7. Ship: *F* (3, 180°)
8. Lighthouse: *H* (4.5, 270°)

NAME

VISUAL THINKING

In each row, ring the letter of the figure on the right that is either an enlargement or a reduction of the figure on the left.

1.

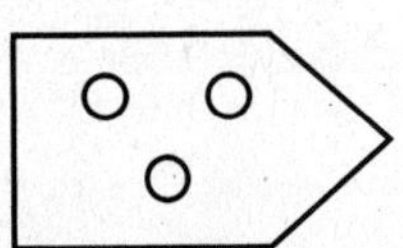
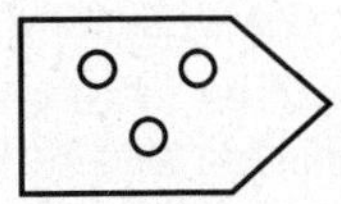
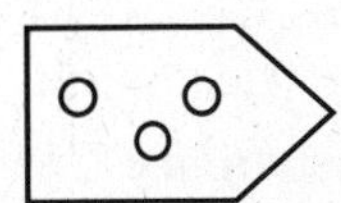
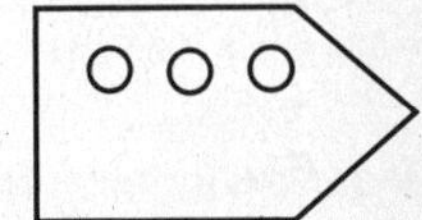

a. b. c. d.

2.

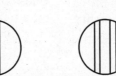

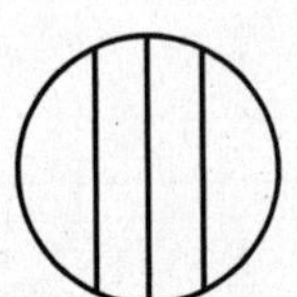

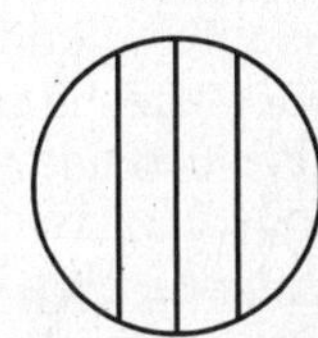

a. b. c. d.

3.

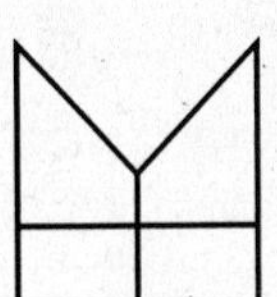
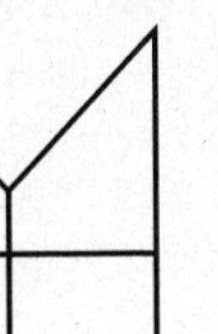
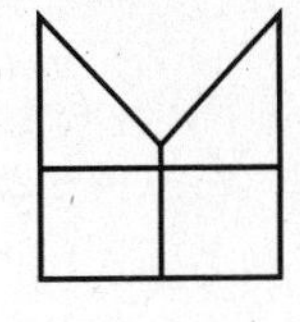

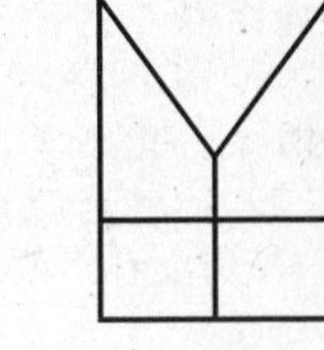
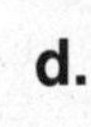

a. b. c. d.

4.

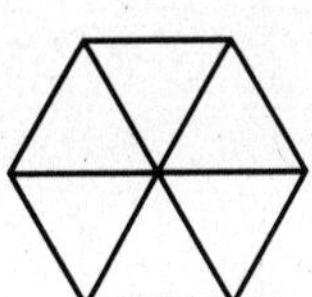
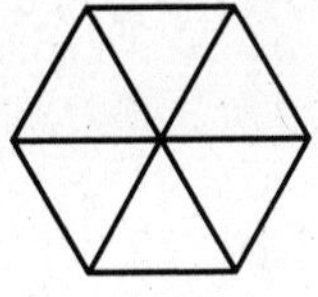
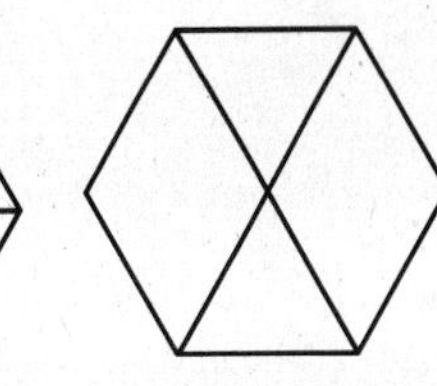
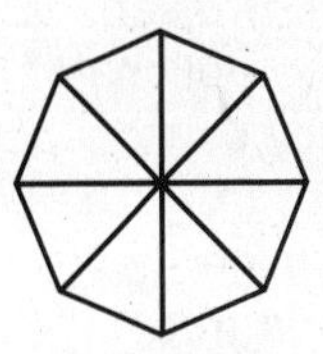
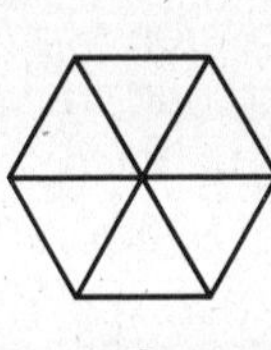

a. b. c. d.

5.

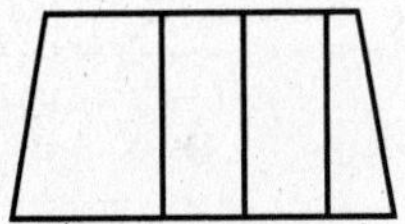
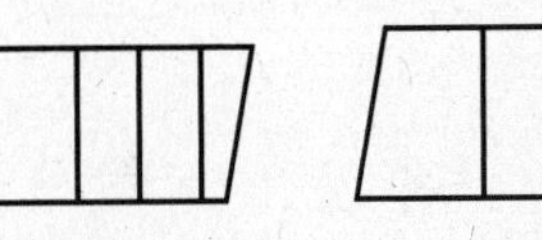
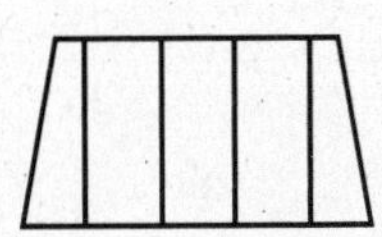

a. b. c. d.

6.

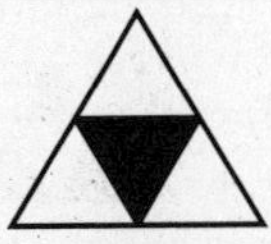

a. b. c. d.

Teacher Notes

Use with
Objective 143
pages 526–527

Focus
Visual Thinking
Spatial Perception

Materials
Visual Thinking transparency (optional)

Overview
Students determine which of four choices is an enlargement or reduction of a given figure.

Teaching Suggestions
Students should see that enlargements or reductions must retain all proportions. If only a part of the figure changes, it is not a true representation of the model. All lines, shadings, and shapes from the model must also be retained.

Alternate Approach: Draw the choices on the board. Project the given figure on the optional overhead transparency over each choice, adjusting the size of the image to determine whether the choice is a true enlargement or reduction.

Extension
Give students simple block figures. Using a ruler and knowledge of ratios, have them make their own enlarged or reduced drawings. If a pantograph is available, it can be used to demonstrate another systematic way to enlarge and reduce figures.

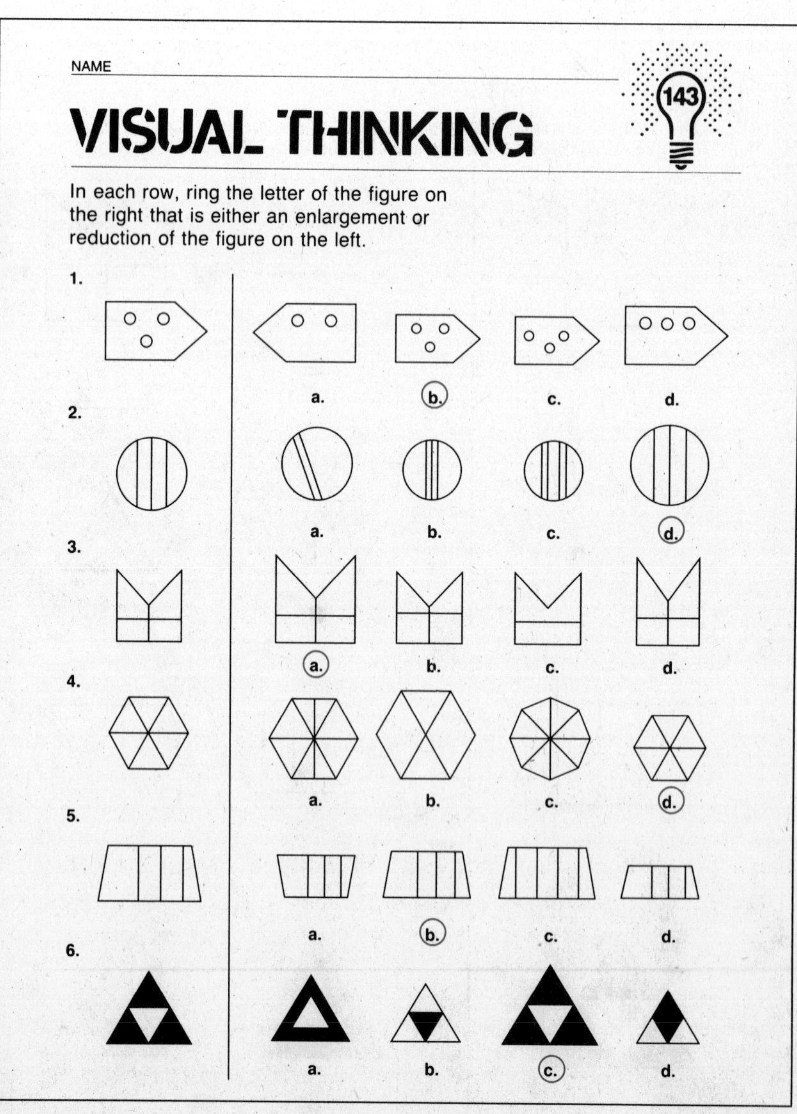
NAME

VISUAL THINKING

143

In each row, ring the letter of the figure on the right that is either an enlargement or reduction of the figure on the left.

1. a. (b.) c. d.

2. a. b. c. (d.)

3. (a.) b. c. d.

4. a. b. c. (d.)

5. a. (b.) c. d.

6. a. b. (c.) d.

NAME ____________________

PROBLEM SOLVING

The menu for La Maison de la Casa Restaurant is shown below. A complete dinner consists of one item from each category of appetizer, entree, and dessert.

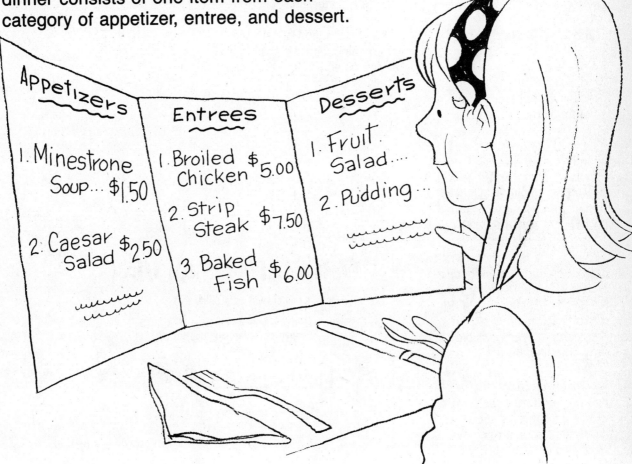

Appetizers
1. Minestrone Soup... $1.50
2. Caesar Salad $2.50

Entrees
1. Broiled Chicken $5.00
2. Strip Steak $7.50
3. Baked Fish $6.00

Desserts
1. Fruit Salad....
2. Pudding...

1. How many different complete dinners are possible? ____________________

2. How many complete dinners have chicken as an entree? ____________________

3. How many complete dinners are available to a customer who will eat fruit only if he or she had steak as an entree? ____________________

4. If a customer lets the waiter order his or her dinner at random, what is the chance that he or she will receive soup and fish? ____________________

Teacher Notes

Use with
Objective 144
pages 528–529

Focus
Problem Solving
Use Logical Reasoning

Overview
Students determine numbers of possible combinations from given choices.

Teaching Suggestions
To introduce the activity, do a simple example on the board. Show that initials or pictures rather than whole words may be used. ***Questions:*** *If Bill has a red shirt and a white shirt, and also has blue pants and gray pants, how many outfits can he put together?* [4: RS-BP, RS-GP, WS-BP, and WS-GP] *Which combinations of pants and shirts are not possible?* [Any combination of two pants or two shirts]

Students should develop a logical system for solving this type of combination problem. The items can be seen as parts of categories that may overlap. A list can be made of the combination possibilities, beginning with the first items in each category, and changing only one item for each subsequent combination.

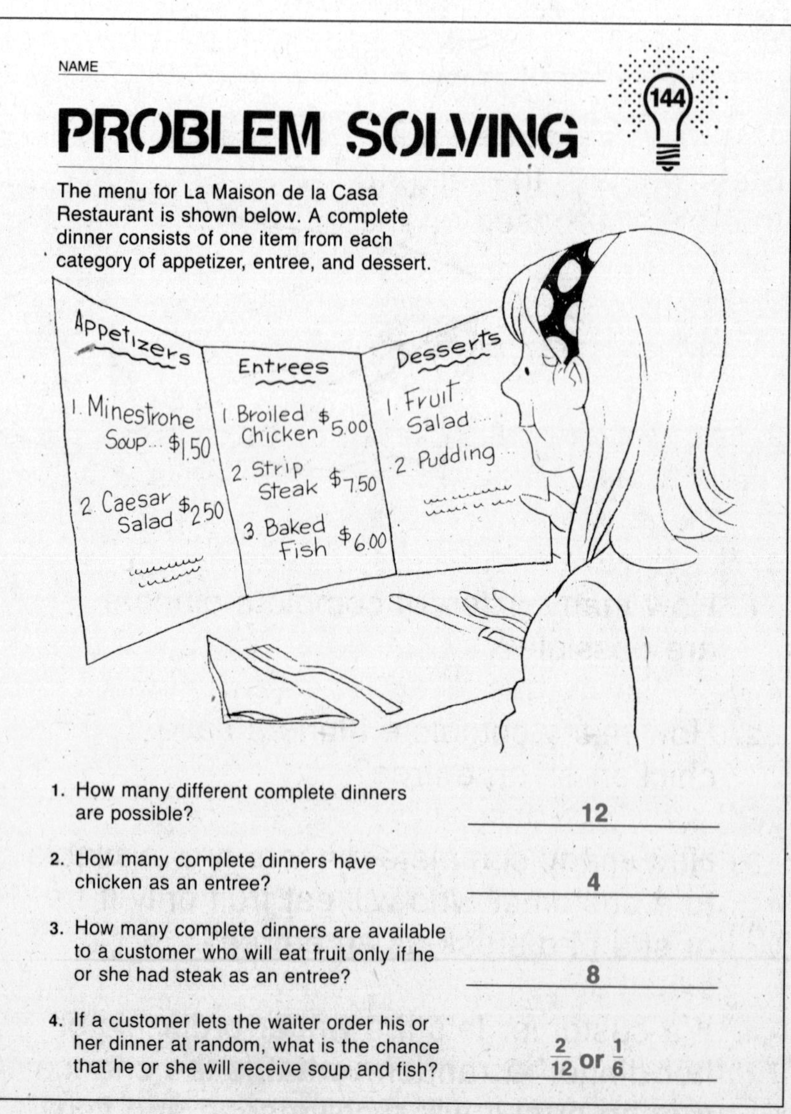

NAME

PROBLEM SOLVING

144

The menu for La Maison de la Casa Restaurant is shown below. A complete dinner consists of one item from each category of appetizer, entree, and dessert.

1. How many different complete dinners are possible? **12**
2. How many complete dinners have chicken as an entree? **4**
3. How many complete dinners are available to a customer who will eat fruit only if he or she had steak as an entree? **8**
4. If a customer lets the waiter order his or her dinner at random, what is the chance that he or she will receive soup and fish? **$\frac{2}{12}$ or $\frac{1}{6}$**

NAME ______________________________

CRITICAL THINKING

There are several types of bicycles sold at Aretha's Wheelies and More.

RACING BIKE
• 10-speed

BMX BIKE
• 5-speed
• wide tires

TOURING BIKE
• 10-speed • Front basket • thin tires

TOURING BIKE
• front and rear baskets
• 3-speed

ADULT TRICYCLE
• 5-speed
• large rear basket
• wide tires

State whether the following statements are true or false based on the information given.

1. If a bicycle has 3-speed gears, then it has front and rear baskets. ______________

2. If a bicycle has wide tires, then it is a BMX bicycle. ______________

3. If a bicycle is a racing bicycle, then it has 10-speed gears. ______________

4. If a bicycle has 10-speed gears, then it is either a racing or a touring bicycle. ______________

5. If a bicycle has a front basket, then it has 5-speed gears. ______________

6. If a cycle has 5-speed gears, then it has 2 wheels. ______________

7. If a bicycle has either front or rear baskets, then it has thin tires. ______________

Teacher Notes

Use with
Objective 145
pages 530–531

Focus
Critical Thinking
Evaluating Evidence and Conclusions
Classifying and Sorting

Overview
Students evaluate "if p, then q" statements to determine logical validity.

Teaching Suggestions
Explain the evaluation process for "if p, then q" statements. In order for a statement to be true, it must be found to be true in every case. ***Question:*** *Is it true that if an animal is a cat, then it has fur?* [Yes] Point out that the reverse statement is not necessarily true. ***Questions:*** *Is it true that if an animal has fur, then it is a cat?* [Maybe] *Can you think of any cases that would make the statement false?* [Possible answers: Dog, mouse, horse]

As a class, discuss Problem 1. Because the statement is true in all cases, the answer is true. Ask a volunteer to read and choose an answer for Problem 2. Then have students complete the activity sheet on their own.

Extension
Have students each formulate 5 "if p, then q" statements based on common knowledge. Have students exchange statements with a partner. Have students determine the reverse of the statements given to them, and decide if these reverse statements are true or false.

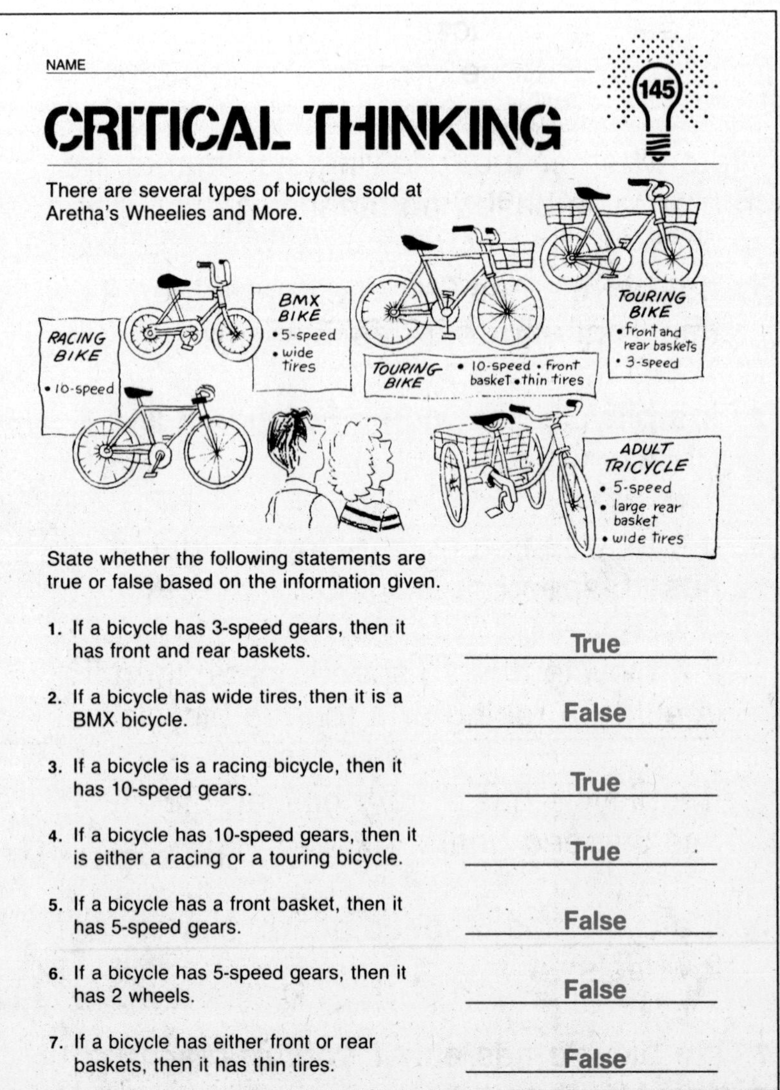
NAME

145

CRITICAL THINKING

There are several types of bicycles sold at Aretha's Wheelies and More.

State whether the following statements are true or false based on the information given.

1. If a bicycle has 3-speed gears, then it has front and rear baskets. **True**
2. If a bicycle has wide tires, then it is a BMX bicycle. **False**
3. If a bicycle is a racing bicycle, then it has 10-speed gears. **True**
4. If a bicycle has 10-speed gears, then it is either a racing or a touring bicycle. **True**
5. If a bicycle has a front basket, then it has 5-speed gears. **False**
6. If a bicycle has 5-speed gears, then it has 2 wheels. **False**
7. If a bicycle has either front or rear baskets, then it has thin tires. **False**

NAME ____

PROBLEM SOLVING

Kiyo is going to a birthday party. She has decided to build a cube calendar to give as a present. One cube or both cubes of the calendar can be used to show every date of the month. Kiyo wants to number the cubes so that they can be used for all the months of the year.

1. Trace on another sheet of paper and then cut out the shapes below on the solid lines. Fold on the dotted lines and tape the sides to form the two cubes.

2. Number the faces of the cubes so that any date of the month can be shown by using either one or both of the cubes.

3. Make another cube calendar in such a way that both cubes must be used to show each date. The first date of the month should be shown as 01.

Teacher Notes

Use with
Objective 146
pages 532–533

Focus
Problem Solving
Try and Check

Overview
Students write digits on the faces of two cubes in such a way that each date of the month can be displayed.

Materials
Scissors
Tape

Teaching Suggestions
Be sure that students understand the problem to be solved. ***Questions:** What dates will you need to represent with the cubes?* [1–31] *What dates of the month can be represented with one cube?* [1–9] What dates of a month need two cubes? [10–31]

Have students cut out and assemble the cubes described in Problem 1. Encourage students to use *try and check* strategies to solve Problem 2.

Alternate Approach: For students having difficulty getting started on this problem, guide them toward this approach: ***Question:** How many different digits will you need?* [Ten, 0 through 9] Have the student number the first cube 1 through 6 and the second cube 7, 8, 9, and 0. On a list of numbers from 1 through 31, have the students cross off those dates that can be expressed with the two cubes. [All numbers except 11–16, 21–26, and 31] ***Question:** Which digits can you write on the remaining two faces of the second cube so that all the dates can be expressed?* [1 and 2]

In Problem 3, two cubes must be used to represent each date of the month. The numbers 0, 1, and 2 must appear on both cubes. This leaves six blank faces on the cubes with seven digits, 3 through 9, to be written on these six blank faces. The solution is not to label a face with 9, but rather turn the 6 over for a 9.

Extension
If possible, let students actually construct the cube calendar. Cut 2 in. by 2 in. wood into pieces to form cubes. Have students sand each face, write the digits on the faces, and stain and varnish the cube to make a lasting gift.

NAME ______________________________

PROBLEM SOLVING

Kiyo is going to a birthday party. She has decided to build a cube calendar to give as a present. One cube or both cubes of the calendar can be used to show every date of the month. Kiyo wants to number the cubes so that they can be used for all the months of the year.

1. Trace on another sheet of paper and then cut out the shapes below on the solid lines. Fold on the dotted lines and tape the sides to form the two cubes.

2. Number the faces of the cubes so that any date of the month can be shown by using either one or both of the cubes.

3. Make another cube calendar in such a way that both cubes must be used to show each date. The first date of the month should be shown as 01.

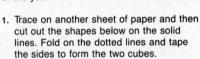

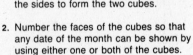

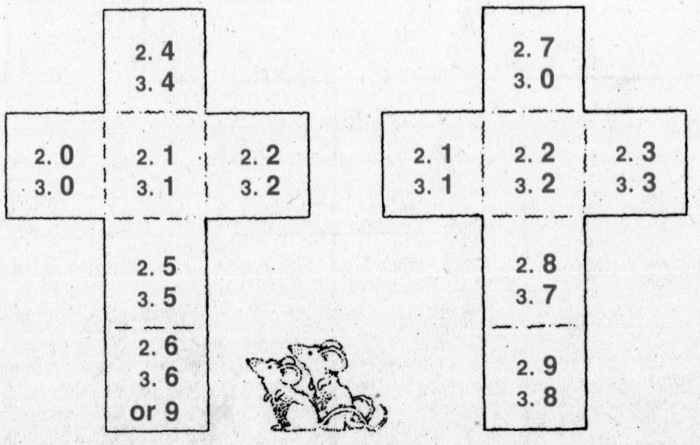